From Superstition to Science

Lionardo DiCapua & the Uncertainty of Medicine

To Linda:
With Kindest Regards
Luke
11-7-23

Luke Magnotto

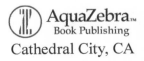

AquaZebra™
Book Publishing
Cathedral City, CA

First paperback edition August, 2023

Book design by AquaZebra

AquaZebra™
Web, Book & Print Design

Cover photo by Sara Kurfeß on Unsplash

Library of Congress Control Number: 2023939485

ISBN 978-1-954604-08-7 (paperback)

Published by AquaZebra

AquaZebra™
Book Publishing

35070 Maria Rd
Cathedral City, CA 92234
mark@aquazebra.com

Luke Magnotto luke@lukemagnotto.com

Dedication

This book is dedicated to Adele DiCapua Lord.
Thank you for your friendship, kindness, and persistence.

Table of Contents

Al Lectorem Benevolum:

(To the Benevolent Reader)

Allow me to begin by introducing myself. My name is William Cantelmo Stuart; by marriage, the Fourth Earl of Bainbridge. Prior to beginning this book, my only writings were short presentations for our local gathering of physicians and scientists. At the time of completion of this work, by the grace of God, in the year of our Lord 1730, I am above eighty-six years.

You might wonder why a man of my age, ill prepared for the task, would undertake writing a biography. Four reasons have compelled me.

First, I had a realization while reading Daniel Defoe's *Journal of the Plague Year.* That book ostensibly concerns the plague epidemic that struck London in 1665, but it also presents an expanded picture of that difficult period in English history. In my opinion, no other writer has captured the dreadful consequences of the disease or the human response to such a tragedy as did Defoe. In so doing, a true accounting of the event and the times emerges, an historical picture that, in its details, would have otherwise been lost.

Defoe reminded me that by delving into the details and focusing on a "minor" character, in his case a fictional one, a fair sense of the times might emerge. Since the devastating plague that struck the Kingdom of Naples in 1656 played such an important role in the lives of us who suffered through it, Defoe's journal became even more poignant. Thus, I began this effort by mimicking his style of using the first-person narrative in the main character's voice, only to abandon the conceit since I did not wish to presume the mindset of a non-fictional character.

This difference of style aside, it was Defoe who inspired me to tell the story of a courageous man whose lifetime spanned a catastrophic war, a massive Vesuvian earthquake, a bloody political revolution, a devastating plague, and a host of scientific discoveries that generated even more uncertainty. Such a precarious setting offered new opportunities for progressive thinkers while, at the same time, frightening those who desired assurance during the transformation.

For the people who were at the center of the intellectual flowering, it was an exhilarating period. A modern world was unfolding before them. On the heels of each scientific discovery came another and then another. Connections and cross-connections between and among the many disciplines (particularly related to the practice of medicine) were being made, and with each link came the realization that the microscopic and macroscopic universe surrounding us were infinitely more complex than what was previously realized.

For centuries, Galen was considered the undisputed expert in medicine. By questioning Galenic precepts, progressive medicine was at the forefront of indirectly challenging Aristotle and, by extension, Catholic orthodoxy. The protagonist in this story, Lionardo DiCapua, was a leader among those Neapolitan physicians and scientists who challenged Galen.

Arrayed against the progressives were traditionalists whose control of civil society was reinforced through Catholic orthodoxy. Ironically, the Catholic Church in Italy, at that time, was an institution in which a questionable number of higher prelates took their ideology seriously. Many were latter-born, aristocratic "Cadet Sons," who, for the continued concentration of their family's wealth, were forbidden to marry. Their future was directed by their parents into either becoming an officer in the military or rising to prominence as a religious cleric. Men who entered the religious life became monsignors, bishops, or cardinals, usually living in opulence. They often believed in and practiced the occult, took lovers, and sometimes begat children.

Yet even though they flaunted their lavish lifestyle, these men were the entrenched masters on matters of faith and morals. Through them, the Catholic Church in the Kingdom of Naples set a traditional tone. All sectors of organized society followed their lead so that, at every turn, antagonism rose toward the unfolding "modern."

I proudly admit to being a firm supporter of DiCapua and his circle, and, as such, it is difficult for me to consider his opposites in a favorable light. Yet, many of those "doctors of physick" who practiced according to Galen's traditional methods were highly motivated men who shared a deep concern for their patients. To them, the concept of replacing a discipline, which had been in existence for literally thousands of years, with an inchoate gathering of ideas—about which even the protagonists often disagreed—was a dangerous gamble. Humans struggle with change. We find solace in the routines of life, and we tend to fall back on what is familiar to make some sense of our days.

However, many in positions of influence who resisted change to the status quo did so for the selfish reason of maintaining rank and power. People who seek power covet it and are loathe to relinquish it, and a functioning society, for various reasons, usually accepts the stability reinforced by their authority. Thus, the most supportive rationale I could offer to justify the designs of the traditionalists is that they understood a need to avoid what they saw as the uncertainty of experimentation, the anarchy of change, and the nihilism of the mob.

These keepers of tradition supported and enforced their inherited teachings and assumed they would bequeath them to their descendants, just as they had received them from their forebears. Often the only argument presented to justify their belief was that Galen or Aristotle or Thomas Aquinas had said it was so. Altering that mindset would be difficult, which meant that a profound clash of ideas arose, with the traditionalists emphasizing that wise men, since time immemorial, have supported the great truths. The established order, they proclaimed, had been built upon them. As a result—either out of fear, complacency, or ignorance—challenging established ideas never occurred to most people. Yet a few can always be found.

Signore Lionardo DiCapua and his circle of like-minded progressives were among that small group of innovators in the Kingdom of Naples during the seventeenth century. They were greatly influenced by the atomist, Stoic, and Skeptic schools of Greek thought. As such, they believed that it was essential that they pursue their scholarship since humanity knew little of what the atomist poet Lucretius called the true "Nature of Things." From his earliest days, Lionardo desired unprejudiced knowledge, which required a skeptical view of established doctrine and reliance upon his own observations and those which his own judgment pronounced worthy of respect. It was not that he considered himself or those he admired infallible. Quite the contrary, he believed that everyone was fallible, and he sought evidence from experimentation to provide veracity. In so doing, he lived a full life—one, I believe, worthy of retelling.

Lionardo is included among other Europeans who changed the way we understand our world. Some of them have already attained the fame they deserve. Others, like DiCapua, remain in relative obscurity. Their discoveries and their writings may hold less importance; yet, like the farmer who plants a nutritious cover crop in the fall and then tills it under in the spring, their efforts made the ground fertile for the bounty of the harvest. The memory of their struggles rests with the few who knew them and with those who have read their opinions and share their passion for intellectual freedom. Within a few generations, they become part of the amorphous backdrop in support of the main protagonists of the time. Hence, they are generally forgotten as individuals. At best, they are lumped together as part of this school or that movement, which brings me to my second reason for this effort.

I believe that one of the main reasons that DiCapua has remained inconspicuous is that he avoided calling attention to himself. He was a reluctant traveler whose only physical contacts—aside from family, friends, and acquaintances—was with members of his Neapolitan intellectual circle and like-minded outsiders who travelled to Naples. Why was he such a reluctant self-promoter, one who held his ideas so closely? Was it out of fear or, perhaps, due to a quirk in personality brought on by a youthful trauma? Maybe he was trying to cover some past failing, some hidden crime, or to protect those around him? Or was he, in truth, a genuinely humble person? I have long considered all these possibilities.

Humility is a virtue that should be held suspect in its intent. Some strive to live a humble life, and their motives ultimately betray their modesty. Pride, as the story goes, was the original sin that snared Adam and Eve with its sublime summons. To escape such a basic impulse requires genuine love for a person or an ideal, and love, like humility, is too often gratuitously proclaimed. I have learned to be suspicious of the person appearing humble. Hence, the second rationale for beginning this venture is to determine the true cause for Lionardo's disinclination toward the fame he might have obtained and, I believe, deserved.

I should add here that whatever the cause of his apparent humility, he was not a spineless pushover nor a fainthearted coward. He was a thoughtful man who considered a question from all angles, based on intense study and investigation. And once convinced of the veracity of an argument, he became a passionate advocate for it, regardless of the possibility that it might place him at odds with the political or religious authorities. In other words, he may have been humble, yet he was certainly courageous.

The third reason for my writing is that no one has told the complete story of Lionardo DiCapua. His official biographer, the poet Niccolo Amenta, published *La Vita di Lionardo DiCapua* in Rome in 1710 and republished it later the same year in Venice. That book was written as part of the second volume of the *Vite degli Arcadi illustri,* biographies of illustrious members of Swedish Queen Christina's Arcadia Academy in Rome— biographies written by a fellow member after the death of the subject. The book Amenta produced is a mere fifty-eight pages. Completely hidden from it (or addressed in a superficial manner) are some of the critical periods of DiCapua's life. Considering these lapses, two possibilities occurred to me: either Amenta was anxious to fulfill his obligation as quickly as possible and with little effort (which seems unlikely, given his admiration for Lionardo) or he intentionally withheld part of the story.

By the time I began serious research into DiCapua's life, Amenta had already passed away. However, other members of the Arcadia and some of Lionardo's closest friends had met with Amenta, who sought their opinions before completing *La Vita.* I learned that those associates requested that DiCapua's early love sonnets be mentioned only regarding their disappearance to spare his wife and children any uncomfortable questions about who his true love, his *Inamorata*, might have been.

One other factor that also may have contributed to Amenta's limited biography was that, around the time of DiCapua's final days, a Jesuit priest of fanatical persuasion had attacked Lionardo's ideas and pushed for inquisitorial scrutiny. This priest proclaimed DiCapua foremost among his group of free-thinking, atheist sinners. If Amenta, who was a member of that group, had recounted all the events of Lionardo's life, he might have placed himself within the very web of the Inquisition at a time in his life inconvenient for such heinous examination. Hence, the publication of *La Vita* was delayed until well-nigh five years after that same Jesuit suffered a painful death from a tightly twisted bowel—an appropriate and well-deserved end, in my uncharitable opinion.

Unlike Amenta, however, I decided to offer the complete story. Many of the most intimate facts were known to me. In pursuit of the unknown, I performed considerable research.

Finally, even now that I have finished his life story, the answer to the most important reason for beginning this book remains uncertain. Despite a great gap in age, why did Lionardo DiCapua and I become such close friends? What was my true connection to him? Why was I raised in a convent? Those questions still haunt me. And indeed, they provide the most nagging reason that I began this effort.

I could go on wagging my garrulous tongue, but I will harness those restive tendencies and allow the narrative to unfold, as it will.

Acknowledgements

During the second half of the seventeenth century, the Kingdom of Naples—those lands on the Italian peninsula extending south from the Papal States in the middle of the calf down to the tip of the boot—experienced a cultural awakening. For more than a hundred years, the region had been ruled by a powerful Spanish monarchy intimately tied to the Catholic Church. But between the years of 1631 and 1656, three catastrophes (two deadly natural disasters and a political revolution) exhausted a citizenry already acquainted with slaughter and mayhem and impoverished by greed and war—greed being the irresistible prerogative of an empire, and war being the inevitable consequence of imperial greed.

That war, now known as the Thirty Years War, was part of a continent-wide conflict that lasted longer than the titular three decades. It involved political intrigues that would leave a swath of death and destruction, and it changed the balance of political power throughout Europe. Coupled with that savage warfare, the three other calamities that occurred in the kingdom created rifts in the social strata through which fertile waters began to flow. A small group of courageous men, united by their passion for scholarship, promoted that undercurrent. It is usually safe and relatively easy to support the ideas that nearly everyone believes. But it takes valor to strive against the majority viewpoint, especially when the accepted political and religious systems oppose the new concept and are willing to resort to whatever means necessary to enforce their will.

For personal reasons and without wishing to slight the memory of others, I have chosen to focus this book on the life of one of those courageous gentlemen, a great man relatively unknown outside of southern Italy. His name was Lionardo DiCapua. As one of his devotees, I appreciated his position on the controversies of that period. He was a central figure in the progressive movement in and around Naples, the largest European city at the time. His life story, beginning in a provincial village in 1617 in the Apennine Mountains east of Naples, encompasses the history of the Campania region during most of the seventeenth century (*Seicento* in Italian).

The particulars of the dialogue in this narrative are based on my recollections and my suppositions, along with the assumptions and experiences of others. With the passage of time, precise recollections blur in the province of memory. However, the quoted exchanges reflect the true or probable substance of the conversations, with allowances for literary license.

Since the study of what was then known as "natural philosophy" gradually evolved into what we now call "science," I sometimes interchange those terms. Also, I use several terms for the progressive thinkers and academicians of the time (*Investiganti:* Researchers, innovators, progressives) and their opponents (*Discordanti:* followers of Galen, doctors of physick, traditionalists, reactionaries).

At the end of the narrative, an appendix includes chapters on the history, philosophy, and the important scientific discoveries relevant to Lionardo's life and times. The purpose is to present background information that would give a more complete sense of the setting. The information came from multiple objective sources including scholarly articles, biographies, historical compilations, and textbooks. Originally, I interspersed these chapters within the narrative, but found that they were too distracting to the flow of the story. Those chapters are replete with names, dates, and facts. I offer an apology in advance for presenting to you, kind reader, what might be too much detail. But alas, it is the stuff of history, by turns interesting and overwhelming.

For a true accounting of this story, I was aided by the writings and gracious help of many experts, particularly Lionardo's biographer, Signore Niccolo Amenta; DiCapua's cousin, Signora Adele DiCapua-Fabrizio; Mr. Defoe; Professors Taradel, Conforti, Leporace; and Mark Johnson.

I would especially like to thank my dear wife whose ideas, edits and support were invaluable. It was she who had to tolerate the many inconveniences and the inattention of a distracted husband at a difficult time in her life. And it was she, more than anyone, who knows that I approached this effort, at every opportunity, with diligence and respect.

—W.C.S., August 1730

Introduction

Mount Cervialto, Campania—1683

Don Pietro was exhausted. He had been walking for over two hours down a path made slick by the passing rainstorm. A nervous tightness gripped his lower back. His feet ached. He was weak with hunger. The frailty of his physical condition distracted him from the task at hand, such that he became careless in his choice of step. At the angle of a sharp switchback, Don Pietro fell awkwardly, his head snapping to the ground, kinking his neck. His soft palms scraped across the prickly thorns of a wild bramble, leaving linear streaks of blood oozing from beneath a mud poultice. The accompanying dizziness and nausea kept him supine on the wet path, while a cold sweat enveloped him. His corpulence made righting his position problematic, so he cried out for help to the others who were too far away to hear his pleas. Through his tears, he cursed the peasant guides for plotting to harm him, and he cursed the Father Superior for nominating him to scribe this miserable affair.

Below the injured cleric, the guides led the four delegates, who were separated into pairs. The viceroy had insisted that both sides of the controversy send two observers along with Don Pietro on this rigorous journey to determine the validity of Lionardo DiCapua's theory on the shape of the rainbow. DiCapua had postulated that a rainbow, the *arco baleno,* would appear as a complete circle if the sun were low on the horizon and the rainbow were viewed from a high vantage point above the cloud burst. The argument, like so many others between the two sides, seemed petty to the viceroy, but he hoped to settle it and avoid the kind of violence his hot-blooded servants were known to employ in defense of such minor points.

The lead pair of Luca Tozzi and Domenico D'Aulisio

represented the traditionalists who denounced DiCapua's theory. They stayed near the front of the group, on the heels of the guides, pushing them forward. They were annoyed at the deliberate pace and the frequent stops, which delayed their return to the village where a carriage awaited to take them from this wild mountain to the civilized comforts of Naples.

Luca Tozzi had been a reluctant volunteer. When none of the younger Galenists accepted the position, it fell to him to assume the challenge. Had he not done so, the viceroy might have appointed someone of lesser persuasion. As a confirmed Galenist, a doctor of physick, he despised his opponents, the Investiganti, who questioned Galen's precepts. Tozzi knew that many of the regional barons, the clergy, and the rest of the traditional Galenist physicians—men who shared his beliefs— needed someone of unwavering conviction to do whatever it would take to discredit their rivals, as well as to keep in line Tozzi's partner, Domenico D'Aulisio, who was appointed by the viceroy.

In nearly two centuries of Spanish control of the Kingdom of Naples, no Spanish king had ever established his court in Naples. They appointed a viceroy to represent them. Like his many predecessors, the current viceroy cared little for his hot-blooded subjects, their ceaseless arguments that sometimes ended in fights with fists or stiletto. And he demonstrated his loathing by refusing to learn the Neapolitan dialect. His goal was to maintain some semblance of peace during what he hoped would be a brief tenure in Naples. Among Tozzi's more suspicious allies, some were convinced that the viceroy secretly favored the Investiganti and thus he had appointed D'Aulisio, whose rants against his uncle, Lionardo DiCapua, they believed to be a ruse.

As Tozzi followed the trail, he considered the counter argument that he prepared after the storm had passed. He would call the sighting a 'mirage' induced by the rigors of the climb, the altitude, the foul weather, the four days of unpleasant food. He would sow confusion to obfuscate the matter. What concerned him was whether D'Aulisio would support his claims.

Throughout the descent, Domenico D'Aulisio remained a few steps ahead of Tozzi, whom he considered a plodding relic encased in the ornate vessel of orthodoxy. D'Aulisio believed that his appointment to this task had been made to bolster his intellectually challenged partner. He liked to think of himself as an independent philosopher, separate from both sides, above the fray. His sarcastic poem (concerning DiCapua's inebriated condition when describing the shape of the rainbow) had unleashed the most recent series of acrimonious exchanges between the traditionalists and the Investiganti. As was D'Aulisio's modus, the poem was meant to create a sensation and turn eyes his way. He was smart and much admired—especially by himself. And now, as he descended the hills, having witnessed the veracity of his uncle's prediction, his boundless ego searched for a way to reinflate itself.

What D'Aulisio had observed during the storm would be difficult to deny. He could emphasize the subjective variables that accompanied the event, like the changing line of sight or the blinding intensity of the wind. But the actual phrasing of his argument eluded him, an unusual situation for a man usually so sure of his words. "Truth can be subjective at times," he had advised the suspicious Tozzi, while still in the high Irpino. "Philosophers spend a lifetime trying to define it. But what is considered truthful today might be revealed as false when other parameters are realized. Why risk one's reputation on a tenuous idea?"

D'Aulisio searched for a compromise, but Tozzi sensed a traitor in his midst. As they continued along their descent, both men remained preoccupied with their own thoughts, their voices restrained save to chastise the guides.

Behind them, a moderate distance uphill, came the two old men whose friendly banter reached those below them in broken phrases and occasional laughs, tumbling down the path like volleys of verbal stones. Unlike their rivals, Tommaso Cornelio and Lionardo DiCapua were certain of what they had seen on the mountain. They were now free to recount stories from their first hike up the Irpino decades earlier with a group of classmates to celebrate Lionardo's eighteenth birthday and to search for the famously elusive black truffle. They recalled that memorable birthday dinner of fresh truffles and sausage they had prepared over the campfire as the sun set in the valley below a stand of castagna trees. They spoke of the repeated toasts of red wine and the beautiful multi-colored sunset that Tommaso heralded as an omen of good fortune. They were venerable friends telling old tales, embellished to the status of fable. Details that one omitted or forgot, the other added.

Despite their age and physical infirmities, they made their way down the hillside aided by long, wooden staffs. Occasionally, they paused in their descent to rest or laugh or emphasize a point in the manner of experienced storytellers. The informality of their conversations was in contrast with the formal discourse they employed while speaking with their antagonists on the mountain. After years of trading verbal and sometimes even physical abuses, they and the rest of the Investiganti had arrived at a tenuous truce with the traditionalists, which held until the uproar created by D'Aulisio's derisive poem. Such was the passionate timbre of the times that any detail slighting the sanctioned canon—even one as seemingly minor as the shape of the rainbow—could cause a heated row with one side arguing to advance its theories, the other bound to preserve the status quo.

The inexorable toll of time had smoothed Lionardo's rough edges and left him with the visceral understanding that change comes slowly, if at all. One needed to savor the rare victories to shore up the spirit for the struggle that every sentient human must confront. This was especially true, he understood, in times like these, when the forces unleashed a century earlier by the Counter Reformation still pursued people in southern Italy who questioned authority. And both Lionardo and Tommaso had spent their careers doing just that.

The two men had remained close friends since their school days in Naples, about a half-century earlier, when a bond had developed between them distilled from their childlike wonder of the natural world. Over the years, they shared their triumphs and supported each other during difficult times. Now, as they made their way down the mountain, they both realized, without saying so, that this would be their last outing together. During the outing Lionardo observed Tommaso's swollen ankles, his quickened pulse, his insomnolence, and his phlegmatic disposition at night—signs that he observed in other patients close to their mortal end.

Before beginning the descent, the guides also sensed Tommaso's fragile state and offered to add his pack to their burden. He refused to allow it. So Lionardo asked the young men to walk slowly and check with him often. He requested this not just for Tommaso's sake, but also out of a selfish wish to prolong this final adventure and cherish every moment for all the years he might live after his friend was gone. He kept a close watch on Tommaso during the descent and signaled the vigilant guides to stop or proceed accordingly.

The two guides who led the expedition were brothers who lived in Bagnoli Irpino, a village in the Province of Avellino, which was also Lionardo's ancestral home. Four days earlier, all seven of the men had departed from the village to a ridge in the Picentini Mountains, a section of the Apennines that towered above the village. The brothers were chosen as guides because they were well acquainted with the area, which meant that they knew the easiest approach to follow, understood the weather patterns, knew where to find potable water, and, most importantly, knew the caves that might be inhabited by wild boar or cats or the more dangerous brigands. They were strong and capable of handling a rapier and a stiletto, and they were fit enough to carry all the provisions, the heavy canvas tents and the monk's books and clothes, because, unlike the others, Don Pietro carried only a goatskin of water.

That vessel now lay ruptured under the weight of the monk's generous behind. Patches of mud caked his heavy, black frock, and his white hood was stained with greasy dirt. Buried inside his vest and still intact, however, was a small flask, half full of dark wine. He rolled from supine into a seated position, freed the flask from the encasing fat, pulled the cork with his teeth and poured a few drops on his wounded hands. He then took a bracing sip to ease the sting and help reconstruct the events that had led him to the point of despair. When his nomination as the recording witness for this excursion was confirmed by the viceroy, he considered it an honor due him for his devoted service to church and crown. Yet, the harsh reality of this odyssey now hardly seemed like a reward. He was physically exhausted, and he could feel the emotional ground slipping away from under him like the path he could barely navigate.

The official findings of the expedition were to be written by Don Pietro and delivered to the viceroy, who would also receive observations from the two opposing factions.

Although he hadn't ever seen a circular rainbow before the expedition, Lionardo had considered the geometry of the theory, and he built a model that convinced him of the soundness of the argument. Still, to observe the phenomenon in real time from on high—with the lightning and thunder and rain sweeping across the dark sky and the magnificent circle of seven colors reflecting the full spectrum of sunlight right in front of him—the experience was breathtaking in its revelation. This was the proof. But whether his antagonists would admit it was the open question. They had demonstrated a willingness to lie about other contentious issues, and he was prepared for their denial of the circular *arco baleno* as well. Regardless of what they might say, once back in the village, he looked forward to savoring this victory over a fine dinner at a local inn with his oldest and dearest friend.

Part One

Chapter 1

A Child Arrives and an Orphan Departs

Bagnoli Irpino—1617

Cesare DiCapua left his resting wife with their new baby boy in her comforting embrace. He stepped outside into the warm night air of this "Night of Shooting Stars" where many other villagers were enjoying the cosmic show. Throughout Italy, folklore held that wishes made on this feast of San Lorenzo would be granted.

* * *

In the Campania region of Italy, some seventy kilometers southeast of Naples, the verdant foothills of the Apennine Mountains begin a steep rise to higher peaks. The rivulets and creeks born from winter snow coalesce into a series of rivers. Among them is the Calore River, which follows its winding course from mountain to valley, separating the village of Bagnoli Irpino to the east from its larger neighbor, the town of Montella. The main road into Bagnoli Irpino from the west crosses the Calore and follows a path along the hillside that is nearly as circuitous as the river itself. Eventually the road levels into a bell-shaped central piazza, lined with trees; the lower branches have been removed and the elevated branches have been trimmed to form a box-like border around the perimeter. This cover provides protection for the people of the village as they rest on the wooden benches or walk about making their *passegiatta* after the evening meal.

Several paths radiate from the piazza into the various quarters of the village. Taking the lowest path down from the south side, one soon arrives at a three-story, square tower attached, on its uphill side, to the building just above it. Wrapped around the face and continuing a level course is a smooth, marble basin, about a meter in height by a half-meter in width, that catches the cool water exiting from a series of metal spigots connected to a spring hidden inside the base of the tower. The locals use the convenient fountain as a reliable source of potable water. They call it *Fontana Gavitone*.

Along the face of the tower, directly behind the fountain, one observes a most amazing sight: an old, twisted carpine tree seems to defy nature by thrusting its roots through the cement base of the tower before rising, in all its gnarly glory, into a wide canopy. The shade from that venerable tree falls over a wide, arched portal and the paved courtyard behind the wrought-iron gated entry. Surrounding the courtyard is a large, three-story compound in which this tale rightly begins on August 10, 1617.

* * *

Cesare waited until a comet streaked across the sky, a blazing arc of light so sudden in its appearance and so dazzlingly bright in its tail that it stole his breath.

Thence, he made his wish that his new son—who would be baptized Lionardo Gerardino DiCapua—would be blessed with health and success.[1]

Lionardo's life was indeed healthy and peaceful until sometime during his tenth year, when his mother, Giovanna, developed a feverish malady that confined her to bed. When the doctor arrived, Lionardo and his older sister Antonia were asked to leave their mother's room while the physician filled a silver bowl with blood let from a vein in Giovanna's neck.

Afterwards, she slept quietly, a bulky bandage covering the site. Later that night, she lapsed into a coma and the priest was summoned. The next morning Cesare awakened his children with the tearful news of her death.

On a clear, fall afternoon about a year later, eleven-year-old Lionardo said good-bye to his Uncle Horace and Aunt Angelina, who lived in the attached house of the compound shaded by the great Carpine tree. He exited the common courtyard, took a drink at the Gavitone fountain, and began a walk that soon turned into a sprint up the hillside to the village *campo*. A nauseous pain had settled in his stomach since his father's health had worsened earlier that day. Horace sensed his nephew's anxiety and encouraged the boy to take some exercise, hoping that it would provide a pleasant distraction.

Lionardo arrived at the *campo*, feeling warmed by the uphill run, just as sides were forming for a game of *calcio*. He was on a team with his best friend, Luciano. It felt exhilarating to run until his legs burned, to steal the ball with a slide tackle, to sweat and breathe the cool fall air scented with the evocative smells of dry leaves and wood fires. Surrounding him everywhere was the vitality of youthful enthusiasm—the sounds, the smells, the physical euphoria.

Lionardo was always an intense competitor, a player who hated to lose. But on this day, the score hardly mattered. Everything was about the game and *only* the game. For a few hours, the distraction was so complete, so engrossing, that Lionardo remained in that carefree youthful cosmos, having lost himself in the sheer joy of the match.

By the time it ended, the soft gray of early evening was settling behind an ebbing sunset. With it came a rush of cool air descending from the surrounding mountains. Hungry and fatigued, the two friends walked home, recounting the key plays of the match. Down they came through a steep canyon of houses before parting. Luciano headed straight to his home near the entry to town, while Lionardo walked down the path toward the *Gavitone*. As he approached the fountain, he recognized the distinctive markings of the doctor's carriage tethered to a post. The boy froze. His heart quickened and his legs turned wobbly; his appetite disappeared, replaced by a nervous grip in his gut.

Lionardo entered the courtyard through the archway, ran up the stairs then hesitated before opening the door. The doctor was inside the portico, preparing to depart. He threw a cape over his shoulders and explained his diagnosis to Horace: "Cesare suffers from a plethoric habit," he said. "Before my treatment, his blood was in a state of great commotion, which had upset the balance between the humors." The physician was certain that by letting the blood, he had reduced the excess circulation, breathed out the heated blood, and calmed the residue. "Now his skin has cooled, and his pulse has slowed," he said. "These are good signs that the inflammation has been reduced and the humors have found balance."

Horace looked at his nephew and smiled at the good news. Lionardo opened the door for the doctor, who offered his final assessment: "We can let more blood tomorrow if necessary. Other than that, we should pray for Cesare, for the outcome is now in God's hands."

By the next morning, the fever had intensified, and delirium had overtaken Cesare. Between bouts of rigor, he conversed in a strange language with the phantoms of his dreams. When the rambling stopped, he would lapse into a deep sleep only to awaken again with teeth-rattling rigors, and he would call the name of his wife, his father, his mother, or some other deceased person, with whom he would engage in another incoherent conversation. The family took turns applying moistened cloths to his forehead to break the resistant fever. At mid-morning, Uncle Horace again sent for the physician.

The doctor felt the pulse, and then lanced an arm vein, this time filling the silver bowl twice. The fever continued but the delirium eased, as Cesare lapsed into a hot coma. The priest was summoned to deliver Extreme Unction. By mid-afternoon, Cesare's skin became pale, cool, and clammy. His breathing pattern alternated between a deep, rapid exchange and increasingly longer periods of apnea.

Cesare never regained consciousness.

That evening, as the bells rang the Angelus, and the last pinkish hues shone on the parapet of the ancient Norman castle that dominated the town, Cesare DiCapua died peacefully in the company of his family. He left behind his fifteen-year-old daughter (already in possession of a fiancé) and her eleven-year-old brother, now an orphan. Uncle Horace and his wife, Angelina, were childless. They adopted Lionardo and did their best to raise him as their own.

* * *

Spring arrived late the year following Cesare's death. In early May, with drifts of snow still present on the mountains and hillsides above Bagnoli, Horace DiCapua received a visit from the assistant priest in charge of the school. The priest told him that Lionardo was a gifted child, beyond the highest level of teaching offered in the village. His mastery of grammar and mathematics came easily, and he could already speak and write in Latin. The priest suggested that other arrangements be made to advance Lionardo's learning.

Since the boy had been living under his roof, Horace had realized what the priest was now confirming. It was the reason for Cesare's final request presented late one night when the two brothers were alone, before the delirium had clouded Cesare's mind. He had given Horace a letter that was to be delivered to a certain Jesuit, an acquaintance through friends in Naples.

Cesare told Horace that preparations had been made through the Jesuit to educate the boy in Naples. When the time was right, Horace promised to follow through with the plan. But, in the interim, the childless parents had grown even closer to their nephew. He was still so young and in need of their protection, they thought. How would they ever let him go?

* * *

About four kilometers to the east and uphill above Bagnoli Irpino is Lake Laceno, a shallow collection of water in the southeast corner of a vast, elevated plateau ringed by the higher Apennines. Hovering above other peaks, at 1800 meters, is Monte Cervialto. Snow covers the heights into early summer while the lower basin warms, drawing the sweet aroma from budding pines. After the spring thaw, the people of the village move their animals onto the verdant plateau for grazing. Vast herds of sheep, goats, horses, and cattle forage the green velvet plain.

On the second Saturday in April 1630, Uncle Horace and Lionardo began a hike into the mountains above the basin. Wild herbs and mushrooms were the prizes they sought. They stopped at the plateau where a serpentine creek wound through the vast field and emptied into Lake Laceno. A cacophony of bells rang from the haltered necks of the many herds and, in the far reaches of the open plain, stray sounds broke apart from the collected din into muted yet distinct notes. The hikers watched the acrobatic Maremma dogs monitor the periphery for those isolated sounds. With relentless directive barks and occasional bites, they ordered the stragglers to rejoin their herd. A great chestnut stallion, the established leader of the horse pack, kicked up his heels at the indefatigable dogs, but ultimately even he obeyed.

Growing along the trail above the plateau were patches of the tall drumstick mushrooms and in a nearby shaded wood they found a collection of prized spring *Funghi Porcini*. The trail led to a meadow thick with wild oregano that clung in scattered patches to the rock studded earth and perfumed the breeze that rustled the savory leaves. In the distance, the hikers could see the unbroken azure blue haze of the Mediterranean Sea to the west and the Adriatic Sea to the east. Horace found a favorable outcropping sheltered from the breeze where they ate lunch while enjoying the view. And it was while there in that rarefied air that Horace relayed Cesare's final request to Lionardo. Horace and Angelina wanted him to stay with them, he said, but the time was right for Lionardo to continue his education in Naples.

Horace sent a formal petition, signed by the local bishop, to the Jesuits in Naples, asking that they receive the boy for admission. A few weeks later, as treasurer of the *Madre* church Horace hosted a gathering of the Society of Jesus on Pentecost Sunday. Arrangements having been made Lionardo was interviewed after dinner that evening. The boy was accepted to start in the fall. He would come to Naples to pursue a course of studies known as the *Ratio Studiorum* that emphasized theology, the classic languages, literature, rhetoric, philosophy, and mathematics.

* * *

A raucous thunderstorm rolled through the mountains the night before Lionardo's mid-September departure. By morning, the wheels of the carriage that would take the boy to Naples cut deep ruts in the muddy roads leading to the center of town. The driver slowed as he approached the main street, where the wide hooves of the draft horses echoed off slippery cobbles and bounced between canyons of stone buildings that lined the sides. In the piazza, mounds of horse manure, reduced to flowing rivulets, collected in puddles that splashed in the horse tracks, filling the air with pungent aroma. When the carriage finally arrived at the Gavitone fountain, in front of the DiCapua gate, the driver's face was splattered with rain and debris. He was two hours behind schedule and in a foul temper.

Hearing the sounds outside, Horace handed the boy a letter addressed, in Cesare's handwriting, to *"Maestro Don Ruggero."* Lionardo was to give it to this priest who would present himself at the school. The boy turned the letter over to look at the red wax impression of the DiCapua family seal. The gray light of the stormy morning left the details hard to decipher on such a small scale and without the background color that placed them in relief. He lifted the letter to his nose and imagined the familiar aroma of his father's shaving balm.

Horace helped load the coach. Then he, Angelina and Antonia hugged the boy repeatedly, caressed his face, kissed his cheeks and, after much weeping and pity had come over all of them, relinquished him to the bilious coachman who coaxed his horses.

Sadness and excitement competed within the boy as he leaned out the window and waved good-bye. The family stood under their black umbrellas in a somber tableau, as the coach wound slowly up the street toward the main piazza. Once on the downhill road that exited the village, Lionardo again leaned out the window while the coachman exercised his whip, and the carriage gathered speed.

Luciano had heard the carriage as it entered town and knew the reason for its coming. He waited beneath the shelter of his front door and flashed a set of finger horns and stuck out his tongue at Lionardo, who laughed and waved back until the transport dropped below the horizon. The driver continued, cutting tracks through the mud toward Montella to the west, in the direction of the capital city.

NOTES

1. I was able to trace Lionardo's paternal family back to the eleventh century when a noble clan, known as the *Famiglia Archiepiscopis*, came from the Capua region to Naples and took the name indicating their original locale, *'di Capua*. Over the succeeding generations, the family produced chamberlains and advisers to Hohenstaufen, Anjou, and Hapsburg kings, as well as archbishops and cardinals of the Church. There were legates, barons, counts, princes, and (as the rounded points in the golden crown hovering within the family crest signified) nine dukes in the family. Cesare was born in Bagnoli Irpino in 1560. What brought his family to the relatively isolated village of Bagnoli Irpino is unknown and likely will remain so.

   What is also likely to remain unknown is the story of Lionardo's childhood. Family records suggest that he had several siblings who died during their earliest days, leaving Lionardo and his older sister, Antonia as the only surviving children. One can imagine an otherwise idyllic childhood for Lionardo spent in the natural beauty of the mountainous Irpino, especially for a boy surrounded by a loving and relatively affluent family.

Chapter 2

Lionardo at the Ratio Studiorum

Naples—1630

After mass on his first morning in Naples, Lionardo was
approached by a tall man of robust proportions dressed in black
cassock, covered by a great priestly cape, his head topped by a
four-sided biretta. A thick crop of dark hair flourished below
the hat, but when the man removed it, all that remained on top
of his head were a few wispy strands. His forehead extended
outward. Green eyes beckoned from beneath. His ample cheeks
held a bright-red blush. Between them was a small, yet sharply
up-turned nose—most appreciated in relief—from which a stone
(or at least a pebble) dropped from his forehead could be launched
a fair distance. "Maestro Don Ruggero di Romano," he announced
with extended hand. "Are you Master DiCapua . . . Lionardo?"

"Yes, Don Maestro, I am," he replied.

"I believe you have something for me, young Lionardo?"

This imposing man hovering above him—enormous by just
degrees—had brought such amazement to the youngster that
he stood momentarily dumbstruck and silent before answering.
"Oh . . . yes, sir, I have a letter for you-u." His voice cracked
with the effect of dropping the extra sound two full octaves
below the rest of his answer.

Don Ruggero's smile lit up his face, covering most of its
daunting crevices and sculpted protrusions like a fresh snow

that smooths the gullies and boulders of the rough Irpinian high-lands. The crow's feet along the sides of his eyes temporarily attached to the corners of his infectious smile. The boy told him that the letter was in his room, so Don Ruggero suggested that they walk together to retrieve it.

Along the way to the dormitory, the maestro gave a brief description of the courses that Lionardo would be taking during his first few years. The priest taught philosophy and would not have Lionardo as a student until the boy's second year. The courses of the first two years could be difficult, Don Ruggero warned, especially if the student struggled with Latin.

"Officium meum faciam," Lionardo replied in Latin (mean-ing, "I will perform my task"). The priest nodded silently, clearly pleased.

Lionardo found the letter in his desk and gave it to the maestro, who reached deep inside his plentiful black cape and removed a case containing his spectacles. He examined the letter and rubbed a finger across the formed molten-wax crest, smiled at his young charge, and split the seal from its attachment.

The envelope contained two written pages. "This letter is nearly two years old. Have your studies progressed since then?" asked the priest.

"Yes, Maestro."

"Well then, based on what your father said in this letter, I think you should be able to handle the Classics without diffi-culty."

"Maestro . . ." Lionardo looked away. "Did you know my father?"

"No. I never met him in person, but we had mutual acquain-tances. On one occasion, we exchanged letters. I can tell you that the people who knew him spoke highly of him—your Uncle Horace as well."

Lionardo grinned and, looking up again, asked, "Could you

please tell me what my father wrote in the letter."

Don Ruggero looked into the boy's eyes. "He said that you were a bright boy and he wished to have you expand your learning." The maestro smiled at his charge. "He asked me to look after you and to teach you. He was proud of you, he wrote, and he loved you very much." He paused and folded the letter. "And I will do what he asked as best I can, young DiCapua."

Before they parted that first morning, the priest explained the location of his office and asked the boy to come after classes, as often as he liked. Lionardo thanked him. The priest turned away in a sweeping wave, only to stop after a few steps and face the boy who stood unmoved in pensive silence. "Is there something else you wish to say?"

"Yes. Excuse me, Maestro." He paused. "May I have the envelope?"

* * *

Aside from bouts of loneliness at bedtime, Lionardo adjusted to the constant activity of the school. He made new friends from places far removed from his home. His inquisitive mind was well-suited for the school's emphasis on scholastics, and he rose to the top of his class. (Niccolo Amenta, his biographer, would later describe him as an agreeable person in possession of a sweet disposition.)

But from Lionardo's earliest days, he also carried a strong drive for whatever might interest him, and he would pursue that passion tirelessly. It could be the learning of a language, or a philosophical argument, or a detail from history, or the plan of attack in a match of calcio. He brought this desire with him on all days and everywhere, into the classroom and onto the pitch.

More than one thousand students were enrolled at the Ratio Studiorum—translated "Plan of Studies"—during Lionardo's time there. Many were day students from Naples who boarded at home. Discipline was maintained by substituting supervision for compulsion and by dissociating punishment from teaching. Much of the course work was given in Latin. The techniques employed included written exercises in imitation of a famed writer, repetition of basic facts, daily disputations, public examinations, and hours of silent study.

The school year opened with a day-long convocation, featuring addresses from the various department heads. The year included a short vacation to celebrate the feast of the Nativity and a shorter break for Easter. Summer vacation lasted for one week for the younger students and three weeks for the upper classmen. The school aimed to teach its students what was necessary to become a prominent Catholic leader. Near the end of the academic year, selected third-year students presented disputations on various philosophers. Oftentimes contests were held between and among the classes, as well as displays of verse written by students of theology and philosophy. Study groups for Greek and Hebrew met an additional three times each week.

At the end of the year, prizes were presented to the best students from each of the classes from within each discipline. The brightest students could be advanced to the next level of a given subject after the Nativity season, as was Lionardo in his first year due to his mastery of the Latin tongue.

Daily life for the boarders was a busy progression of organized events that left virtually no free time for the idleness of youth. The first bell rang at 5:50 a.m. Morning Prayer began at 6:10, followed by mass and then a short meal, at which the "Grand Silence" that began after prayers the night before concluded. Time was allotted for room cleaning and a change from cassock and surplice to school uniform.

Classes began promptly at 8:00 a.m., proceeded until noon, broke for a half-hour lunch, resumed at 12:30 p.m. and ended at 2:30 in the afternoon, allowing a short break for exercise before first study at 5:30.

A lecture of a spiritual nature was presented by students of rhetoric in Latin in the auditorium, which preceded dinner at 7:00 p.m. The first half of dinner was taken in silence, listening to the reading of a book or another lecture in Latin, and always of a spiritual nature. Second study began at 7:45 in the evening, followed by night prayers at 9:50, after which all had arrived again at the Grand Silence.

This schedule was repeated five days each week when classes were held all day. Classes met on Saturday mornings as well, but Saturday afternoons were set aside for recreation—although special studies might intervene.

The Lord's Day was filled with activities designed to promote spiritual growth. That meant either all-day retreats held in silence or all-day spiritual lectures and readings, with periods of adoration of the host. Novenas to a particular saint and Sunday evening study hall, followed by Compline, completed the Sunday routine. Exceptions to any of the schedule would be announced in advance.

Critics of the schools complained that the methods employed were too formal and mechanical, that independence of mind and love of truth for its own sake were suppressed. Supporters would assert that the rigorous schedule, on the face of it, was meant to produce a well-educated elite group of men whose faith was securely anchored to Catholic orthodoxy. Some would also add that it had a more practical and immediate purpose, which was voiced by an elder Jesuit who had taught in one of the schools.[1]

Aside from the scholastic curriculum, time was allotted for formal debates and dramatic productions. Classic Greek and Latin plays were staged along with more modern offerings—again, of a spiritual nature—presented in the vernacular. Students wrote, acted, and managed the plays, built the scenery, and created the costumes. Lionardo quickly took to writing his own pieces inspired by a religious theme from the life of various saints.[2]

* * *

In 1620, nine years before he met Lionardo and when he was fresh out of the seminary, Don Ruggero di Romano was among the earliest group of Jesuits to go to the New World to set up a mission for the native people at a site near the Uruguay River. Influenced by the call of the gospels and perhaps by the ideals of Thomas Moore's *Utopia,* the fathers set up several communities along the line drawn by the pope that cleaved the New World into Portuguese and Spanish halves.

Aside from the theories as to why the Jesuits felt it necessary to protect the natives from extortion by the European powers, the result was that many devoted and courageous men took passage across unpredictable seas, hacked their way through a dense and primitive rain forest to set up camps reminiscent of those first established by the early Christians. They pursued their calling by learning the native language without forcing the European tongues onto the indigenous people. For the children, they set up schools in which they taught a basic curriculum plus music, drama and religion. Enterprises were developed for adults to sustain the community, including the production of various goods and the means to provide sustenance. The priests looked after the physical health of the people using traditional cures whenever requested. In these efforts, all members of the community, including the fathers, shared the work and the bounty.

This model of Christian goodness has not met with the kindest approbation from Christian countries in Europe where the ministrations of the Jesuits have, by turns, wavered in support of Christ's ideals on the one hand and the political intrigues of Peter's descendants on the other. Recently, both Spanish and Portuguese mercenaries have redoubled their efforts to extort the natural and human capital. In response, some of the fathers have been doing their best to shield and protect the natives in the jungles of the New World.

The youthful Don Ruggero worked at a mission that bordered the Uruguay River for more than three years before succumbing to a feverish disease that extracted nearly all the vital elements from him to the point that he was forced to return to Europe. He'd planned to come again to the New World after he had regained strength, but he never did; he turned instead to the idea of sharing his experiences with younger men in the hope that they might be inspired to accomplish charitable goals. Thus, until the end of his life, he carried forth that mission to the best of his abilities with those students who seemed likely to receive his suggestions. From within the group that entered in 1630, Don Ruggero chose two: Lionardo DiCapua and another boy from the small town of Rovito, near Cosenza in Calabria. His name was Tommaso Cornelio.[3]

NOTES

1. The acceptance of the priest's suggestion is left to the reader, although any observation of the hectic daily schedule affords some truth to his assertion that the real purpose was to keep the boys active with little time for private contact, thus minimizing the chance that they might engage in exploits of an illicit nature, one with another.

2. Suffice it to say that Lionardo DiCapua blossomed in the environment. Amenta tells us that sometime during his years at the Ratio Studiorum, he began calling for an open approach to discourse regulated only by deep study of the subject at hand. The biographer assures us that Lionardo began writing his thoughts in arguments

against the blind acceptance of Aristotle's teachings. Such an impulse ran counter to the structured curriculum of the school and leaves one wondering when it came to him and why. (Amenta remained silent on the source.)

3. In fact, Lionardo would have two influential mentors during his years of study. One we will meet later in this story. The other, the earliest, was Don Ruggero. The liberal methods he employed in teaching philosophy to Lionardo, during both regular and extra classes, freed the boy's imagination to question established authority. This freethinking would remain a central principle during his academic years and a constant theme throughout his life. Certainly, Lionardo's birth parents, his adopted parents and, perhaps, other early Irpinian influences affected his viewpoint. But it was Don Ruggero who combined those influences with the ideals of an alternative philosophy—all of which begs the question as to how the impetus to question orthodoxy came to the kindly priest.

Chapter 3

Don Ruggero's Extra Classes

Naples—Autumn 1631

Lionardo met Tommaso Cornelio on the calcio pitch. Unlike the boyish Lionardo whose fair skin and beardless face had yet to catch up with his cracking voice, Tommaso was on the other side of puberty—hairy arms and legs, black stubble on his face, and a deep and stable voice. In a contest of sport, Cornelio (much like Lionardo's friend Luciano) was an aggressive defender uninhibited in the application of physical force. He was also a bright boy, especially gifted in mathematics. He quickly surpassed the limited offerings in math at the Ratio Studiorum, which ignored subjects like biology and history and placed minimal emphasis on mathematics, save for what might be useful in commerce.

Friendship between the two boys grew throughout their initial year of study. In their second year, they were enrolled in Don Ruggero's class on ethics and natural philosophy. At the end of his lecture on the first Friday of the new term, Don Ruggero asked Lionardo and Tommaso to wait in their seats as he dismissed the other students. "I have been following your progress over the past year," he said, "and I have a suggestion for heightening your comprehension of natural philosophy. I would like both of you to come to my office tomorrow after lunch and plan to stay for a few hours."

On the way to their next lesson, the boys complained to each other that this extra course would interfere with their recreation time. So they made an agreement to minimize their questions and discussion with Don Ruggero so that they could still find time on the pitch.

The next day, they arrived at the priest's office. Tommaso rang the bell. Several seconds passed without a sound from inside. They looked at each other and smiled. Tommaso rang again. Still, no movement. Tommaso whispered, "Maybe we can still get into the match." He rang again. Lionardo leaned his ear against the door. It opened suddenly and he fell sideways into Don Ruggero.

"Ah!" the priest greeted them, his head bobbing side to side, from one surprised face to the other. "You're here. On a Saturday afternoon as beautiful as this! I'll bet you were hoping that I had forgotten. Huh? *Huh?* Uh-huh." He offered them seats in front of his desk.

The office was a large, drafty room with a high ceiling stabilized by twisted chestnut beams in support of terra cotta tiles. The walls held shelves of books and loose manuscripts that sometimes spilled over the edges like loose rags. Behind a wide wooden desk, a marble mantel (blemished by the soot of many a fire) encased a hearth full of cool ash. The bronze bust of a bearded ancient sat in the center of the desk with eyes that seemed to squint at the sunlight streaming through a pair of windows high up on the opposite wall. The boys sat behind the desk facing the bust, their backs warm to the sun. Don Ruggero handed each a copy of a book. He told them that they would be meeting on future Saturdays to discuss its contents.

The boys leafed through their copy in silence. "Well?" Don Ruggero asked. "Would you like to do this?" They looked at each other with uncertainty and offered tepid consent. The priest pulled a chair from his desk and sat. "Having finished your studies of the Classics, you are quite steeped, I'm sure, in the history of the *Rinascimento,* the 'rebirth' of ancient art and literature that began in Florence in the early 1400s. Have either of you heard of a Florentine from that time by the name of Bracciolini?"

The boys looked at each other and shook their heads, answering nearly simultaneously, "No, Maestro."

"Poggio Bracciolini was a member of the Curia who became famous for discovering and translating ancient manuscripts. In 1417, Signore Bracciolini uncovered a poem written by a Roman poet named Titus Lucretius Carus. The title of the poem was *De rerum natura (On the Nature of Things).* The book you are holding—like mine—," he said as he raised his copy, "is that poem, and the poet, this Titus Lucretius Carus, is known simply as 'Lucretius.' Have either of you heard of him?"

The boys again responded, "No, Maestro."

Ruggero paused to gather his ideas. "If I'm to explain Lucretius' poem, I must digress to an earlier time, because Lucretius put into rhyme theories that had been developed well before his day, during the age of the great Greek thinkers. *De rerum natura* is a compilation of theories from three Greek philosophers: Leucippus, Democritus and Epicurus. Together they formulated the theoretical concepts of a branch of philosophy that came to be known as atomism. I doubt that either of you have heard of it." He stood and poured a glass of water from a pitcher, took a drink, and returned to his chair. "The original proponents of atomism were Leucippus, who flourished about 440 years before the birth of our Lord, and his pupil Democritus. Leucippus was influenced by Parmenides, the southern Italian who developed logic, and Zeno, the original Stoic. Democritus was a contemporary of Socrates and came to prominence around 420-odd years before our Lord's birth.

"For decades, their predecessors had been locked in a debate to define the primordial element. Now, my boys, the genius of

Leucippus and Democritus was their novel idea that the four candidates—earth, wind, water, and fire—could be equated by breaking them apart and finding the same constituent elements in all of them. They came to designate these similar particles as atoms. 'A-tom' in the Greek means 'un-cuttable.'" He chopped his right hand hard into the top of his left fist to emphasize the point. "They believed that the atom is the basic element composing all matter, and that the universe is made up solely of atoms and the empty space, the void between them. The atoms are always in motion within the void, and collisions between them cause the mechanical formation of vortices, which make things, bodies and, ultimately, worlds."

As he proceeded, Don Ruggero warmed to the topic, emphasizing his words with a physicality of twirling hands and flapping elbows that mimicked the wings of a great bird about to be carried away with his thoughts. "Atoms come together to form matter." He clasped his hands. "But, the quantity of matter—again, a most important point, my boys—always remains the same." Here he stood onto the tips of his toes, released his clasped hands, and began pinching both index fingers to thumbs while slowly repeating each word: "The quantity of matter always remains the same; none can be created or destroyed. Apparent destruction is merely a mutation to another form." He dropped from his toes to his heels, rested his fingers, relaxed his arms to his side, and regained his seat.

"Neither Leucippus nor Democritus postulated a source for the atoms," he continued. "They were thought to be infinite. The atomists were thus strict materialists. That is to say, to their way of thinking, everything comes from a physical process, from atoms and the space between them. The soul is made of small, spherical atoms, fast-moving and, hence, invisible; the same with fire and thoughts. But surprisingly—and by the way, rarely does this get mentioned by their critics—they were the first philosophers to say that something could be real without having a visible form." With his large eyes flashing beneath his wrinkled forehead and his eyebrows rising and falling like waves in a rough sea, he had become one with his subject.

"Atomists believed that the gods had foresworn any involvement with humans or the world we inhabit. Their suggestion that the atoms were infinite has, in recent times, led to the assertion by the Inquisition that atomism and atheism were evil twins. But tell me," he said, staring into Cornelio's eyes and pointing at him, "if the Greek gods created the world, Tommaso, who created the gods? Well?"

Cornelio fumbled about in his chair. Not hearing a response, the priest answered his own question. "You see. By not defining the origin of the atoms, they left open the possibility of an 'un-caused' Creator. The gods or *a* God could have started the process. So, the atomists were not necessarily of an atheistic persuasion.

"As for what we perceive of matter through our senses, Democritus believed that all sensations are due to atoms released from the object and landing on our sense organs. Humans by convention call something sweet or cold or of a certain color or smell, but these characteristics are the opinions of our senses. All that we know for certain are the effects upon our body of the mechanical forces acting on it. True knowledge is buried deep, and only comes through deep thought and serious investigation."

A tall, wooden ladder leaned against the corner of the bookcase to Ruggero's left. The upper end of the steps slid on wheels inside a metal rail running above the shelves; the legs also rested on wheels. The maestro stood and walked to it with purpose in his step, and, with a quick upward jerk, he detached the ladder from the rail, carried it to the fireplace wall, reattached it, and slid it to an area above the hearth. He climbed the ladder and removed a heavy book that occupied an elevated position, and then he returned to his seat.

"I have here a copy of Aristotle's *Metaphysics*." He leafed through the book to a certain page. "Let me ask you, what was Aristotle most interested in defining?" He again stared at Cornelio, who basked in the glory of possessing an answer.

"The final cause of an occurrence, Maestro."

"Yes, the final cause. The purpose. Very good, Tommaso!" The maestro again took to his feet and turned the book to show them the chapter he was paraphrasing. "Aristotle wanted to know why something happened, what was the purpose of an event. But, unlike that Aristotelian concept, the atomists held that there was no purpose in the universe, only atoms governed by the natural law. However, the atomists also believed that the actions of the atoms were not left to chance. Instead, everything happens out of necessity, in accordance with natural law. Leucippus's one and only surviving fragment says it all: 'Nothing happens for nothing, but all things happen for a reason and of necessity.'"

Don Ruggero returned to the ladder, climbed it, and replaced the book in its lofty niche. He walked to the front side of his desk where a hanging oil lamp hovered directly overhead, partially obscuring his face and catching his voice in a tangle of filigree metal and painted clay.

"Which of the two original atomists worked out the details of their argument remains uncertain. The details of Leucippus's life are vague and, of his writings, only the one assertion that I just repeated survives. After spending some time studying logic and Stoicism, Leucippus came to Abdera, an Ionian settlement in Thrace. There he met Democritus; much more of whose writings remain. As a result, Democritus receives the most credit for developing the philosophy and is the more famous of the two."

Lionardo twisted in his seat trying to get a better look at the teacher through the decorated lamp. "Democritus was the son of a wealthy family from Abdera," Don Ruggero continued. "He had spent some time going and coming widely. Everywhere he went, he sought the wisdom of the locals. Early biographers said that his sojourns took him to Athens, Egypt, Ethiopia, the Red Sea region, even unto Persia and India. He was determined to absorb the knowledge of each region and to develop a unified worldview. He believed that good people everywhere shared a common brotherhood, which he summarized in one of his surviving sayings: 'To the wise and good man, the whole earth is his fatherland.'"

The frenetic maestro again took a seat behind the bulky desk made of a fine-grained wood, stained dark, and highly polished. Covering the middle of the wide top was a leather pad blemished with random spots of dried ink. Abutting the upper edge of the pad was a square-shaped inkwell ornately decorated with scenes from the four seasons, one on each corner where four brass lids were lifted to expose four glass vials, containing the drying remnants of red, green, black and brown ink. A collection of gold tipped pens lay in parallel in front of the well. Nearby, resting tenuously, was a much-used blotter that rocked on its U-shaped base to absorb the excesses of an overly ambitious paragraph.

"In early Greece," the maestro continued, "because of the dominance of Socrates and Plato, atomism never came to the level of inquiry that was afforded the other contemporary philosophies. However, in the book *Lives of Eminent Philosophers,* which he wrote in the third century after our Lord's birth, Diogenes Laertius repeats the claim of other early Greeks who said that Plato wished to burn all of Democritus's writings. Diogenes Laertius adds that Plato, who commented on almost all the early philosophers, never mentions Democritus. According to Laertius, this omission was intentional because, otherwise, Plato would have had to match himself against Democritus, whom Laertius called the 'prince of philosophers.' But Democritus was a modest man. After his sojourns, he lived a simple, rather austere life in strict pursuit of knowledge through repeated habits, the kind of code around which the monks of our day build entire communities, although it is probable that his approach was more austere and certainly holier."

Ruggero paused to smile with an evocative twinkle in his eyes. "Democritus shunned sensual pleasures and material extravagances. He preferred studying and writing to endless discussions. The fragments of his manuscripts that remain cover a wide range of subjects from philosophy, medicine and mathematics to mental therapy, art, and music."

Ruggero pointed to the bust of the ancient on his desk. "I think he was a handsome fellow. What do you think?" He lifted the bronze to stare at it as he spoke. "One of the surprising things about the man was that he never gathered a group of followers, even though he had the time to do so. You see, he lived a long and productive life of somewhere between ninety and nigh one hundred and nine years, according to contemporary sources."

He returned the statue to its spot on the desk and continued. "Leucippus and Democritus were the last of the free-thinking philosophers. They wished to understand the universe. Not— and this is the key to their importance," he emphasized the point with a knobby, elongated index finger pointing upward, "not its relevance to the individual person living within it. Their ideas were boundless, vigorous, imaginative, and filled with the delight of adventure. They believed in the power of the intellect, the power of the mind, my boys." He tapped his head with the same pointed index finger and slowed his enunciation. "The power of the mind," he repeated slowly. "And their enthusiasm made a path for those of us who now delight in walking upon that trail." He concluded with a plea: "I hope it will come to both of you to join me on this adventure. Questions?"

Caught up in the theatrical performance, the pupils forgot their vow of silence. "Signore Maestro," Tommaso asked, "why do you think Democritus did not start his own school?"

"Hmmm? Many people have wondered," Don Ruggero said with a nod. "And the truth is that we really do not know." He reached for his chin, took a few steps to his right, reversed course, and returned to his original spot. "We know that he came from a wealthy family and that he spent much of his fortune travelling about and studying in the places he visited. When he returned home, as I explained earlier, he lived simply, as a philosopher, devoted to learning. Diogenes Laertius said that he went to Athens but did not want to be recognized because he despised fame."

Don Ruggero resumed his back-and-forth pacing, this time completing two rounds before continuing. "I believe that Democritus was a profound thinker who had much to give those who might have studied under his tutelage. But he was influenced by the Stoics and, as such, practiced the ways of modesty. He was interested primarily in the attainment of personal knowledge, whereas taking on students and running a school would have been distractions. He probably realized that. Lionardo, any questions?"

"Yes, Signore Maestro. My question is why the atomists were considered atheists, since you said that they believed the gods existed and that their theory left open the possibility of a creator."

The priest smiled and explained that the atheist designation came about because the atomist philosophers after Democritus were particularly strident in their statements against religion. Those other philosophers, Epicurus and the poet Lucretius, would be discussed when they met the following Saturday. He asked Lionardo to hold that question for their next meeting, wherewith he suggested that they begin translating the first part of Lucretius's poem. Before they departed, the maestro told them he had one more request—an important one. He explained that the study of atomist philosophy is not looked upon favorably by the Church, although he believed it was important to pass on the ideas for the sake of the evolution of natural philosophy. "It would be best for everyone," he concluded, "if we kept our meetings and our discussions confined to the three of us."

Chapter 4

The Rector Seeks a Spy

Naples—Autumn 1631

The weather on the following Saturday was much different than the week before. A hard rain began in the morning and a chill hung in the air. The boys planned to head for Don Ruggero's office after noon meal, but that changed when Lionardo received a note requesting his presence at the rector's office immediately after lunch. Tommaso would let Don Ruggero know of the delay and Lionardo would meet them at the maestro's office after the rector's meeting.

It was the first time that Lionardo had been summoned to the rector's office. He hadn't had any difficulties with prefects, teachers, or other students. He was doing well in his studies. Perhaps there was some problem at home—sickness or injury—although he hadn't received any word of illness or other problems in recent letters from his sister or Uncle Horace. The unknown nature of the summons created anxiety, and his nervousness increased as he walked to the office.

When Lionardo arrived, the rector sat behind his desk, wearing a sweater over his cassock and a scarf around his neck. He appeared to be an older man of indeterminate age, perhaps fifty, maybe seventy. His hair was thinning and gray. His excessive wine consumption and his protuberant belly, exaggerated in the sitting position, were fodder for jokes among the students. He wore a serious look on his face, which was marked by a bulbous nose of reddish-purple hue.

The rector greeted Lionardo but did not offer him a seat, so the boy remained standing next to the cold hearth as a feeling of nausea suddenly swept over him, along with a cool sweat. His knees weakened and, for a moment, he feared he might faint.

The priest observed the color drain from the boy's face and sensed his anxiety. Thus, he began the conversation with small talk about Lionardo's home life, his village, his early lessons in the village, his favorite subjects at the Ratio, his favorite extracurricular. Then he removed a piece of paper from a folder on his desk and read each side carefully, with tremorous hands that caused the page to shake in response. His frown turned to a smile as he praised Lionardo for his excellent scholastic work. "Congratulations," he said. "I see that you have done well in your studies, particularly in your Latin classes."

"Thank you, Father."

The priest paused and returned the trembling grade sheet to the folder, sat back in his chair, and looked up at the boy, as his smile again gave way to a frown. "You are probably wondering why I called you here."

"Yes, Father."

"Well, it has come to my attention that you have been meeting with Don Ruggero di Romano for some type of extra instruction. Is that true?"

Lionardo did not want to drag Tommaso into wherever this was headed, so he answered in the singular. "Yes, Father. I have met with him."

"Where was the meeting?"

"In Don Ruggero's office."

"And what did you discuss?"

Lionardo recalled Don Ruggero's admonition to keep their meetings secret due to his concerns about atomist teachings.

But, at the same time, he wanted to avoid lying. "We discussed Aristotle's method of questioning 'why' things happened," he answered.

"That is all?"

"We have had only one class, Father," he said, again in an evasive yet truthful manner.

"In the future, I want you to keep me informed as to what you discuss in the sessions with Don Ruggero. I have received complaints about his methods and his philosophical positions. I would like for you to report to me monthly, so that I can verify or negate those complaints. Can I count on you, young DiCapua?"

"Yes, of course, Father."

"Good," he said with a smile. "That is all." He stood, walked around his desk, placed an arm over his shoulder and walked him to the door. "I will see you in a month." he said. "Goodbye, for now."

* * *

On the way to Don Ruggero's office, Lionardo tried to figure out who might have told the rector about the extra classes. When Don Ruggero had first proposed the Saturday sessions after their regular Ethics class, he'd waited until the classroom was empty of other students. Lionardo and Tommaso did their translating in a quiet area at the back of the library away from everyone else. Furthermore, he was careful with his satchel, always leaving Lucretius's poem between his papers, inside a side pocket so that no one knew its whereabouts. And what about Tommaso? Why was he not called to the rector's office with him?

Don Ruggero was tending a fire in the hearth when Lionardo arrived at the office. Tommaso sat in a chair placed near the glowing fire that gave off a pleasant warmth. The priest offered Lionardo a chair next to Tommaso, who had a concerned look on his face. The light from the oil lamp lit above the great desk projected the brass figures into dancing shadows on the ceiling. Don Ruggero tossed another log on the fire, and then he asked about the meeting with the rector.

Lionardo felt guilty that perhaps he had done something to jeopardize Don Ruggero's position at the school. "Honestly, Father, I don't know how," he began, almost in tears, "but he somehow knew about our first meeting, and he wants me to report to him monthly as to what we discuss."

Don Ruggero sat down next to Lionardo. "Don't worry," he said. "He's done this to me and others before. Did he ask what we talked about at our first meeting?"

"Yes, and I told him that we discussed Aristotle's questioning the 'why' of things. And we did. I didn't lie."

"Very good," the priest said smiling. "That was some quick thinking, my boy, and you didn't lie. Did he say why he wanted to know about our classes."

"Yes. He said he'd received complaints against you—your methods and what he called your 'philosophical positions.' He didn't say from whom."

"The same as always," the priest said. "He's been trying to get me for years. He knows my sympathies for the natives of the new world, how we spoil their lives and their traditions while supposedly trying to save them. But he and I know that his wealthy friends hope to profit greatly from those conversions." Don Ruggero stared into the fire. "Indeed, what they truly want is the gold."

"But why was I called without Tommaso?"

"Yes," Tommaso asked. "Why was I not called?"

"The both of you most likely were seen by one of his henchmen interacting with me. I would guess that you will also be called by him," he said, nodding at Tommaso. "I suspect he does that to see if you have your stories straight. But don't worry, my boys. Many Jesuits support my beliefs. The rector and his friends have been trying to build a case against us for some time. But we have strong support within the order, and he and his friends know in their hearts the righteousness of our position." He stood before the boys, spread his arms wide, and smiled. "Enough now. We are wasting valuable time. Let's get on with Lucretius. Tell me how the translation has gone."

The boys told him that they had been working on it separately until yesterday, when they compared their efforts and began working together on the more difficult passages. They had completed up to line 483 in the first section.

The maestro complimented them. He told them that it had been some time since he had read Lucretius and that the poem, once again, impressed him with its beauty and power. "Titus Lucretius Carus was the most famous follower of a philosopher who had lived about two hundred years before him," Ruggero began. "That man, as you have already found in the poem, was Epicurus. Decades after Democritus's death, around 310 before our Lord, Epicurus expanded the atomist theories in the garden of his home on the outskirts of Athens, where, unlike our modest Democritus, he opened a school that attracted a large following.

"Mention the term 'epicurean' to a sober Dominican and he will describe a seeker of pleasure whose main goal is the pursuit of enjoyment, especially in the form of a glutinous meal." He placed the side of his hand next to his mouth and added in a whisper, "Of which our holy brother would secretly love to partake. But, in truth, Epicurus disdained pleasure for pleasure's sake and proclaimed the absence of pain as the main goal of life. He preached prudence, not gluttony; individual happiness, not unmodified indulgence. He was a materialist who followed the basic atomist premise of atoms and the void, yet disagreed with them on the idea of necessity.

"Remember last week? The one fragment from Leucippus: '. . . but all things happen for a reason and of *ne-cess-i-ty*.'"

He dragged out the word. "What Epicurus disliked about the notion of necessity was its potential linkage with religion. And he fiercely opposed religion and wished to separate it from philosophy. He believed in the existence of the gods but said that they lived in a distant realm, never involving themselves with petty human affairs. And, as far as he was concerned, the two greatest sources of anxiety were the dread of death and religion, which promoted ignorance and fear."

Don Ruggero looked at the boys and could see in their faces the weariness induced by the warmth of the fire. He stood and grasped a brass rod on the side of the fireplace and stabbed at the center of the burning pile, collapsing it into a growing heap of white-hot coals, a spray of red cinders rising in the draft. He asked that they move their chairs away from the hearth to the front of his desk.

Then he resumed his lecture. "Epicurus did not believe that the atoms were governed by natural laws out of necessity. Instead, it came to him to propose a kind of *spontaneous motion* of the atoms, swerving from the perpendicular as they fall through the void. This swerving was responsible for creating the material world." His hands swiveled under the spell of the swerving like a conductor of a wild symphony trying to keep up with staccato notes.

"After his own death, some of his followers took his 'absence of pain' notion to a hedonistic extreme, and these excesses soon became associated with his name. This, of course, is a shame." Don Ruggero walked to the sliding ladder and pushed it across the track of the wall, then climbed to a point where he faced a haphazard heap of manuscripts. He leafed through the pile. "Ah," he smiled. "Here it is."

He climbed down to his warming station. "It's a shame," he repeated, "because when you read the poem of his renowned disciple, our friend, Lucretius," he raised the manuscript toward them, "you understand the true nature of epicurean ideals presented in a lyrically elegant fashion. *De Rerum Naturum* became the introductory source for atomist philosophy to Renaissance thinkers."

He carefully leafed through the folio, which was a copy of the original Bracciolino manuscript given to him by a friend from Florence. He handed the copy to Lionardo and asked the boys to share it carefully. "As you already know, it's a lengthy poem. In fact, I would be willing to guess that the first thing you did when you opened your copy was to go to the end to see just how much work you were in for." The priest looked back and forth between the boys. "I'm right, huh? 'My God,' you probably thought, '7,400 lines of Latin contained in five books, all written in Latin, hexameter rhyme. How will I get through this?'" He retrieved the manuscript, climbed the ladder, and re-deposited it in its elevated perch.

"You said that you had translated to line . . . what was it? Four hundred something?"

"Four hundred eighty-three, Maestro."

"So, you have already covered the foundation of his philosophy—the cardinal principle of atomism that nothing exists but atoms and the void. That the atoms are infinite in number, constantly in motion, and can never be created or destroyed. Some of these atoms support life. Others make for disease, volcanic explosions, wild beasts, death, and so on."

The maestro went on to describe how Lucretius explained the mechanical laws of nature and the moral ideal of the pursuit of pleasure. "As you will see in later chapters, Lucretius debunks the superstitions surrounding natural phenomenon like earthquakes, lightning, rainstorms. Like his atomist predecessors, he was a complete materialist who felt that religion was the great deceiver of mankind. He was convinced that the soul was composed of atoms that were dispersed when the body dies." The teacher stopped speaking and rose to the full height of his toes.

From there, with fingers pinched, he started bouncing on every syllable, slowly, as he did whenever he wished to emphasize a thought. "Therefore," he said with repeated bounces, "there . . . was . . . no . . . reason . . . to . . . fear . . . the . . . hereafter." He held his elevated position and then, in an exaggerated tone, with an elongated finger pointed to the heavens, he loudly proclaimed, "'Heresy! Pure Heresy,' the Church says."

With a great sigh, he lowered himself to his seat. "To the legitimate skeptic who might then ask why humans should live a moral life, Lucretius would offer Democritus's improbable and yet highly moral ethic: 'The generous man is he who does not look for a return, but who does good things by choice.'"

He stared off through a window and held the thought for a moment. "Imagine that. People should lead a good life out of conviction, not out of some compulsion or in the selfish hope of receiving eternal reward."

A wide smile settled on his face as he turned back to his pupils. "The poem reveals a passionate man who saw in the simple wonders of nature the most marvelous examples of existence, and his words express that grandeur. But do we know what he was like as a person?" he asked. "Well, of his actual life, little is known. What we do know is that he lived in the years from about 99 to 55 before the birth of our Lord, during the last part of Julius Caesar's life, when the teachings of Epicurus were popular among the educated class. Later, during the Emperor Augustus's reign, the Roman Empire was forging its order within the known world, and it needed the ethic of a martial populace to endorse its imperial motives."

The maestro took Tommaso's copy of the poem and paged through it. "For generals and politicians, philosophers and scholars, and even the common public," he said, "the feverish pitch of imperial times can lead to a restless anxiety. Do we not know of this ourselves, in our own time and place? And as for the poet, the person of soulful persuasion who cares more for the beauty and fragrance of a flower than for the power and plunder of conquest? Tell me. How can he escape the mayhem? Here it is: 'For neither can we pursue our task with tranquil mind in this untranquil time of our country.'

"He could not escape it. Not when the emperor Augustus had revived pagan religion, and the fashionable epicurean antagonism among the higher Roman classes was no longer appreciated. Lucretius agreed with Epicurus about religion. Both men believed that the gods do exist in a realm far removed from the petty problems of humanity. The fixed laws of nature govern our world, thus obviating the need for interference or the usurpation of divine beings."

Ruggero continued searching through the text, as he spoke. "Lucretius expressed Epicurus's anger at religion for its manipulation of humanity's common fears when he said that religion thrived on ignorance and promoted superstition. The priests and the soothsayers of Roman times exploited the fear of perpetual punishment for personal and political gain. Hear this: 'O unhappy race of men! They attributed such acts, besides bitter wrath, to the gods! What lamentations did they then prepare for themselves and what sufferings for us! What fears have they entailed upon our posterity!'

"Is there any surprise then, my boys, that Lucretius's poem was suppressed and nearly lost to us? And as for the poet, what happened to him?" Ruggero stared back and forth between them in the knowledge that they lacked. "A single brief assertion, written by St. Jerome over two centuries after Lucretius's death, claimed that the poet committed suicide due to insanity, which resulted from a love philter. Jerome added that *De rerum natura* was written between bouts of madness, and that Cicero then edited it to its final polished form. None of these assertions have ever been corroborated."

The priest began pacing back and forth, his hand pulling at his chin. "If Lucretius did suffer from mental illness, it may have been a symptom of depression, perhaps brought on by the political situation of his time, or due to the efforts of his detractors, or because of a failed love affair; for indeed, as his poem testifies, he was a passionate man. And as you will learn in time, the unfinished nature of the poem lends some support to the suicide theory or at least to a sudden death from some unknown cause. In any case, a fervent man of the Church like St. Jerome could hardly be considered an unbiased historian on the life of an iconoclast who was said to have despised religion.

"Which brings up the crucial point that you asked about last week, Lionardo." Don Ruggero stopped pacing and stared back and forth between the two boys. "We know Lucretius disliked organized religion, but was he really an atheist?" He paused to consider his answer. "To me, the moderation that he suggests as a path to happiness echoes the basic principles of religion. I am of the persuasion that an unbiased reading of *De rerum natura* reveals a spiritual conviction that negates the 'atheist' epithet. He may have opposed organized religion, but he was a very religious or, perhaps more accurately, a very spiritual man. It seems obvious to me that most human beings need to practice religion to find a better way to live—most humans, but not all. People who can arrive at a truthful life through a humble process of study without resorting to the narrow precepts of religion, whether they know it or not, they are the descendants of the atomists.

"At the time that Poggio found the copy of *De rerum natura,* the Church was amid troublesome times with multiple popes, an irreverent clergy, heretics, and wars. Of course, wars always seem to be raging, and they often involve the religious crisis of the day. It took nearly fifteen-hundred years before the beauty and imagination of Lucretius's poem was rediscovered. The rebirth of his poetry was, I believe, an example of the atomist principle that the forces of creation and destruction were in perfect balance, and that atoms—of which even ideas are composed—never die.

Don Ruggero concluded by, again, contrasting the atomists' desire to understand how nature operated with the Aristotelian concept of purpose. "In the thirteenth century," he explained, "Thomas Aquinas, the pre-eminent Scholastic philosopher of the Catholic Church, codified Aristotle's philosophy as the basis for the Church's teachings. These days, any progress in natural philosophy usually forces one to usurp some precept or idea of Aristotle. As a result, the underpinnings of Catholic theology have also been shaken, and no one, it seems, can make the ossified Sacred Curia realize that it does not need to come to this. Which means, my good boys, that we must proceed with our efforts; yet, as we discussed last time, we must do so cautiously. But don't worry. We will come up with an anodyne statement—true, of course—to offer the rector prior to your next meeting with him."

As the kindly priest had predicted, Tommaso was summoned to the rector's office after dinner that evening. This erased the lingering doubt that Lionardo ashamedly harbored regarding any collusion by his friend with those opposed to Don Ruggero.

* * *

The maestro's sessions continued through autumn and into the early months of winter, 1631. He was pleased enough with his pupils' progress that he shortened the classes to allow more time for Saturday exercise. He announced that decision at a session near the end of November, calling an end to the class after an hour and assuring the boys that they would follow this new schedule for the next three classes in December until Christmas holiday.

For a few months after their initial meeting with the rector, the boys reported the same summary of the classes during their conferences with him. However, the need to continue reporting ceased completely in the new year after a tragedy that struck the rector and several others at the school and throughout the city.

Chapter 5

The Eruption of Vesuvius

Naples—December 1631

According to written accounts, around midnight on the fifteenth of December 1631, a servant in the Neapolitan *palazzo* of the Marchese d'Arena saw a bar of fire rise from the volcano in a long arc that seemed to stretch all the way to Pozzuoli. Other people in various locations around Mount Vesuvius confirmed this fire-arc apparition, and many of those witnesses spoke of repeated tremors that shook the area with increasing force throughout the night. Around 4:00 that morning, the entire city of Naples—including Lionardo DiCapua and the other students at the Ratio Studiorum—was suddenly awakened by the violent shaking.

The tremors lasted for several minutes, vibrating and, in many cases, collapsing the rigid stone buildings throughout the city. In every public and private structure, every home and every place of business, materials were strewn about, resulting in numerous injuries and conflagrations. Although this brief demonstration of nature's violence had abused many and terrified even the most resolute, it was just a precursor of the destruction yet to come. Within a few hours of those first shakes, the great, giant Mount Vesuvius awakened from its slumber. Fables abounded in their time, yet none of the inhabitants of the area had been alive when the fire and fury of the mighty volcano had last been unleashed over a hundred years earlier.

The top of the mountain opened, producing flames, smoke, and ash, followed by an explosion of rocks exiting from multiple fissures. One nearby observer described the site as appearing like pyrotechnics on a holiday. As the vents continued to widen, a cloud of smoke, silhouetted by lightning and intermittent explosions of hot stones, produced a column of ash that smelled of sulfur and burnt bitumen. It drifted toward the city and across the region as far away as Dalmatia to the east. Residents who lived nearest the mountain tried to run; many were suffocated in the exuberance of smoky ash. Survivors could not decide on a course of action; by turns having run outside to escape the dangers of fire in their homes, they were likewise fearful of the smoke and debris that filled the air.

When the tremors started, Lionardo awakened in his dark dorm room to a disorienting confusion of crumbling plaster, shattering windows, projectiles of books and other objects, accompanied by the surging motion of the earth and the screaming of terrified and injured students—all of which made getting out of his room a frightening hazard. Once in the hallway, he ran for an exit and headed to the open campo as the shaking temporarily ceased. In the dawning light, he saw blood coming from cuts to his bare feet and felt a tender swelling on the back of his scalp. Like the others, he was inadequately dressed against the weather with little time to perceive the cold once the mountain soon began to rumble again in violent spasms and shooting flames. An older priest removed the rosary from around his neck, fell to his knees on the field and led the gathering in prayer. Lionardo spotted Don Ruggero, his great bald head swerving above the crowd from side to side like a lighthouse in a raging storm. Lionardo limped to him and hugged him tightly. The priest checked his injuries then asked, "Have you seen Tommaso?"

"No, I haven't."

"You have some cuts, but you're going to be fine," Don Ruggero tried to calm the frightened boy. "Everything will be all right, Lionardo. Stay right here and don't leave. I'm going to look for Tommaso. Do you hear me? Stay here, Lionardo. Do you understand?"

Lionardo nodded then sat in the grass, shivering and on the verge of tears. Some indefinite time later, the priest returned holding onto Tommaso wrapped in a blanket. He had cuts on his face. His thick black hair was matted with blood. The priest had another blanket for Lionardo, then gathered the two boys under his arms, assuring them that they were safe. Both boys sobbed and held onto the kindly priest who looked in awe at the Vesuvian display.

"Do you recall the passage from the fifth book of *De rerum natura?*" he asked, hoping to distract the boys. "Lucretius advises the reader to avoid giving in to the powerful urge to lay the blame for cataclysmic events on superstitious origins." He paused to stare at the violent, flaming volcano. Then from memory, he quoted the text:

> When the whole earth totters under our feet, and cities shaken to their base fall or threaten to fall, what wonder is it, that the nations of the world despise and humble themselves, and admit the vast influence of the gods over the world, and their stupendous power to govern all things? . . . These points, then, being laid down and admitted, the earthquakes on the surface, when it is shaken by great falls of substances beneath.

* * *

An eyewitness to the great eruption was the founder of the famous Neapolitan literary academy known as the *Oziosi* ("the idle ones"), the Marchese Giovanni Battista Manso. He was a close friend of the cardinal archbishop of Naples, who told him he had been forced to flee his residence in Torre del Greco by boat, narrowly escaping the complete destruction of the town. In a letter Manso sent to an acquaintance in Rome a few days after the events, he described how, around 1:00 in the afternoon on that terrible day, the rising sun could not penetrate the thick curtain of smoke. The shifting winds carried a rain of smoldering ash that strangled one's breath and became the source of numerous fires.

By 3:00 in the afternoon, Naples was on full alert. With the earth tottering beneath their feet, as Lucretius had noted, the people of Naples tried to appease their God by following the call from the cardinal archbishop to form a procession through the streets. When another episode of violent shaking began during the parade, the participants panicked, fearing that the Day of Judgment was at hand. As the procession arrived at the Carmine church later that evening, another powerful earthquake shook the ground and rattled the buildings. The people joined their cardinal in the sincerest supplication to their patron, Saint Gennaro, proclaiming that if he could ease God's fury and spare the city, Naples would be forever grateful.

That night Lionardo and other students at the Ratio saw fire glowing on top of the angry giant and red, hot streaks flowing in fast-moving, fiery rivulets down its flanks. A dense covering of ash hovered several kilometers into the sky above the volcano before settling on the city, obscuring Vesuvius until late morning on Wednesday the seventeenth, when the eruption reached its climax with another strong *terremoto*. This last quake caused a dramatic retreat of the coastline, followed shortly thereafter by a surging wave said to be ten meters in height. Lava again poured out of the crater in flowing rivers that quickly reached the agitated sea. Thence a violent thunderstorm flooded the region with heavy rains resulting in mudflows that cooled and tempered the lava. Later that afternoon, the crater collapsed, causing a reduction in the height of the volcano by a third of its original size.

Mount Vesuvius had vented. The worst was over.

* * *

The next afternoon, another procession departed the cathedral, this time with the viceroy in attendance. On that same Thursday afternoon and on the following day, a pious competition erupted between the Jesuits and the Franciscans, with each order arranging a procession carrying relics of their patron saint who, they hoped, would unseat San Gennaro as patron saint of Naples.

Ultimately, San Gennaro maintained his position, especially after the Marchese Manso reported a miracle witnessed by the people who were crowded outside the cathedral at the beginning of the first procession. They claimed to have seen San Gennaro in a magnificent episcopal outfit hovering in the great window above the entry doors where he blessed the people. This flying apparition convinced the public that it was he who had interceded with God to save Naples. Hence, to this day, he maintains the undisputed title as patron saint and protector of the city. The Neapolitan artist Domenico Gargiulo's *Eruption of Vesuvius* captured that confirming scene. There—in a cloud above the teeming streets, assisted by several putti bearing his relics—is San Gennaro with his hands raised in the direction of the volcano that looms close-by in its most angered state.

All of Naples and the surrounding countryside was convulsed by the cataclysmic events that ended the year of our Lord 1631. In nearby Herculaneum, the accumulation of ash rose to fifteen palms and in Bagnoli Irpino's provincial city of Avellino, some seventy kilometers from Naples, five palms of ash gathered. For provincial villages like Bagnoli Irpino, some good came from the disaster. Villagers were forgiven their taxes and the necessity of providing soldiers for the war effort in the north. But the damage to farms and grazing lands had a pronounced impact on grain harvests and the survival of livestock. The resulting shortages would affect the kingdom for years afterward, and contributed to the social problems that led to a calamitous political upheaval in the following decade.

The sudden and inexplicable fury of the awakened monster provoked deep terror among a citizenry grown comfortable with it as a tranquil backdrop. Hence, regardless of their status, the people experienced a return to penitential practices and pious devotion. Indeed, Vesuvius released not just ash and lava, but also an outburst of religious passion that enhanced financial support for artists whose work focused on their redemptive patron saint, San Gennaro. This energy culminated in the completion and decoration of the Chapel of the Treasury of San Gennaro in the Cathedral, an assemblage of paintings, frescoes, marble work, and spectacular silver busts—one of the greatest collections of art in all of Italy.

* * *

For Lionardo, Tommaso, and the other students, the Ratio Studiorum closed for an extended vacation during the Feast of the Nativity, the longest vacation they would have throughout their years of study. During that break, a temporary rector was appointed to replace the old rector. He had been knocked unconscious by falling debris, leaving him with a loss of memory and occasional convulsive fits, such that he never returned to his former position.

Most of the boarders, like Lionardo and Tommaso, were forced to remain at school, due to the destruction and the accumulated debris that made the roads impassable. Beyond the logistical problems, the emotional ordeal suffered by Lionardo reopened the scar of the wound caused by the loss of his parents, forcing him to encounter, once again, the uncertainty of life, the fragility of existence. In some ways, this trauma was worse than the one before since he was now in the city, far from home, without the support of his extended family. True, he had Tommaso and other friends, and the kindly Don Ruggero did his best to console the boy. But try as they might, none of them could ease the isolation Lionardo felt nor the overwhelming sense that he had been abandoned by cruel fate. It would take all that vacation for him to recover from the strain. Although, in truth, like all children orphaned at a tender age, he carried that stifled burden for the rest of his days.

Chapter 6

Medical School and Marcaurelio Severino

Naples—1635

Lionardo and Tommaso continued meeting with Don Ruggero through their years at the Ratio Studiorum. He was like a kind uncle who shared his knowledge and life experiences, celebrated their successes, guided them through difficult times, and was always available to counsel them.

In the summer of 1635, the boys (now young men) completed the formal curriculum of the school. Tommaso Cornelio, possessing a more adventurous spirit, decided to travel outside southern Italy in search of inspiration that might give some direction to his life. Lionardo DiCapua would continue his studies, entering the curriculum of law at the University of Naples. The two friends parted and would not see each other again for several years.[1]

Lionardo remained in the law school for a year, then abruptly switched course and entered the medical school. According to his biographer, Niccolo Amenta, the main reason for switching from law to medicine was a petition by family and friends from his hometown of Bagnoli Irpino, urging him to take up medicine. Lionardo had returned to Bagnoli during the Christmas season of 1635 and while there, he observed the doctor of physick in town give a purgative, and an emetic coupled with two applications of the *salasso* to a feverish and delirious child of a friend.

In a matter of hours, the child deteriorated and never regained consciousness. She died, with lips parched, and the skin on her face pale and shrunken, which brought back to Lionardo that horrible visage of his mother after her death. Afterwards, when Uncle Horace and others approached Lionardo to consider switching his curriculum to medicine, it took little convincing.

Lionardo was above eighteen years of age, and he held in his heart the unsettled longing of an orphan for what had been lost. The Irpino was in his blood. His family lived there. His parents and his ancestors were buried there. This deep connection, fractured at a young age by the death of his parents, reinforced his decision. But in truth, there was another reason, equally as important to him, one that Amenta, whose life's work centered on literature, may not have fully appreciated.

As the seventeenth century unfolded, the study of medicine, burdened for centuries by unchallenged Galenic assumptions, was the discipline in which the most dramatic innovations were occurring, particularly regarding human anatomy. In the milieu of the university, the excitement surrounding those discoveries, which followed one upon another, soon challenged the hold of traditional authority. Students with Lionardo's philosophical leanings were emboldened to pursue other methods of securing the truth.

It was a time of great change. It could be argued that the key pre-condition to this awakening was Poggio Bracciolini's rediscovery of Lucretius's *On the Nature of Things,* which had great influence on those natural philosophers who were making the breakthroughs. Lionardo's exposure to atomism during Don Ruggero's special classes inspired him to pursue the new and evolving investigational approach to medicine. Thus, as his family and friends had hoped, in the fall of 1636, he gave up legal studies to enroll in the medical school in Naples, one of the oldest in continental Europe.

* * *

The medical school at the University of Naples was closely affiliated with the *Ospedale Santa Maria d'Incurabili* (the Hospital
of the Incurables), which had been built in 1522 by a woman
named Maria Longo, wife of the Prime Minister to the King of
Spain. She herself had suffered from a debilitating and painful
arthritic disease that confined her to bed until she obtained a
cure while on pilgrimage to the shrine at Loreto. Thereafter, she
devoted herself to the care of the sick and built the hospital that
was intended to care for sufferers of chronic diseases.

Naples enjoyed a memorable and joyous moment on March
23, 1522, for it was on that spring day that the new hospital
was officially opened. Signora Longo herself led a procession
of the sick from the old hospital at Angevin Castle to the new
hospital on Caponapoli Hill. Imagine the site: A succession of
patients, sickened with a variety of physical and mental ailments,
walking alone or with the assistance of staff or family members,
perhaps on crutches, some bandaged, some carried in a litter
or transported in a carriage through the crowded streets, up the
cobbles to the new hospital on the hill.

Signora Longo was inspired by her mission to treat the poor
at what she hoped would be the best hospital in the kingdom;
hence, she recruited the best doctors of the day. In time, this large
facility of over 1600 beds became famous all over Europe. Indeed,
it became so renowned that one of the ancillary provisions offered
to the patients and their families was an interpretive service for
the many foreigners who came to Naples for treatment.

The hospital specialized in incurable diseases such as apo-
plexy, epilepsy, burns, pleurisy, kidney stones, and the three
categories of insanity—mania, melancholy, and *taciti* (extreme
melancholy). One of the more interesting aspects of the administration of the *Ospedale* was that it abolished the strict hierarchy
that continued to exist in many other hospitals. Thus, it was

possible for a physician to evaluate and call for a consultation with a specialist without the permission of the chief of service.[2]

* * *

By the time Lionardo began the medical curriculum, the long-standing proscription against human dissection had disappeared in Naples. As a result, medical students no longer needed to rely on the erroneous theories of a professor whose human anatomical expertise had been gained through the dissection of lower animals. Instead, patients who died and were left unclaimed at the *Incurabili* provided a steady supply of cadavers. Furthermore, an arrangement had been made between the priests of the Company of *Santa Maria Succurre Miseris* (the "Providers of Mercy" who cared for the spiritual needs of criminals set to be executed) and the hospital anatomy department that accepted the corpses after they had been dispatched.

Medical students also had a reliable textbook, Andreas Vesalius's remarkable *De Humani Corporis Fabrica (The Structure of the Human Body)* to guide their dissections. After years of diligent, surreptitious effort, Vesalius published an incomparable combination of art and science in which students discovered the correct nature of the human body. The *Fabrica,* originally published in 1543, is one of the most remarkable products of the Renaissance both in its artistic form and its pedagogical function. Anatomists who did not wear the blinders of Galenic tradition stepped down from their lecture podium, took instruments in hand, and performed the dissections, using the *Fabrica* as their guide. To Lionardo's benefit, his anatomy professor was one who never wore the Galenic blinders. That man, Maraurelio Severino, became the second great intellectual influence in Lionardo's life. Like Don Ruggero, Severino developed a fond regard for his pupil and remained, not just his mentor, but also a close friend.

Severino, like Tommaso Cornelio, was of Calabrian origins and had studied philosophy under his fellow *Calabrese,* the Dominican monk Tommaso Campanella, who insisted on questioning orthodoxy. Like Lionardo, Severino began his professional studies in law and then switched to the study of medicine.

Propelled by Versalius's *Fabrica,* Severino became a man possessed by a passion to understand the evolving field of anatomic studies. He was also greatly influenced by atomist ideas. He dissected and studied a wide range of vertebrate and invertebrate specimens and encouraged his students to do the same. His book on the comparative anatomy of animals, *Zootomia Democritea,* is testimony to his innovative genius.

Severino corresponded with many of the important physicians and scientists of his time from outside Italy. His willingness to embrace new ideas was best illustrated by his stance on William Harvey's *De Motu Cordis (On the Motion of the Heart).* Harvey had studied medicine at the renowned University of Padua under anatomy professors who had a direct link back to Vesalius. In 1628, eight years before Lionardo entered medical school, Harvey published his groundbreaking opus, which detailed the continuous circulation of blood within a closed circulatory system.

At first, Marcaurelio Severino refused to accept the theory. However, he reversed his position after proving it to himself through careful dissection and observation. In truth, few men of Severino's status, in any field, from his or any other time, would have the integrity to admit his mistake. This intellectual honesty and devotion to his art is the mark of a truly enlightened man. Thus, he had a profound effect upon the many students who learned from him, including Lionardo DiCapua.

* * *

The spirit of investigation that propelled Severino enlivened young DiCapua to focus on the study of anatomy, which, thanks to his maestro, became the most exciting course in the medical curriculum.[3]

Few professors approached their specialty with the openness of Marcaurelio Severino. He was the brilliant exception who would, like others throughout history, pay a dear price for his unbiased and courageous pursuit of truth. Yet he and his methods would live on through a new generation of physicians, like Lionardo DiCapua, who helped formulate a new, modern direction for medicine.[4]

For the rest of his life, Lionardo applied the principles he had learned under Severino and Don Ruggero to question unproven orthodox precepts. DiCapua disputed the discrepancies between what the doctors of physick were teaching him and what he was directly observing in his care of the infirm. He became convinced that medicine, like natural philosophy, must start from free experimentation and open dialogue. Long-accepted principles should be scrutinized and followed only if they have withstood vigorous, open investigation; otherwise, they should be modified accordingly or abandoned altogether.

The revolutionary concepts that DiCapua held aggravated the Galenists, who made up most of the practicing physicians in the kingdom at that time. Their bitter response to atomist-inspired thinkers like Severino and DiCapua demonstrated that the practice of physick in southern Italy—nay, in all of Europe—was mired down in the parsing of Galen's words.

Despite the intellectual fervor percolating in the kingdom during the first half of the *Seicento*, religious authorities and the doctors of physick remained strongly persuaded in their orthodox ways. Such thinking was enhanced by the fact that the Kingdom of Naples was the most papist-supportive monarchy in all of Europe.

NOTES

1. If the two men stayed in touch through letters, none are known to have survived.

2. The hospital to this day contains a renowned anatomy laboratory, a pharmacy, and a medical herb garden *(orto medicale),* which, as will be seen in due course, is an important part of Lionardo's story. The school became known for its gifted instructors and its rigorous curriculum that emphasized hands-on, bedside care of the sick. It was so admired that the English modeled their own medical schools after the strict teaching program offered at the medical school in Naples and the affiliated *Ospedale.*

3. Amenta tells us that this discipline—so basic and so essential for a true understanding of the functions of the human body—consumed Lionardo. Until the late sixteenth century, the only accepted source of human anatomic truth had been Galen's teachings, which were based mostly on animal dissection. And even after Vesalius, the doctors of physick refused to accept the findings of human dissection if they conflicted with Galen.

   Thus, the study of human gross anatomy and, later, the details of chemical analysis, which men like Lionardo would advocate, became the double portal through which young physicians could discover a new paradigm. During the early part of the *Seicento,* the university became the repository of tradition, which was reinforced by a repetition of classic teachings.

4. Lionardo DiCapua (and others who knew Severino) told me that the drawing of his visage in the front of his brilliant book captures the essence of his personality.

In that depiction, his trunk is turned slightly to the left, but he stares at the viewer, who is immediately drawn into the large, intense eyes. His wrinkled forehead appears pinched by a low hairline above and high arching eyebrows beneath. These brows drop into vertical creases in the middle of the forehead just above the nasal initiation like arrow tips, right and left, pointing toward the keen eyes. His neck is hidden under the white collar of his vestment. Thus, his head rests, it seems somewhat precariously, above a small torso. This effect is exaggerated by shoulders that fall away quickly to a pair of hands, the right holding a pen above scripted paper, the left resting on the crown of a skull. The long, narrow fingers are finely detailed, suited for the pursuit of excellence on the pianoforte or to the careful dissection of an artery from its accompanying nerve.

Taken in its entirety, the drawing presents the impression of a man consumed by passion for his work. A man who never wasted time. A man who applied his considerable capacities to the vigorous exercise of his intellectual pursuits. Scholars rank Severino first, above all others of his time, as the most illustrious teacher at the *Incurabili*. Yet, beyond his abilities as a professor, he was also a renowned physician-surgeon and a great scientist. Unlike many of his contemporaries, he was a clinician who was comfortable with medical therapy, as well as performing surgery.

Chapter 7

La Famiglia Carazutto

Campania—1636

After she finished a slice of lemon *torta,* Faustina lowered the black veil across her face and waited as her eldest son, Giacomo, began his third serving of dessert. She watched him nearly inhale the sweet and wondered how a person could eat so much, yet remain so thin. She rang for the head servant. She told her to serve tea in the sitting room and then have the other servants finish packing the coaches and retire to their rooms. They could clean up after the family departed in the morning.

All four of Faustina's children—Giacomo, the older sister, Diana, their younger brother, Giulio, and the baby of the family, Celestina—followed their mother into the sitting room. A fire had been lit in the great stone hearth, warming the velvet chairs arranged in a half-circle around it. The servant deposited the tea and left as instructed. Faustina raised her veil. Giulio poured a cup of tea, to which he added sugar by a measure of two spoonfuls, then handed the cup to his mother, who stirred the mixture while addressing her brood. She told them that now that their father had been buried for a fortnight, it was time to discuss the future.

Faustina reminded them that, for the past three decades, the harvests in their fiefs had been declining, leaving little extra grain to feed the greatly expanded cattle herds that their father, Carlo, had purchased despite Faustina's protests. At the same time, the crown had been extracting more resources to cover the expenses of the ongoing war in the north, causing a shortage of materials and labor that inflated the costs of completing the new Carazutto palace in Naples. By these and other circumstances—his gambling debts were still being tallied—Carlo Carazutto had been forced to borrow to maintain their accustomed lifestyle. Now that he had passed, his creditors were swarming like jackals seeking their share.

"This may be a low time for our family," Faustina said, rising to face her children, "but we are of ancient, noble clans. We are authentic. Our roots in these lands are long and deep. One will seek in vain for another family with ties that are as tightly woven as ours." She took a sip of tea and continued. "The prestige of our name will always be sought. The old ranking families will wish to ally with us, and the well-placed foreigners need our name to claim legitimacy. What we have is invaluable and we must preserve it."

She told them that the first step in holding their titles would be moving the entire family to the new palace in Naples. Several related reasons for the move had occupied Faustina's mind, and she had considered all of them. By custom, the eldest son could not marry until the death of his father, and now that Carlo had passed, they would have a better chance of finding a suitable partner for Giacomo in the capital. Giulio would finish his studies in Naples at the Carazutto college. Diana would be introduced into Neapolitan society in the hope of arranging a worthy mate, who would be seeking a small dowry. If need be, Faustina would rely on the support of the *Monte di maritaggi,* which had been established by noblemen from the *Seggio* of the *Capuana* (the Capuan section of Naples) to cover the costs of marrying-off a female. Carlo had been one of the original investors in the months after the birth of his first daughter.

The idea behind the Monte was to pool and invest the money on more favorable terms than an individual could attain, so that by the time of a daughter's wedding, enough interest would have accrued to cover the costs. It was a shrewd response to the ever-inflating expectations placed on the brides' families, many of whom (like the *Famiglia Carazutto*) were facing increasing economic difficulties. Faustina knew that other members of the Monte had daughters about Diana's age. If all of them married around the same time, they wouldn't have accumulated enough interest on the investment for all the young brides' families; it could take a considerable period before enough interest would again accumulate. Therefore, it was important that Diana be wed quickly—or not at all.

The youngest child, Celestina, was fifteen years old. There was no rush to arrange her situation, so she would remain with her mother at the palace in Naples while Faustina dealt with her older children—most importantly, with her eldest.

As the first-born son, the *primogeniture,* Giacomo would inherit most of the family patrimony, including the lands, titles, palaces, and miscellaneous investments. But he would also inherit his father's considerable debt. Faustina explained that, after a careful review of the claims against the family with the accountants, if all the demands had to be met immediately, the family would be bankrupt. They would be forced to repay the financiers with their *feudi* (their ancestral properties) and, once gone, they would lose not only the income generated by the lands, but also the noble titles that accompanied them.

Giacomo had been continuously pacing behind the row of chairs since his mother began speaking. When he stopped to sit down in his chair, his legs continued bouncing on the tip of his toes. "But mother," he said with quivering voice, "how do we prevent the inevitable? You know that all of father's debtors will demand immediate repayment. If we have no funds, what else can we do but forfeit the holdings?"

Faustina placed her half-empty cup on the silver tray. For the past few weeks, whenever she ate or drank anything sweet, the first molar in her left upper jaw would begin to throb. She reached inside the pocket of her black dress for her vial of cloves, which, she realized, she had left in her bedroom. So she wiped her mouth and pushed the napkin against the painful tooth. Added to her nights of insomnia, the toothache kept her mind in a tempest, on the edge of a foul temper. She couldn't remember the last time she had laughed.

"In order to protect the patrimony," she said to her anxious son, "I will demand that my dowry be returned to me, as permitted. I will also ask for the *antefato* that was promised to me by your father's family before our wedding. Now that Carlo has passed, by law, both are mine. My dowry was thirty-six thousand ducats. The *antefato* was another twelve thousand."

Giacomo stared at his mother while his chin dropped down his bulbous neck with each breath. Suddenly, he sprang from his seat, as if released on a tight spring, and resumed his pacing. He reminded his mother that her demands would have to be met by the same nearly-bankrupt family estate.

Faustina answered, "You are correct, Giacomo. And because there is not enough in the patrimony, you will give me title to the *feudi* of Sostegno and Fonte. My claim will have precedence because it began on our wedding day, years before your father incurred any other debts. The Sacred Royal Council of Naples will undoubtedly recognize me as lord over the *feudi*. Once that is accomplished, you will give your brother his legacies due him from his father, his uncle and his two aunts, which will come to another twenty thousand ducats."

Faustina paused to take a sip of tea, which, again, caused her to grimace. Her salted hair was held in a bun. Shadows from the fire added severity to her face along with a hint of foreboding. She looked at her second son. "Giulio, you will buy Fonte with the twenty thousand from your legacies and you will obtain the princely title attached to it. I will create a legal receipt saying that I also sold Sostegno to you for eighteen thousand ducats, although you will not pay anything for it. That will give you full right to another title. On paper, both *feudi* will be yours. You hold the titles. However, I collect the revenues."

While Giacomo was recovering from this last blow, and the others were still trying to digest their mother's complicated scheme, Faustina announced that the discussion was over. She reminded her children that they would be leaving for the city in the morning. The servants would have everything packed, and the coaches would depart at seven. Diana protested the early departure, but her mother refused to listen. She dismissed them all, except for Giacomo, who grabbed the poker and jabbed at the logs while the others left the room. A rush of glowing sparks snapped like fireworks, ascending into the draft and cracking against the brass screen. Faustina held the pressure on her molar as she watched her agitated son.

Nice things could be said about him, she thought. He was kind to his siblings and respectful of his parents. Yet his odd looks and anxious mannerisms would hardly prompt a woman of taste to ever find him attractive. He was fortunate that noble blood ran in his veins, she reasoned, otherwise he might have fallen in with a travelling circus. If only the handsome and fit Giulio had been her first-born. He would have made a great catch, and families would have lined up to pay dearly for that connection.

Faustina removed the napkin from her tooth and addressed Giacomo. "Why do you worry? You are the first-born male, and I know that all must pass through you. But can't you see that what I am doing will save your patrimony and our titles? Consider the alternative. The debtors would take all our money and most of our holdings. You would end up with little. Your brother and sisters would end up with nothing. Our lands would be lost, and our heritage destroyed."

Giacomo replaced the poker and pulled his chair away from the fire. His cheeks were flushed. The tight, starched collar gripping his bulbous neck was stained with sweat. "That is true, Mother," he answered. "But if those lands survive, by rights they should remain in my line, not my brother's."

Faustina returned the napkin to the tooth and stared at his profile now animated by the play of the flames. He possessed the prominent Carazutto nose defined by a central hump that turned a gradual descent into a precipitous drop. Like the thinning hair on his head, his black eyebrows were narrow, insignificant lines that ran along the ridge above his almond eyes. A full-frontal view of him was like looking at double targets, closely spaced. The eyes bulged from their sockets, revealing a black, bull's-eye pupil surrounded by a band of brown, encompassed by an excessively protruding circle of white. Even on the coldest days, a thin layer of sweat covered his pale skin, yet his lips were usually dry and cracked. Kissing him was an unpleasant task. Faustina knew that finding a bride who might someday actually love him would be difficult. He was the kind of a man that only a mother could love. And that inclination did not come easily to her.

"The lands will remain in your line," she assured him, "and your brother will remain a cadet son. He will not marry with my blessing. If he chooses to do so, he loses everything. Any legitimate heir he might sire would not be recognized. Arrangements would be made to deal with illegitimate ones. I have already considered your objection and you will be named proxy to administer the properties should something happen to Giulio. The lands and the titles will be retained through your line. The only situation in which I might bless a marriage by Giulio would be if, God forbid," here she paused to cross herself then kiss her rosetted fingertips, "something happened to you and your line was left without a son. In that case, we would need to preserve the family name."

"Have you mentioned this part of your arrangement to my brother?"

"No, but as I said, I will let him know, in no uncertain terms, what is expected from him. After he finishes at the college, his uncle can secure a place for him as an officer in the Spanish army, or we can call upon our ecclesiastical preferments for the bishopric of Bovino or the abbey of San Frediana and our other four chapels." She hesitated as a hint of a smile crossed her face. "I always thought that Giulio would make a good presentation with Crozier and Mitre. I suppose he was destined for bishop's robes."

Giacomo again rose to his feet and paced in front of the hearth. His mother watched him, recalling how, since his childhood, she knew that he was possessed of some tremulous illness. Doctors had diagnosed an excessive heat in his blood, which they let on several occasions, allowing his anxiety to ease and rest to come upon him, if only for a while. An old healer in Sostegno once claimed to have developed a potion that could cure his problem. Faustina refused to allow it because her grandfather, who had suffered from similar symptoms, nearly died after taking a locally concocted cure. She would rely instead on the stubborn notion that noble people can overcome their physical debilities or at least compensate for them.

"Giacomo, please try to focus and consider my plan. If we play our roles correctly, we can make our situation appear as though our legal disagreements are substantial, and we can draw them out indefinitely before the council. That would give us the time we need to delay payment to our creditors and repair our misfortune."

Giacomo stopped in front of Faustina and asked, "What of

my sisters, Mother? What will become of them?"

"Diana's temperament is ill-suited for life in a convent." Faustina responded. "A marriage will be arranged. But there is a problem in that the Brienzi, the Alfieri and the Monteforti all have daughters her age who will probably marry in the next year or so, although I can assure you that none of them will make a more elegant wife than our Diana. I will lavish her with the necessary accoutrements to create a quick arrangement, and we can then rely on the *Monte* for the dowry. If we cannot make a quick match, we might not have any choice but to enroll her with the convent of San Gregorio, where your aunt is now the Mother Superior."

"I take it that you have not mentioned this last option to Diana?"

"No, I have not."

Giacomo again set to pacing. "Well . . . that should be interesting. And what of Celestina?"

"For Celestina, I think the convent would be the best option. As it is, she leads a quiet life. She does not mind being alone with her books. She prefers studying to socializing." Faustina paused and lowered her gaze. "Fortune has placed strength and wisdom within her that the rest of you lack. She is content with her life. She does not need a husband to make it more complete. I think she will be fine at San Gregorio."

Giacomo would not admit it to her, but he was surprised at the shrewd calculations that defined his mother's plan. He had always thought of her as his father's passive partner whose main concerns were with the welfare of her children, the decoration of the palaces, the purchase of clothes, and the attainment of fine jewelry—not necessarily in that order. Considering her compelling scheme, he was now re-considering that assessment, as perhaps his father should have. Since the death of her husband, the legal restrictions placed by aristocratic society on the dowry and the *antefato* could give his mother ultimate control of the family fortune. By using the legal system to enforce her preferences, his mother had apparently prevented him from inheriting the entire patrimony due the *primogeniture*. But he also realized that, by protecting those assets from the debtors, her ingenuity would ultimately save it for him and his descendants.

Faustina again pressed the napkin to her painful tooth and held it for some time before offering her concluding thought. "Before you leave this room tonight, Giacomo, I want you to promise me one thing. Your father, God rest his soul, came up with some foolish ideas in his life. If I, in earnest, proposed another viewpoint, he would refuse to consider it no matter how reasonable." She stood and faced her son. "Remember this: A foolish idea is one thing, but to hold to it stubbornly for the sake of pride is to resign all claims to wisdom. We are living the results of that dreaded combination within your father. Henceforth, I ask that you listen to the counsel of others. Do not allow your pride to blind you in your choices, and do not place your family in a predicament that could have been avoided had you acted judiciously."

Giacomo agreed to heed his mother's advice. With that promise, he kissed his mother good night. She lowered the veil over her face and headed for her bedroom. Her toothache had finally eased.

Chapter 8

The Carazutti Come to the City

Naples—1636

After establishing her family in the palace in Naples, Faustina set in motion the deliberate plan that she believed would reclaim the economic fortunes of her family. With desperation in her voice and severity in her manner, she staked her claims before a sympathetic court, asking that her eldest son return her dowry plus the *antefato*. She also asked for Giulio's legacies. Her sons heeded her advice and played their roles as advised: Giacomo protested with righteous indignation as did Giulio, who cited his looming poverty. The court, as Faustina anticipated, did its part to entangle things in a protracted settlement, which usurped the prerogatives of the financiers and kept them at bay for an indefinite period.

While the legal case proceeded, preparations for Giacomo's marriage continued, but at a slower pace than Faustina had hoped. It took over a year before a suitable agreement was made between Giacomo and the daughter of a wealthy Spanish financier and bureaucrat. Faustina set aside her innate displeasure in dealing with the newly minted Spaniards to negotiate terms that brought Imola Portola's enormous dowry of 50,000 ducats, along with an additional 10,000 ducats for Giacomo to buy back the titled fief of Sento, which his father had lost just before his death. Unlike the usually slow exaction of an arrangement between Italian parties, Imola's dowry would arrive on the wedding day in hard assets—cash, capital on tax-farms with guaranteed yields, land and jewels. In exchange, the highly bred and tightly strung Giacomo brought to the Portola family what they needed most. He was the flawed, yet properly credentialed, thoroughbred that would transport them into Neapolitan high society.

This combination of new money with old society did not sit well with members of the established Neapolitan families, particularly, as in Giacomo's case, when an aristocratic man married a woman of lower rank. Nonetheless, for Faustina, the end of her need to preserve the status of her family clearly justified the means used to secure it. Other noble Neapolitan families, equally desperate, had withdrawn from similar arrangements by dint of their pride, only to witness the eventual dissipation of their patrimonies. Ultimately, the one truly embarrassing aspect of Faustina's current predicament was her thought that others were laughing at her for the mistakes that her prideful husband had made—mistakes that she had tried to prevent. More than a year had passed since Carlo's death, but her anger at his poor judgment was keener than ever.

Giacomo's wedding was set for the fall, after the harvests of 1639, which would give Faustina time to complete her crafty plan. In the meantime, Giulio had resumed his final year of studies at the Carazutto college in the *Capuana* quarter. A wealthy Carazutto count had donated the original monies to create the college for the purpose of providing education for the sons within the extended Carazutto family. Each titled member of the clan invested one thousand ducats, while each untitled member gave five hundred ducats, with the result that students received a comfortable annuity during their years of study. The expenses of the teachers, building upkeep, room and board of the fifteen or so students, and the miscellaneous costs for servants, barbers, cooks, the doctor, and the pharmacist were covered by the interest on the original investments, which fortunately (unlike those of the *Monte di maritaggi*) had been spread outside the region. The priests of the Somaschian order were recruited as teachers. The subjects included Catholic doctrine, philosophy, rhetoric, Latin, mathematics and civil law. Lay instructors taught French and the chivalric arts of fencing, music, dancing, and riding. These latter courses had been particularly troublesome for Giacomo when he had attended the college. Giulio, on the other hand, excelled in them.

Indeed, the brothers shared few physical traits. Giulio was tall and handsome. His lips were sumptuously thick, his nose slender, his hair and brows full, and his blue eyes betrayed a distant Norman connection. Whereas Giacomo was jumpy and clumsy, Giulio was tranquil and athletic. Hieronymus Bosch would have found the perfect model in Giacomo, while Giulio was Raphael's ideal. All of which seemed to substantiate the rumor among those who knew the family that Giulio was the product of his mother's passionate *mesalliance*. Why else, they would say, did Carlo relieve the dashing, young, blue-eyed priest of unusual devotion to the family from his pastoral responsibilities and send him to an isolated village in Sicily soon after Faustina began to show?

Giulio finished college in the summer of his twentieth year. As a cadet son, his mother had considered placing him in the church as titular head of their ecclesiastical benefices. In time, he would become a cardinal, like his paternal great uncle through whom the preferments were passed. Having a son directly in charge of these holy offices would be economically beneficial to him and politically beneficial to the family. The endowment of an abbey or a chapel was an exercise in devotion common among wealthy women. The money was invested directly or loaned to peasants, either as cash or in the form of grain at an interest rate typically of 8 percent. A small part of the acquired interest would be donated back to the village for the welfare of the peasants, through the maintenance of hospitals and medicines for the poor, and dowries for a small number of girls who excelled in catechism, while most of the annual income of each benefice went to the priests and the jurisdictional bishop. Added together, it represented a substantial amount of money.

Faustina's unspoken concern about a religious life for Giulio was the possibility that Giacomo might be too fragile and weak in the loins and thus unable to leave a son for the possession of the titles. In that case, Giulio would need to marry, which could prove difficult should he become a bishop. Thus, instead of having Giulio pursue the religious life, Faustina asked her brother, Pietro, who was himself a cadet son, to secure an appointment in the Spanish army. He found a captain's position for Giulio, far from the battlefronts.

After his time at Carazutto college, Giulio enrolled in the military academy in Naples. When his officer training was finished, he gathered his things and wished a sad farewell to his beloved sisters before heading north to Flanders to assume an administrative position in support of the Spanish against the Dutch forces. But Giulio clamored for more than the administrative job chosen for him. He was a young man of high spirits, who was hoping to escape his staid life. He made it clear to his sisters that his new appointment was a disappointment. Celestina recognized the despondency that replaced his usually carefree nature for, in it, she sensed a reflection of her own increasing desperation.

As for the Carazutto daughters, Diana was happy with her new life in the capital. Being from a powerful clan that moved in the best circles meant that Diana participated in the events of court life. Naples, like Paris, was, for the high aristocracy, the center of the marriage market where the prestige of the Carazutto name was substantial. Faustina had beautiful gowns cut for Diana that complemented the coiffures and the expensive family jewels that also enhanced her natural beauty. Diana was a tall, sensuous woman with the fine features of her mother's side of the family. She had the same sumptuous lips as Giulio, her hair was thick and naturally curly, and her blue-green eyes mesmerized like a clear pool on a quiet day. She was present at every formal ball, at which she danced nearly every dance. Graceful like her younger brother, Diana's natural rhythm kept her light on her feet. Her mood, in public, was light and gay. Several young men expressed interest.

One of her suitors, from a clan with membership in the prominent *Seggio di Porto,* was particularly intent. Preliminary discussions ensued through the established rituals of the aristocratic network. The intermediaries met to discuss a substantial dowry request from the prospective family. As Faustina had suspected, the groom's elevated position naturally demanded a handsome fee. She appealed to the *Monte*. The board of governors apologized and told her the same thing they eventually told three other imminent petitioners: The initial investments of the *Monte* had been made in enterprises within the kingdom where the regional economy had remained stagnant. Thus, even though the original principal had not been tapped, the interest had not accrued as scheduled. The board voted to apportion the available accumulated interest equally, but they were constrained by their original charter from dipping into the principal. The amount that could be distributed to each petitioner would be less than half of what the prospective groom's family had suggested to Faustina.

If the marriage would have been profitable, Faustina somehow would have raised the balance after the *Monte* contribution. But in the tightly structured mores of the old aristocracy, no economic advantages came to an established family by marrying a daughter into another equally ensconced clan. Consequently, arranging a daughter's marriage to a lower family was a common and well-accepted practice; it also presented an opportunity for the lesser aristocracy to reach the highest echelon simply by shedding some of their recently obtained resources. Shrewd Faustina was aware of this and let it be known that other offers would be entertained. This outraged the originally intended *Porto* clan and afforded Faustina a measure of satisfaction by letting it be known that she did not care a pin over their perceived insult.

Three lower families quickly pursued the opportunity with more reasonable requests at much better terms. Their intermediaries were anxious to meet the demands. Faustina decided to use the necessity of concentrating on Giacomo's more immediate arrangements as a delay maneuver to hopefully start a bidding tangle. Diana did not mind. She was happy to remain on the glittery social circuit for as long as possible.

Having convinced herself that Celestina favored a contemplative life, Faustina enrolled her youngest with a private tutor, a Jesuit priest who met with her six days a week. The curriculum included Latin grammar and the classics, philosophy, French and some mathematics. Celestina did well in all of them, especially Latin grammar. Perhaps because of her own history with ordained instructors, Faustina made sure that the teacher was a plain-looking man with a sincere calling to the priesthood. She chose a cadet son of a wealthy Neapolitan family who lived a contented life focused on learning and teaching. Celestina was impressed with his love for knowledge, a passion that she shared.

During her childhood, Celestina's father often took her on riding excursions into the countryside surrounding their feudal lands where the fields of grain rolled in the wind like waves in a golden ocean, and the meadows were scented with wildflowers and pungent herbs. Now a walk in the palace garden would have to suffice her desire for wider exploration. She kidded with one of the servants (a young woman her same age) that she would someday escape the surrounding walls to visit her. The servant,

Sophia, reminded her how unpleasant the city could be for a young woman not used to its rough ways, which only enticed the naïve Celestina even more.

One Thursday afternoon in the spring, while her mother was distracted with preparations for Giacomo's marriage, Celestina left the Carazutto palace, which was near the Church of *San Giovanni di Carbonara,* and headed downhill in the direction of the bay, holding to the wide street that ran beside the stone ramparts. At the *Capuana* portal she headed back into the maze of pathways and buildings. The streets were crowded with pedestrians and carriages. Piles of horse dung dotted the pavement and a strong smell of excrement hung in the air. She covered her head with her shawl and entered her first destination, the ancient *Basilica of San Lorenzo.*

In contrast to the sights and smells outside, the interior of the ancient basilica held the fragrance of incense from innumerable liturgical ceremonies within its Gothic splendor. After her eyes adjusted to the subdued light, she walked along the main aisle of colored marble toward the apse, genuflected, and knelt at the altar rail. Her teacher had told her the history of the Basilica. It was a palimpsest upon which the story of Naples had been written over the centuries, beginning in the era when Naples was *Neapolis,* one of the great cities within *Magna Grecia.* The basilica rose upon an early Greek *agora* built, according to the legend, after the siren Parthenope had failed to seduce Ulysses and was washed ashore. The Romans expanded the space with a road that held a large open market on its flanks. In medieval times, Boccaccio had met his Fiametta inside the church. And more recently, Celestina's teacher had been ordained before the high altar. She looked up to the soaring wooden trusses and said a short prayer then retraced her path up the marble canyon, exiting through the great wooden door.

Using the old walls as a guide, Celestina turned down hill,

toward the bay. Near the *Nolana* portal, a breeze off the Mediterranean covered the rancid smells of the streets as the crowds grew larger near the entry to the open market. She followed the crush of people through the narrow portal that opened into the spacious *Piazza del Mercato*, a semi-circular piazza that, at the far end, held sheets of rough hemp separated by wooden poles into individual stalls. The fabric undulated in the light ocean breeze, shading the vendors and their goods in its billowing swells. Customers gathered about the stalls of enterprising merchants who hawked their produce, dry goods, live poultry, fish, or mollusks. In the center, a delicately carved marble fountain provided continuous streams of fresh water. Around it, small groups of men huddled in animated conversation, using a repertoire of hand and facial signals to accentuate their points. Their rough dialect often neglected the final vowel thus chopping each sentence into near grunts.

Celestina passed the rows of stalls and came to a tapered street that exited the piazza on the side opposite the entry portal, where Sophia said she lived. Celestina wandered through the warren of tall buildings searching for Sophia's tenement, but she became disoriented beneath the lines of wet laundry that hung in the air high above her from one building across the narrow street to another, obscuring the sky. The occasional breeze off the bay caused the limp articles to awaken and dance a lively *tarantella*. People chatted across balconies crowded with plants and birdcages. Children played games along the crowded streets, dashing around pedestrians and carriages in the dark passageways, which again took on the smell of refuse and human waste. Everything seemed as if in a frenzied motion. Celestina was fascinated and frightened at the same time.

The inescapable smell of fresh pastry drew her to a line of customers who stood outside a small bakery where the latest batch of *sfoglitelle di crema* was being sold. The evocative smell brought back memories from her childhood, the time her father—who was concerned that she was not gaining enough weight—added a special cook, an expert at crafting the luscious treats. In her home village, they were known as *boccatelle,* triangularly shaped "little mouths" stuffed with rich custard tinged with lemon peel. Famous throughout Campania, they were Carlo's favorite pastry and, for several months, were one of the few solid foods that his baby girl would eat.

This memory of her dear father brought a sudden aching sadness to her. Despite his faults (recounted by her mother), the smell of that pastry evoked the kindness that he always showed her. In the bustle of this Neapolitan neighborhood, however, the sights and sounds and aromas soon distracted her from those sad thoughts. She climbed the hillside away from the bay, still looking for Sophia's apartment—which she never did locate—arriving instead at the entry to the hospital of *Santa Maria d' Incurabili,* where a cluster of medical students had gathered. The *campanile* clock showed that over two hours had passed since the start of her adventure. She needed to return to the palace, but she had no idea how to get there. So she asked directions from the students, addressing them in the formal Tuscan idiom. One of the students described the route and Celestina stepped closer, out of the shadows and into the sunlight and raised her hand to shield her face as she listened.

Standing near the back of the gathering was another student who observed that gesture, the grace and confidence of her bearing despite her obvious anxiety. He surprised his classmates (and himself) by offering to escort her home—a proposal that resulted in some teasing by his fellow students. Celestina refused his courtesy, thanked him with a pensive smile, and departed in the direction given her. He lingered, watching her disappear into the crowded street.

It was the first time that Lionardo DiCapua beheld Celestina Carazutto.

Chapter 9

Return to Bagnoli Irpino

Bagnoli, Irpino-1639

Lionardo DiCapua completed his medical studies in the autumn of 1639 at the age of twenty-two years. In appearance, he was a man of medium height with a face that featured a prominent elongated nose, humped in the center and narrow at its terminus. He had wide, dark eyes, thin lips, and a prominent forehead below a thick crop of dark hair, already beginning to show signs of gray. Taken only for his physical attributes, he would not stand out in a crowd.[1]

With his formal education behind him, Lionardo thought of travelling north to France and England, with the hope of contacting some of the great scholars whose works he had read under Maestro Severino. However, from his youngest days, he carried a strong aversion to travel, especially when a bloody war still raged, causing devastation throughout many parts of the northern continent.

So, at the request of friends and family who appealed to his kind and agreeable nature, he moved back to Bagnoli. Once there, he quickly became even more convinced of the uncertainty of the medical arts as practiced by the doctors of physick, and he realized the need for more study. It was not enough to just tear down the old system. He had to work on developing viable alternatives, and his small village, where there would be few distractions, seemed the ideal place. In addition, he would stay in contact with his anatomy instructor, Marcaurelio Severino, and arrange to return to the medical school once a year to spend a few weeks with him performing dissections and caring for patients to increase his knowledge of the functioning of the body.

Before departing Naples, he met with Don Ruggero and Severino, packed his possessions, paid all debts, and chartered a carriage to take him to his home village in the foothills of the Apennines. He arrived in Bagnoli Irpino on a fall day, late in the afternoon, just after the sun had set behind the western foothills. The air held the chill of winter's approach as the last rays of an abbreviated, sun-filled day ebbed in the twilight. Lionardo asked the coachman to stop briefly at a house on the steep road that led into the center of the village, where his friend Luciano lived.

Luciano's mother answered the door dressed in black. She started crying as she hugged Lionardo, for she had not seen or heard from her own son since the duke's soldiers had taken him from their home in early July. She told Lionardo that over the past few months, many young men from Bagnoli and other nearby towns were forcibly conscripted to fight in the northern war against the Protestants. "I hid my Luciano under the floorboards in the kitchen," she explained. "But the guards knew he was somewhere inside. They said they would shoot into the floors and ceilings if he did not appear in five minutes. They surrounded the house. There was nothing else I could do." She brought her hands together in prayer position and, through tear-filled eyes, gazed at Lionardo as if seeking his forgiveness. "They bound his hands behind him and collared him in a long chain that held, maybe, twenty others about their necks. 'Do not worry Mamma,' he said as they led all of them away. He promised, 'I will come back.'"

"Do you know where he was taken?" Lionardo asked.

She had heard through others in the village that the men were taken north. Exactly where, she did not know. She asked Lionardo if he might intercede with people in Naples to discover Luciano's whereabouts. By the circumstance of her husband's death a few years earlier, she was a widow with few resources. The small piece of land the family had worked for the local duke would sit untilled without her son's help.

Lionardo promised to help find Luciano and the others. "In the meantime," he said, "I will be staying at my family home and will need to hire a cook and housekeeper, if you are interested." She gladly accepted the offer.

Lionardo asked the coachman to continue to his family home near the *Gavitone* fountain. He would stay with his aunt and uncle until he could prepare his parents' home, which had been left as it was after Cesare's death. Uncle Horace kept track of the DiCapua holdings and was pleased that Lionardo would be staying in the abandoned house. The aunt and uncle had been anticipating the arrival of their nephew, and they accompanied him with the keys to Cesare and Giovanna's home just across the courtyard.

It was a large stone *casa*, standing three floors above a large *cantina* with a stable of such girth to accommodate a carriage and four horses. The interior was gripped in a cool humidity. Dust and flakes of plaster crunched under their shoes. Most of the furniture and paintings in each room were still as they had been, only hidden under hemp throws, which likewise endured a skim of dust and debris. Large sections of the walls would require repairs and the windows and marble floors were much in need of cleaning, yet the house was otherwise secure. There were large fireplaces in the living room *(salotto)*, the dining room, and Cesare's study, and a *forno* in the kitchen wide enough to cook an abundant feast. The second floor held four bedrooms with a fireplace in each. The third floor was one open room pinched on all sides by a beamed ceiling hung from a four-cornered roof, which showed no sign of leaking.

Lionardo asked the coachman to pull the carriage into the courtyard where they unloaded his clothes, his collection of books, his instruments, and his personal items into the large cantina. With the help of Luciano's mother over the next few days, he rearranged the house to accommodate its new functions. He would use the *salotto* to interview and examine patients. He borrowed a small, one-horse carriage from Uncle Horace to make house visits.

Lionardo had returned home as an educated professional, a rarity in this mountain community of farmers and shepherds. He was much influenced by his atomist beliefs and by the teachings of Marcaurelio Severino to continue a detailed study of comparative anatomy, for which he possessed a great natural aptitude. Hence, on the top floor of his family home he set up his laboratory. There (as Amenta wrote) he began dissecting various animals in appreciation of Democritus's exhortation to study the forms for the purpose of understanding the function. Severino had advised him to focus on the cardio-respiratory system to clarify the evolving concepts of a closed system propounded by William Harvey more than a decade earlier.

Galenist physicians, in blind acceptance of their master's teachings, condemned Harvey and ignored his idea. But Lionardo believed that he would arrive at the truth through hands-on effort, not through endless discussion. He became most interested in understanding how the respiratory system interacted with the flow of blood in the vessels since Harvey had failed to elucidate how the blood thinned and darkened and transferred from one set of vessels to the other.[2]

The locals thought it a bit strange that Lionardo carried on as he did. However, his family was known and respected throughout the area, and many villagers remembered him as a child. He spoke their dialect, and most importantly, he took the time to listen to them by eliciting a complete history of their physical complaints. Thus, they came to respect and admire his thoughtful and caring ways, even if this young man employed methods unlike those of his predecessors.

Suffice it to say that he loathed prescribing haphazard cures of a questionable nature. Instead, he spent a great deal of time taking the patient's history and observing their symptoms. Lionardo did not hold to Galen's four humors idea and its necessity for balance. Plus, he possessed a particularly strong aversion to the letting of blood based on his parents' experience and, more recently, that of the young daughter of his friend.[3]

Lionardo led an intentionally busy life in his ancestral village. In addition to his medical practice, he occupied his time by teaching himself the Greek language and advancing his understanding of mathematics, natural phenomena and philosophy. He also continued the practice, started during his school days, of writing tragic and comedic plays, fables, translations, essays, poetry and commentary on other poets. He also stayed connected to his close advisers and friends in Naples.

Having lived for more than a decade in Europe's largest city, he missed the active life of Naples, so that the benefits that came with returning to Bagnoli Irpino were offset by the reality that life would never be easy for him there.

NOTES

1. Lionardo's biographer, Amenta, described him as "more handsome than not," which was probably a polite way of looking past his plain appearance. An extant portrait of Lionardo, painted when he was much older, reveals a wizened man with flowing, gray hair and a somber countenance. The burden of his years shows

in his deep-set eyes and in an inscrutable expression, caught between a smile and a frown.

Yet, despite his scholarly inclinations, he was not an egotistical stuffed shirt. Amenta said that he was courteous and in possession of a pleasing personality. He loved jokes, and his face was often illuminated with a smile. I can assure you that he enjoyed teasing others, and that he was lighthearted enough to laugh when he was the subject of a proper tease.

2. In my opinion, if fortune had gained him a microscope, we would be referring to the capillaries—the connectors between the arteries and veins—as the "DiCapuan tubules" instead of "Malpighian tubules," the common eponym used in honor of Lionardo's friend Marcello Malpighi, who discovered the connections.

3. Through Lionardo's firm advocacy and influence over the ensuing years, Amenta confirms that he became a leading antagonist of the practice in Naples and elsewhere in the kingdom.

Chapter 10

The Continued Unfolding of Faustina's Plan

Naples—1640

The fourth spring after the Carazutto family arrived in Naples brought mixed blessings for Faustina and her brood. Giacomo's marriage to Imola had gone as expected. The dowry had been delivered, as well as the additional ten thousand ducats, with which he reclaimed the *feudo* of Sento. Shortly after their wedding, Giacomo and his new bride moved to his home village in the mountains. Up to that point, Imola had spent her entire life with her family in the capital, so the thought of leaving the city for an isolated village far from contact with friends and family was more than unsettling. Her parents pitied her plight but would not intercede. They were not about to jeopardize their new status that came with a marriage to the Carazutto clan. Ultimately, she had no choice.

After taking his post with the Spanish army, Giulio remained in his administrative role in Flanders. He petitioned to be given command of a cavalry contingent. When his uncle Pietro made sure that his request was denied, the restless nephew asked for a transfer to the army in Milan, which, in due course through the uncle's agency, was also denied. Giulio was placed in charge of training new recruits that had been forcefully conscripted from throughout the kingdom to join the Spanish army. Compared to his previous desk job, the new position allowed for more physical activity, which his uncle hoped might dissipate some of his nephew's martial energies. For Giulio, however, teaching a bunch of poor conscripts hardly compared to the rush of leading a cavalry charge. He was mired in an unchosen position due to his station as a cadet son. Administrative drudgery and procedural weariness were the result. But Giulio was too high-spirited to accept such a despondent existence. The opportunity to prove his gallantry, he hoped, would still come as the endless war dragged on.

As for Celestina, every Thursday, in celebration of the day she had escaped into the city, Sophia would buy a batch of *sfoglitelle* on her way to the palace, and the two of them would take their treats with tea under a pergola in the garden. It was during one of those outings that spring that Sophia told her of a premonition she had just before awakening that morning concerning her baby boy. "Should something happen to me and my husband, would you help my son?"

Celestina urged her to stop worrying.

"But if something *were* to happen . . . would you help Rosario?"

"Of course I would," Celestina replied. "But why do you ask this? Because of a dream? We all have bad dreams."

"I suppose," Sophia said. "But I would like for him to meet you sometime, so that you are not a stranger to him. Do you think we might do that? I could bring him here to the palace. Do you think the Baroness would allow it?

"Mother doesn't have to know," Celestina said. "Or I could sneak away from here to meet you and Rosario somewhere easily located. I'd like to meet him, but as I said, I really think you are overreacting to a bad dream. Consider, instead, your good fortune. You are lucky to have a child, to have a home, to have a husband. Look at me," she raised her arms and turned about. "I'm caged in my mother's palace. I never get out. I'm like one of the songbirds that live on the tenement balconies, except that," she pointed at the surrounding walls, "I am not permitted their view. All that life going on out there—the noise, the colors, the smells. I imagine it. Sometimes I even get a whiff of it." She plugged her nose and they laughed together. "But you're lucky because you get to be a part of it."

"Maybe you'd like to exchange places?" Sophia asked. "There's no glamour in my life, dear Celestina, believe me . . . only work. You'll marry soon. Probably a prince. You'll live in a castle. Have a nice family. Servants. Gowns. Jewelry. I'd make the trade with you anytime."

"We all receive our blessings one way or another," Celestina conceded. "And I guess you are right, dear Sophia. We should be prepared because we never know what may come."

The following Thursday, Sophia brought little Rosario with her into the garden, while the Baroness was occupied with her dressmaker. Like most two-year-olds, he had a mind of his own. He refused any help walking, and would not greet the stranger, Celestina, who received a kick on the shin when she tried to pick him up. Sophia handed him the bag of pastries and asked that he place it on the table beneath the pergola. He walked toward the table, stopped midway there when he saw the stranger holding out her hands to receive him, reached inside the bag for a pastry, from which he took a bite, and proceeded to drop the rest of the *sfoglietelle* onto the ground. During the rest of the visit, Rosario remained hesitant around Celestina and never let her touch him.

Celestina did not have any nieces or nephews and lacked any experience dealing with children, especially a headstrong two-year-old. When it was time for Sophia to take the child home, she knew what a mistake the meeting had been. Celestina tried to present an understanding attitude, but her expression betrayed her true feeling of concern that she did not like Rosario, that she might not like any children, and probably never should have children of her own. But those were concerns that hardly mattered to her now since, unlike her sister whose life centered on finding a husband to produce more children, much of her day involved classes, especially the study of Latin.

Celestina did not participate in the social exercises that busily occupied Diana, although she did occasionally wonder if any of the family assets would be available when the time came for her to enter the marriage game. When those thoughts arose, she tried to suppress the accompanying jealousy and pretend that she didn't care. But with all the activity and expenses centered on Diana, it was impossible not to feel at least somewhat envious.

Nearly six years had passed since Carlo's death. The plans for Giacomo had gone as hoped. Giulio was settled safely in the north. Faustina's main concern now centered on Diana. The family from the *Seggio di Porto* slighted by Faustina spread the story among the aristocracy, causing all potential interest among the established families to quickly dissipate. The engaged lower families had been kept on hold until after Giacomo's wedding, and for the half-year since the marriage, Faustina had avoided pursuing a match, hoping that a lively season at court would make the newly minted families that much more anxious to find entry into the baronial sphere. Once they caught a whiff of that rarefied air, she knew it would be hard for them to contain their desire. Hence, she believed a bountiful request was sure to follow.

Diana continued to enjoy the pampered frills of court life in Naples. She was pleased that the arrangement with the groom from the *Porto* had fallen apart since the castle and patrimony of the prospective groom were centered in the wild mountainous Abruzzo region, which meant that Diana, like her sister-in-law, Imola would have been banished to the isolated hinterland far from the social scene in the city. Diana let her mother know that she desired an alliance with a family based in the city. The naiveté that accompanied her privileged youth convinced her that she would get what she wanted. One sweltering evening in the summer of 1640, however, reality set in.

Not a drop of rain had fallen for four weeks during a particularly hot and humid July. Diana had awakened on the morning of the twenty-second with a mild sore throat, a dry cough, and a slight headache, but she did not complain to her mother for fear that she would be kept from a ball hosted that evening by the viceroy—the social event of the season.

A bejeweled Diana, dressed elegantly in a powder-blue, silk gown, arrived at the great hall of the royal palace at dusk. It was terribly humid inside, and the many dancing bodies—plus the heat and smoke of hundreds of candles—added to the uncomfortable closeness. After a lively round, the pain in her head returned and she began to feel feverish, achy, and slightly nauseous. She stepped onto the veranda to take some air and waved her intricately carved, ivory fan rapidly in front of her face. Things began to fade around her periphery. People standing nearby were soon spinning around her and the flickering candles blurred into undulating strobes of flame. Voices blended into an indistinct hum. The next thing she remembered, she was riding in a carriage in the arms of her servant. Perspiration had soaked through her silk gown. Her joints ached. She felt completely drained of vitality. Through that long night, her sleep was hectic. She sweated profusely, such that her nightgown and bedding had to be changed several times. By the next morning, the feverish rigors had passed, leaving her fatigued and thirsty. Faustina attributed the outbreak to overexertion in the close climate. She ordered her daughter to remain in her room. Diana was too exhausted to do anything but comply.

Celestina's classes were cancelled so that she could remain with her sister. They reminisced about tales from their childhood and took their siesta together after lunch. When they awakened,

Celestina read stories from the *Decameron*. After a light dinner, Diana was so exhausted that she fell asleep again for the night.

The next morning, she was still sleeping when Celestina stopped by her room on the way to class. During her mid-day break, Celestina returned to her sister's room to have lunch. Diana had a mild headache and pains throughout her body. She took liquids, but no solid food, and fell asleep soon after Celestina departed. When Faustina checked on her later that afternoon, she was still in a deep sleep and had to be awakened for dinner. Her headache and body aches were worse. She managed to drink only a cup of broth. That evening Diana asked her sister to read more from the *Decameron*. Midway through the reading, Diana stopped laughing at the comedic scenes. Her face flushed crimson and her facial muscles tightened, snapping her teeth together in a rhythmic rattle that kept cadence with a strange, fearful moan that vibrated with each rigor.

Celestina walked hesitantly toward the head of the bed repeating her sister's name, terrified by the snapping teeth, the primal moans, the fixed stare, the lack of response. She yelled to Sophia for cool water and towels, and then she ran to her mother's room and asked her to send for the doctor immediately. Sophia and Celestina soaked the towels and lay them around Diana's face, arms, legs and chest. She remained unresponsive and wracked with the shakes. Finally, the doctor arrived.

Doctor Luigi di Grazia was the most renowned practitioner in all of Naples. He catered to the prominent families, which brought him wealth along with fame. As Faustina led him to Diana's room, she explained the events of the past few days. Behind the doctor, came his limping coachman, carrying a large, black leather bag, perspiring profusely in the humid night. The coachman deposited the bag on an empty table, all the while averting his eyes before quietly exiting with a bow.

Di Grazia introduced himself to Celestina. He took a seat next to the bed to observe his patient. Diana was unconscious. Her breaths were quick and shallow. She was covered in sweat. The doctor felt the pulse at her wrist with his right hand and held the back of his left hand on her flush forehead. He directed Sophia to fetch a bucket of hot water and more dry towels and proceeded to open his bag, which expanded outward from its steepled top, displaying rows of shiny metallic instruments. As he searched through the contents, Doctor di Grazia explained his diagnosis and treatment plan.

"Baroness, I believe your daughter suffers from ague. I have seen other cases in the city already this year. From what you tell me, she has had two bouts of the rigors, and if we do nothing, she will certainly have more."

"But how did she become so ill so quickly, Doctor?" Faustina asked.

"You said that she first took ill at the ball," the doctor replied. "Does she enjoy dancing? Music?"

"Yes, very much so."

Sophia arrived with the hot water and towels, and the doctor instructed her to soak them and place them on the break between her upper and lower arms and around each ankle. Turning back to his bag he pulled out a purple velvet box and opened it, revealing a collection of silver blades of various sizes, each tied in place with silk bows.

"Well then," he concluded. "Your daughter is obviously of a phlegmatic humor. As I mentioned, I have recently seen several cases of ague, and I am convinced that she is suffering from the extreme and intermittent fevers that accompany that illness. She is of a plethoric habit, and her blood is in a state of intense commotion." He paused and walked to the bedside. "Thus, we must let this agitated blood for the sake of attaining a balance to the humors."

He placed the box of blades and a silver basin near Diana's right arm, and then he unwrapped the hot towel from her arm. He ran his fingers across the brachial crease, in search of a vein. Having found an adequate specimen, he asked Sophia to place pillows under Diana to elevate her back and head and to remove the hot towels from her other extremities. Celestina lifted her limp sister while Sophia placed the bolster beneath.

The doctor lowered Diana's extended arm over the edge of the bed and again ran his fingers across the crease. From the velvet box, he untied an oval-shaped, silver ring with a sharply pointed, diamond-shaped blade attached to one side. He slipped the index and middle fingers of his right hand inside the ring with the blade on the palm side. The three women watched as he palpated the course of the vein a few inches apart with his middle and index fingers of his left hand. DiGrazia scored a small vertical opening in line with the vessel between his fingers, causing Diana to flinch slightly. The mark was true. Dark-red blood began flowing from the site. The doctor collected it in his silver basin, which was curved to fit around the arm. When it was half full, he placed a white towel over the wound, flexed Diana's arm over the towel and held the arm in place. He felt for a pulse. In short order, he announced that it was slowing and was not as forceful. With the back of his hand, he again touched her moist forehead. "The fever is easing as well. She should rest comfortably the rest of the night."

The doctor wiped the blade with a towel and tied it in place in the velvet box. Sophia handed him the emptied basin, which he also returned in his bag. He asked her to call his coachman then addressed Faustina. "Baroness Carazutto, ague oftentimes does not respond to one treatment. It may be necessary to let more blood if the fever returns. I am, of course, at your service. Please, call me should you need anything. If the fever does return send your servant for me immediately, any time, day or night."

The baroness thanked him for responding so quickly to her call. The coachman limped into the room to recover the doctor's bag, and the three of them walked to the entry. Faustina again thanked him. He bowed. "Please call me at any time," he reminded her before turning to leave. After a few steps, he stopped and turned around. "Baroness, excuse me. I almost forgot to ask. Since tonight was an emergency, I did not have time to ask beforehand, and I would never presume without first asking. You see, I have a young protégé, a graduate of the medical school, who is spending a few weeks with me on a tutorial. I would like your permission to have him accompany me should it be necessary to return. Young physicians need to observe and treat patients. This young man is a gentleman from a respected family in the kingdom, and I give you my word that he will act with utmost courtesy and propriety."

Faustina agreed with the request. Doctor di Grazia thanked her with another bow and walked to his waiting carriage.

Chapter 11

Reacquaintance

Naples—1640

Two days following her first bloodletting, Diana's fever, head-ache, nausea, and body aches returned. Since that first *salasso,* she had remained asleep much of the time. Sophia had to awaken her to eat, and even then, she took little nourishment. Celestina continued to meet with her Jesuit teacher, but was much distracted by her sister's plight, unable to concentrate on intellectual pursuits. She and her teacher decided to cancel classes indefinitely so that she could stay with her sister.

The excessively humid weather persisted without a rainy respite. The doldrums hung at sea, and the air inland remained oppressively close and hot. Nerves frayed. Tempers flared. Swarms of black flies and mosquitoes added to the general discomfort. Sophia and Celestina did their best to keep them away from Diana, as the familiar pattern of symptoms progressed. By mid-afternoon, Celestina requested her mother call the doctor, this time before the fever turned into rigors.

＊ ＊ ＊

Luigi di Grazia pulled the starched collar of his shirt away from his sweaty neck as he listened to the young doctor's question. They were in a side room of a palace just inside the gate of the *Porta Reale,* discussing the case of congestive humor that was plaguing the owner, a baron from Calabria, when the urgent message from the Baroness was handed to the doctor. He quickly concluded the discussion and left with his student.

Di Grazia ducked his tall, thin frame inside the carriage door. His student followed and took the seat opposite. As they rode to the Carazutto palace, the doctor presented Diana's case. He reminded his young pupil of the standard Galenic treatment of ague and his intent to follow it when caring for the countess, regardless of their previous discussions on the matter.

The student responded with his own conclusion on the topic. "*Maestro*, what do you have to lose by trying the Jesuits' bark? You have told me that the fevers of ague are often resistant to the letting of blood. The stories that I have heard about the bark suggest that a tea steeped with it can cure the fevers immediately, and written reports from some of the Jesuit fathers in the New World have confirmed that fact."

Di Grazia fidgeted in his seat, trying to free his pants from the sticky leather. He removed a small, silver container from his jacket. Inside was a pleasantly scented balm that he applied to both sides of his face and under his nose, which helped buffer the street odor within the tight carriage. The humid weather had left the doctor on edge. He had a hard time sleeping in the heat, and his busy practice had kept him in the city rather than at his second home in the countryside that he would have preferred. His practice required constant availability to his wealthy patients who seemed even more demanding as the unremitting heat wave continued to take its infernal toll. "And if your famed bark does not work, Signore DiCapua," he said with a smile and more than a hint of sarcasm in his voice, "I suppose that you will then ask me to consult with an astrologer. After all, the folk healers and even some of those renowned Jesuits claim that the periodic fevers are tied to the stars."

Lionardo leaned forward to plead his case. "Signore, Galen

taught that physicians should try to discover useful treatments based on their own experience. He would support you in this effort. I am certain of that."

The smile widened across di Grazia's face, revealing a pair of dimples that dotted the sharp points of a black mustache. Drops of perspiration glistened inside the sculpted crevices. He stared intently at his protégé. "Oh, so now that you have read Galen, you think that you can interpret his teachings. What happened to the great agnostic of traditional medicine? Aristotle's skeptic? You know, Lionardo," he teased, "you have a reputation to uphold. I agreed to a tutorial with you because I was told that you were a Galen-skeptic, as well as an atomist . . . therefore, possibly an atheist. My goal was to make you understand the error of your ways. I guess I was far more successful than I ever thought possible. Listen to you . . . paraphrasing Galen."

Lionardo smiled and relaxed back into the seat. Marcaurelio Severino had arranged this tutorial with di Grazia, hoping to challenge Lionardo to match wits with the man considered the foremost Galenist doctor in Naples. If the influential di Grazia could change, Severino thought, perhaps other Galenists might follow.

Out of respect for the renowned di Grazia, Lionardo remained congenial when disputing him. Like a gifted fencer, he had learned when to lunge and when to parry. By the time a tease evolved, it was a clear signal for him to withdraw, secure in the fact that he had at least come close to a score with his opponent who had resorted to sarcasm for lack of a better retort. By late June, the two men had spent virtually every day together for the previous two weeks, and despite their differences, they had established a warm friendship. Di Grazia was an honest man, secure enough in his position that he accepted the challenge from a younger physician whose ideas were critical of Galen, and he believed that the advantages of his wisdom could be more fully exerted on an inquisitive physician than on one who passively accepted the given word.

Di Grazia was impressed with the fact that Lionardo had taught himself the Greek language in his free time so that he could read the manuscripts of Hippocrates, Aristotle, Galen and others in their original text. This practice aided the young doctor in avoiding the pitfalls of other later interpretations, which often guided the contemporary doctors of physick. Lionardo had equipped himself to debate the Galenists on their own terms. Indeed, he was better equipped than most Galenists to do so since few traditional physicians ever read the original Greek texts.

What di Grazia could not understand, however, was why Lionardo would waste his time studying mathematics—the language of the new and evolving inquires. He realized that to take on such intellectual pursuits while also practicing medicine was no small feat. And despite their differences, di Grazia developed an admiration for Lionardo's intellectual honesty and his work ethic, which were driven by his inquisitive nature. He found that DiCapua would question the sweeping theoretical proclamations whenever he observed a contrary detail, yet he always did so in a respectful manner.

On a personal level, the teacher could see the tenderness with which Lionardo approached the sick, proving that he was an empathetic and compassionate physician struggling to find the truth and apply it to his patients. These qualities were the same ones that animated di Grazia when he was a young student; although, during his training, no one would dare question the exalted professors. He held to the traditional teachings like one keeps to the well-worn path through a wood at night. He was not so rigid as to completely rule out an alternative path. He simply loathed risking his established career in pursuit of one. In this respect, he envied Lionardo, who was able to consider other ideas precisely because his lack of orthodox belief opened his mind to opposing possibilities.

Their mutual respect aside, however, the two men could only approach the other's philosophy; rarely could they agree. It was as if they stood on opposite peaks, close enough for conversation, yet separated by a deep chasm. This abyss—between physicians of consecutive generations, between teacher and student—had only recently formed. New discoveries had begun to fracture traditional medicine, making it unlikely that either this teacher or this student would jump to the other side. Di Grazia could come only so far forward, while it was inconceivable that DiCapua could retreat to the past.

"No, Lionardo!" The teacher concluded as they arrived at the Carazutto palace. "We will not use the Jesuit's bark. Ague comes from within, and it must be healed from within by balancing the humors."

The butler greeted the doctor at the entry and directed him, his young associate, and the burdened coachman to Diana's room. Faustina heard them coming and met them in the hallway, where the doctor bowed to her then introduced his student, who also bowed. She led them into her daughter's room.

Celestina was placing a moistened towel across her sister's brow with her back turned to the group as they entered the bedroom. Sophia stood on the opposite side, waving a wide fan over Diana. Lionardo noticed the long, chestnut-colored hair curling haphazardly across Celestina's back. When she turned around, his mouth dropped open. She caught his eyes momentarily then looked back at her sister. In that fleeting moment, Lionardo saw all the worry and sadness that he himself had once felt when his parents were ill. The doctor introduced his student, who continued to stare noticeably longer than he should have before bowing to Celestina.

Celestina described the pattern of symptoms that had begun

earlier in the morning. She recognized that they were the same as with the last episode, which was why she had asked her mother to notify the doctor before the rigors began. She spoke in a dispassionate tone with the confidence of an experienced physician. Di Grazia complemented her for the careful observations and announced that he would need to perform another *salasso*. He turned to Sophia, who had anticipated the doctor's request and had a basin of warm water and several towels already in the room. He opened his bag, pulled out his velvet box, untied the ring-shaped knife, and positioned the basin along with the tools on Diana's left side. He nodded to Sophia who handed him a moistened towel that he wrapped around the brachial crease of her left arm, then another one upon the left side of her neck.

Di Grazia looked at his student. "This case of ague has a Quartan presentation," he said. "The fevers are recurring every two days. The last *salasso* was performed on the right arm. This time we will take it from the left, which will, of course, increase our chances of balancing the humors. Questions, Signore DiCapua?"

"Maestro, how much blood did you remove previously, and how much will you remove with this *salasso*?"

"I removed above 200 *oncie* on the right; I will remove the same from the left this time." The doctor paused, draped Diana's left arm over the edge of the bed and checked it for a suitable vein. "Other questions?"

"No, maestro. No more questions." Lionardo walked to di Grazia's side of the bed to observe the procedure.

The skin of the patient's arm was so white that it appeared almost translucent, yet there were no viable veins evident. Faustina and Celestina positioned themselves around the footboard of the bed and craned their necks to maximize their line of sight. Sophia took a position nearby. The doctor moved to the neck. He removed the towel and was pleased to see the outline of a vein running from the angle of the jawbone. "If there are no adequate specimens in the arm, most likely the leg will also be dry." He pointed to the neck. "But this one," he said gleefully, "this one will be easily scored."

Lionardo looked at Celestina whose face filled with anxiety. She turned to her mother with a pleading look. The doctor grasped the ring of the knife with his right hand, placed the receiving basin against the skin below the vein and felt across the specimen for the exact location.

Faustina sighed. The room hushed. As the doctor approached Diana's neck, blade in hand, Celestina suddenly cried out, "Before!" which froze the action. She lowered her voice. "Excuse me for interrupting you, Doctor, but before you proceed, I would like to ask a question."

The baroness and Sophia exhaled, while Di Grazia removed the ring from his hand, stood upright facing Celestina, with a peevish look on his face.

"Yes, Countess," he said. "What is your question?"

"Doctor di Grazia, the last time you let the blood, my sister weakened, and she has remained so. Are there no other therapies?"

"Yes," the doctor continued. "If the *salasso* does not heal the fever, perhaps we can try purgatives or an emetic. The excess humor must be released. However, sometimes the humors are so imbalanced that a return to complete health is impossible."

Celestina looked at Faustina who let out another more audible sigh, punctuated by a groan of resignation. The older woman pulled out her handkerchief and turned her back on the group.

Celestina faced the doctor. "I discussed my sister's feverish disease with my teacher, who told me about a tree that grows in the forests in the province of Peru, which the native people call 'the fever tree.' When the bark of this tree is ground and steeped into a tea, it is said to cure the fevers of ague."

The doctor asked, "Is your teacher a Jesuit?"

"Yes, he is."

"Well, then, perhaps you should address yourself to my protégé?"

Celestina faced Lionardo who stared into her determined eyes. He watched her lips move to words, which did not register until he heard her say "Jesuits' bark." Her lips stopped moving and she probed his spellbound face. "Have you heard of it, Signore DiCapua?"

Lionardo cleared his throat and looked at di Grazia who raised his black eyebrows as if to ask the same question. "Yes, Countess," Lionardo answered. "I have heard stories from the provinces of 'the fever tree' and its healing bark from some of the Jesuit fathers that I know."

Celestina's face lit with a smile. "My teacher told me a story about the wife of the Viceroy Chinchon," she said, still facing Lionardo. "She suffered with ague soon after arriving in Peru and was cured when she took a tea made from the Jesuits' bark. Can you confirm this story?"

"May I respond, *Maestro*?" Lionardo asked his teacher.

Di Grazia extended his arm and nodded. "Certainly."

"Countess, I cannot confirm your story. However, I've heard that in the colonies, the Spanish soldiers who have the fevers prefer to be treated by local healers because the bark works better than the treatment of their own doctors."

Celestina asked the older doctor if he would consider trying the bark on her sister. He politely refused, adding that he could not imagine how it would decrease the excess blood humor. He reminded her that such fantastic yarns of colonial potions might be interesting, yet they were merely unconfirmed accounts. He asked Faustina if she wanted him to continue treating Diana in the method he had described. The pensive matron became even more anxious, sighing deeply as she looked from the doctor to her younger daughter and then back to the doctor before answering. "Please continue your treatment, Doctor. If there is no improvement, we can decide what to do then."

Di Grazia completed the *salasso*, scoring a small vertical incision on the neck vein as the others watched with a combination of aversion and fascination. Diana remained unresponsive during the procedure, which yielded a half basin of dark blood. The doctor applied pressure with a towel on the neck for a few minutes as he checked the pulse and then asked Lionardo to continue doing the same. He gathered his equipment and requested a private conference with Faustina, who appeared pale and more apprehensive. The two of them left the room.

Celestina walked to the opposite side of the bed from Lionardo. She stared at her motionless sister and lifted a hand to her forehead as a worried look spread across her face. It was the same gesture of vulnerability that had haunted him since she had turned up lost in front of the hospital several months earlier. Once again, he felt her anxiety and her fear, and—along with the other emotions she had demonstrated that afternoon—her confidence and strength. She was, he thought, the most animated woman he had ever seen.

She raised her eyes to him in a questioning gaze. "What will happen to her, Signore DiCapua? Tell me the truth. Do you think she will improve?"

Lionardo realized his precarious station. To respond honestly would likely upset her further, plus it could compromise his relationship with di Grazia. "Countess," he answered, "as to myself, I have very little experience in caring for the fevers of *Ague*. The doctor believes that his treatment will help."

"Yes, but what do *you* believe?" she asked in a probing tone, emphasizing the "you" and thus leaving little room for judicious vacillation.

He asked her to hold the cloth on Diana's neck, and he walked to the doorway to see if the doctor was returning, then he continued in a soft voice while looking at the sleeping patient. "Countess, in these circumstances, I am in a tenuous situation. To be honest, I think it would be worthwhile to try the bark and I said so to the doctor on our way here."

He paused, straightened himself and looked directly into Celestina's eyes. "Allow me to speak frankly. I believe the reports from the New World. And unlike Doctor di Grazia, I do not hold to the balancing of humors idea nor most of the treatments prescribed by the doctors of physick. I've witnessed the negative effects of the *salasso*, and contrary to what physick teaches, I am a firm believer in the potential for chemical cures. There is much that we do not understand about medicine, much to be learned particularly about chemical treatments. But he is the doctor. I am merely his protégé. Plus, the Baroness has pronounced her desire to follow his course of treatment."

Celestina paused and lowered her gaze toward her sister. Then she lifted her head and stared directly into his eyes. "Yes, then you *do* think it would be worth trying?"

"Yes, Countess Carazutto. I do." The words fell from Lionardo's mouth as if she had slipped him a truth potion and he was powerless under its spell. He realized that if the bark did not work, he would lose any chance of seeing her again. But here was the moment for him to stand for what he believed, regardless of the consequences.

"Well then, I would ask that you return tonight, about eight o'clock. Her last bout with the chills began around then. If this *salasso* does as promised, she should be fine. Correct?"

Lionardo nodded his agreement.

"If not, we should obtain some of the Jesuits' bark. Do you know anyone in possession of it? Money is no object."

Lionardo placed his open hands in front of him with palms turned towards her. "Countess, before we continue with these plans, I must have a discussion with the doctor." He paused, lowered his hands, and turned away from her face, toward a nearby corner of the room. "I can assure you that I know a Jesuit who has access to the bark. It is given to those in need without a fee." He faced her again and bowed. "And I would be honored to return tonight to serve you . . . and your family, of course. But, as I said, I must first have a discussion with *Dottore* di Grazia to see what he has planned."

"Will you come back tonight regardless of his plans and bring along the bark?" she asked.

"Will you have a talk before then with your mother?"

"Yes, I will," she responded in a lower tone. "And I am willing to actuate our plan, even by a clever method, in order to deliver the medicine to Diana."

"Then I will return tonight with the bark," Lionardo whispered so softly that Sophia, who had remained at the foot of the bed taking in the conversation, had to bend over the high footboard to hear.

Celestina told Lionardo that she would leave instructions with the servant to admit him and escort him to Diana's room.

Lionardo bowed as he departed. "I look forward to seeing you tonight, Countess."

Celestina curtsied. "Until tonight, Signore DiCapua."

Chapter 12

The Cure

Naples-1640

The doctor and his student rode in the carriage to the home of their last patient of the day. Lionardo asked Doctor di Grazia about his discussion with the baroness. Di Grazia told him that they had agreed that he would return to the Carazutto palace if she called him. He told her that in his experience, if the *salasso* did not work, Diana probably would not benefit from other treatments. There was no reason to put her through more agony. The outcome, he said, was now in God's hands—a phrase that carried a familiar and uncomfortable sentiment to Lionardo.

"Excuse me, Sir, but that is not what you said to her in the room when the countess interrupted you. You said you might try a purgative or an emetic."

Di Grazia reiterated that years of experience had taught him that, most likely, further treatment would be useless in a case of ague that did not respond to bloodletting. "Thence, Doctor, would you consider using the Jesuits' bark?" DiCapua asked expectantly.

The doctor looked through the open window of the carriage as if searching for the patience stolen from him by the combination of his unrelenting student and the unbearable weather. He pulled out his handkerchief and wiped his brow. To use the bark, he reminded Lionardo, went against everything he was taught and all that he believed. A chemical taken by a patient could not be effective unless it balanced the four humors, and he could not imagine that the taking of a tree bark steeped into a hot tea could perform such a feat. He patted his brow and continued staring silently into the distance.

A slight breeze generated by the movement of the carriage conveyed with it the foul smells of the city. Di Grazia reached into his jacket for his silver tin and placed a dab of balm under his nose. This time he did not offer it to his protégé.

The sticky weather had gone uninterrupted throughout all of June, and the pace of life had slowed with each passing day. It was early afternoon. The streets were deserted. He was weary from the incessant demands of his practice and thankful that his tutorial with Lionardo was ending. He looked forward to a short holiday at his country estate. DiCapua, on the other hand, was too distracted to feel tired or be bothered by the weather.

They rode along quietly for some time before Lionardo broke the silence. "Signore, I understand your position, but it seems to me that we must do something to help the countess."

"Tell me Lionardo, do you really believe that there is a chance that this treatment will work?"

"Sir, yes, I do. I am not certain of that, but I believe the bark is worth a trial. After all, she is suffering and, as you have noted, there is probably nothing more to be done."

Di Grazia leaned close to his student and whispered slowly, "Her time on this earth is now in the hands of the Almighty. We can let her go peacefully. Why prolong her agony?"

Lionardo leaned forward in response. "It is not my place to lecture you, sir, but with all due respect, allow me to offer that there may be some undiscovered method by which the Jesuits' bark heals without bringing equilibrium to the four humors."

"And what might that mechanism be, Signore DiCapua?"

"I cannot say. I believe that there is much uncertainty to the art that we practice, sir. By the cases we have observed together these past several days, it has become apparent to me that more is unknown than known about physick. The atomists, whom I know you despise, did not differentiate between the four primal elements of fire, earth, water and air. They taught that all four are composed of the same basic structure. Galen, on the other hand, differentiated the four elements and equated them with the four humors. I need not tell you, he built his system on that theory. However, like the atomists' teachings, Galen's ideas are only a theory without any actual proof."

Lionardo paused to gather his thoughts. "Perhaps there is a chemical within the bark that can do what the Jesuits have reported by a mechanism unknown to us. Do you appreciate such a possibility? Chemicals from the earth, in proper mixtures, might produce cures. That I believe."

"As did that crazy alcoholic . . . Paracelsus!" came the doctor's sharp reply.

"Sir, I agree that much of what Paracelsus preached was wrapped in strange enigmas. His was a life on the edge of sanity and his chemical cures were uncertain mixtures offered with his own brand of astrology. But let us be honest." He leaned forward and continued. "In our time, few can escape the lure of superstition. Many people in the highest spheres—including our pope—are amateur astrologers or regularly seek their guidance. Important decisions are often made only after consultation with men who supposedly can interpret the stars. You can dismiss Paracelsus as a crackpot, but at least there was more than a particle of wisdom to his madness."

Lionardo sat back on his bench and observed the doctor, staring out the coach window with disparagement written across his face. Based on his experience over the past several weeks, he knew that Luigi di Grazia was an honest and caring physician. But despite those qualities, he also knew how constrained di Grazia could be, the same as every other doctor of physick that

Lionardo had encountered during his studies. They were, all of them, straightlaced and narrow minded. They marched in step and were governed in their working lives by fear—fear of change, fear of losing their standing, fear of losing their wealth. They did exactly as they were taught, without questioning, regardless of the failed outcome. Their inflexibility was a great frustration to Lionardo, who was a passionate advocate for the patient, despite the discomfort it might create for his opposites or himself. Indeed, the vexation he felt for the constrained Galenic creed further incited him to search for a better way.

"The use of the bark could provide the cure," Lionardo persisted. "As far as I know, the Jesuits from the New World are not trying to establish a concession for monetary gain. They have no reason to exaggerate what they have observed. Sir, I would ask that you give me your permission to use the bark even if you refuse to actuate the trial."

Di Grazia was surprised, and a bit angered by his subordinate's insistence. He was about to continue the argument, then hesitated and scanned the horizon outside the carriage, searching once again for some patience. "We have no reason to continue our debate during our last day together, Lionardo. You know that I will not use the Jesuits' bark, nor can I give you my permission to use it. However, I will not try to stop you, nor will I report you."

When they finished their work that afternoon, the doctor told his protégé that a trusted colleague would look after his patients. He was leaving for the country to escape the heat, and he encouraged Lionardo to do the same. Lionardo bowed to di Grazia and expressed his appreciation for his instruction, his insights and, mostly, for his patience. The doctor smiled, reached for Lionardo's hand, and told him how much he had enjoyed their time together, even though he was uncertain if he had left him with any new knowledge or simply more questions.

They promised to stay in touch and, just before parting, the doctor offered a final thought. "What I say to you now, Lionardo DiCapua, is this: At one time or another, men in our profession come to think of ourselves as titans, only to eventually learn—some more quickly than others—that we are not. We are humans, subject to the weaknesses and prejudices that afflict our times and our human condition. Remember that, and always try to keep your mind open to other possibilities. It suits you to do so now in your youth. Maintain that attitude if you can."

They shook hands and went their separate ways.

* * *

Lionardo returned to his apartment to change his sweat-drenched clothes. His former teacher, Don Ruggero di Romano had Jesuit friends who had remained in service in Peru and had written to him expounding on the wonders of the bark. The kindly priest had assured Lionardo that he had access to the purest bark available should the young doctor ever have a patient in need.

Lionardo walked directly to the Jesuit rectory. He apologized for the intrusion and explained that he had an urgent need for the bark. The priest sensed the excitement in his voice. He left Lionardo in the entry way and returned presently with two large, coin-sized circles of ground bark. They were wrapped in thick paper, tied with black string, and sealed in a dollop of wax, which was marked with the impression of a circle with lines radiating from the circumference. In the center of the circle were the letters IHS, the H supporting a crucifix, and three nails with points nearly touching beneath the letters—the symbol of the Jesuit order. The priest wanted to know more about the patient and what Lionardo's teacher thought of the bark. Lionardo promised to return and explain the details of the case when time allowed, for the patient was very ill and he needed to make haste to treat her.

*＊＊

By the time Lionardo arrived at the palace, he was perspiring so profusely that his clothes were again soaked. It was just after eight o'clock. As instructed, the butler led him to Diana's room where Celestina greeted him. Lionardo apologized to her for his unkempt condition. She waved off his concern. "I am glad to see you, Signore DiCapua, in any condition. Thank you for coming to help us."

"Lionardo, Countess" he answered with a bow. "Please call me Lionardo. I am honored to serve you."

Diana lay asleep breathing rapidly. Her flushed cheeks contrasted with the rest of her pale skin. Lionardo felt her radial pulse with his left hand and placed the back of his right hand on her forehead. He looked to Celestina. "Has she awakened since I left?"

Celestina's features bore the stigma of exhaustion. "Only briefly to take a little broth." She sighed. "The nausea began after she had a few sips. Her cheeks began to flush as the fever rose. I am afraid she will soon begin the shakes."

"Did you speak with your mother?" he asked.

"Yes, she's frightened. The doctor made her understand the gravity of Diana's condition. She realized that we had to try something. Did you find any bark?"

"Yes, I did." Lionardo handed her one of the packages. "Here is enough for one treatment. It should be steeped into a tea. I was assured from a most reliable source that this is pure Jesuits' bark. If it works, I can obtain more."

She recognized the distinctive wax emblem of the Jesuit Order, opened the package, held it to her nose and sniffed. "The color is of cinnamon," she proclaimed, "but the smell is much different." She excused herself and ran out of the room, returning presently with a kettle of hot water and a large cup.

Lionardo placed the circle in the cup and filled it with hot water. He pressed the bark with the back of a spoon to soak it and stirred the mixture into a greenish brown tea that emitted an unfamiliar, pungent smell. He took a tiny sip, and his face quickly contracted into a caricature with lips curled and eyes squinted. The taste nearly gagged him.

Celestina followed him with the same result. "My poor sister," she said. "Her medicine is almost as bad as her illness."

They lifted Diana's limp upper body into a sitting position and bolstered her with several pillows. Celestina slowly and repeatedly told her sister what they were doing and urged her to drink the bitter-tasting liquid that Lionardo held to her lips. It took several minutes of constant encouragement before Diana, whose facial expressions mimicked those of her attendants, emptied the cup. They placed her back on her pillows and began what would become a long watch. Celestina made the sign of the cross and bowed her head in prayer.

Over the next hour, Diana remained asleep. Periodically she would grimace as her hand reached for her belly. Otherwise, she gave no indication of improvement or deterioration. Lionardo checked her pulse and her skin temperature repeatedly, while Celestina held her sister's hand and changed the cool compresses on her brow.

Around ten o'clock, Diana's breathing began to slow. The blush in her cheeks, which had given her some sign of life, was almost gone. Her pulse rate had dropped, and her face no longer radiated heat. Lionardo had no experience using the bark, but he chose to present Diana's physical changes as favorable, to offer Celestina some solace. "Perhaps the fever is broken. Certainly, the shaking chills have not developed. These are good signs, Countess."

They sat on chairs placed on opposite flanks of the bed. Celestina continued to hold her sister's hand. She leaned forward, bending her head onto the mattress. By half-past ten, she had fallen asleep in that position.

From his station across the bed, Lionardo watched the soft glow of candlelight cast tall, wavy shadows throughout the room. He quietly stood to stretch his back and extend his neck. Lines of brightly colored flowers in a trail of ivy, stenciled into the upper reaches of the plaster walls, climbed over the intersections with the high ceiling where they were woven into an intricately designed meshwork of painted wood. The irregular waving of the flames animated the flowers, causing them to dance wherever the shadows met the flickering light.

Nightfall had brought little relief from the uncomfortable humidity. With some difficulty, Lionardo removed his sweat-soaked jacket and returned to his watch. He picked up the wide grass fan from the bed stand, waving it over his patient, her sister, and then himself, before reversing the order in a continuous, slow arc, back and forth.

Celestina's long brown hair spread across the bedspread. She remained asleep for nearly an hour in that awkward position, bent at the waist and breathing loudly, occasionally producing a snore. Just before midnight, she awakened with a start. Her hair on the side against the bed was held firmly against her cheek by a gathered layer of perspiration and drool. She did her best to regain her composure while Lionardo turned away smiling. She excused herself from the room and returned in a few minutes looking refreshed.

The baroness accompanied her daughter. Lionardo rose and struggled to put on his jacket while attempting a bow. Faustina cast a look of displeasure and then asked how Diana was doing.

"Baroness," he responded, "it has been almost four hours since the countess has taken the tea. I am pleased to tell you that the fever has eased, her pulse has slowed, and so far, the shaking chills have not developed. She had some pain in her abdomen soon after taking the tea, but that apparently has passed. She has remained at rest and her breathing has not been labored."

Faustina went to the side of the bed and observed her sleeping daughter, and then she cast a piercing glance toward the young doctor. "Signore DiCapua," she said. "You address me with these details as if I have some experience in these matters. What I want to know is this: Do you think she will recover?"

His youthful inexperience left him struggling to answer. "I have never used the Jesuits' bark, Baroness." He searched for the right words. "I cannot say for certain if she will, but the lack of symptoms appears opportune."

"Lionardo," Celestina asked, "how long will we have to wait before we know for certain?"

"Countess, again, I have no experience with the treatment, but I would guess that we should know by morning. By then, if the rigors have not developed, and if she awakens with an appetite, we could feel blessed with at least a temporary cure. She is weak and needs nourishment."

Celestina asked her mother if it would be possible for Lionardo to stay a while longer to be certain the chills did not develop. Faustina agreed. Then, while glancing back and forth between them, she added, "I believe his name is Signore DiCapua. And as a representative of his profession, I would ask that he maintain a professional manner in this home."

Lionardo bowed. "Certainly, Baroness." She stared back and forth between the two of them again, and then she gathered her dress and swept from the room like a tempest passing.

Hours passed without an obvious change in Diana's condition. She continued sleeping, and around one-thirty in the morning, Celestina accompanied Lionardo to the door. She apologized for her mother's harshness and thanked him for all that he had done. She asked if he would return in the early afternoon. Elated by the possibility of being with her, he eagerly agreed to her request.

He took her extended right hand into his, bowed deeply and kissed it. Then he stood up straight and looked into her tired eyes. "Countess, I admire your courage. Try to get some sleep to save your strength."

"Celestina," she whispered. "Please call me Celestina."

"I will then, Countess . . . Celestina. At least when we are away from your mother." They both smiled. "And I will always keep my coat on in your home. If I become feverish, you can administer some of the bark to me."

"If doctors were forced to take their own concoctions," she assured him, "they would be far advanced in better-tasting treatments."

"Before I leave, Celestina, may I ask you a question?"

"Of course."

"Do you remember walking alone near the *Ospedale Incurabili* on a spring day several years past? You stopped a group of students to ask your way home."

"Yes, I remember. I was lost while attempting to find Sophia's apartment. I never found it, but I did run into a group of students. And one of them, a polite *Cavaliere*, offered to escort me home." A smile lit her face. "But little did I know at the time how brave he truly is. Good night, Lionardo. I look forward to your visit tomorrow."

She offered her hand again and again he bowed and kissed it. "Good night, Celestina. It will seem like an eternity to me until then."

* * *

As he walked through the humid city, Lionardo felt as if he were suspended above himself. With his vague memories of childhood and constant academic pursuits, he had grown into a solitary young man. For the past decade, he had buried his loneliness in his studies. Like a true pupil of Democritus, he had not allowed the possibility of an emotional attachment interfere with his vocation as a scholar.

But that was his life before his visit to the Carazutto palace. Suddenly, everything had changed. And no matter how impossible the thought of being with her might seem, at that moment, nothing in this world was more important to him. It was a feeling unlike any that he had ever experienced. He floated through the deserted streets in a state of exhilaration, considering the words that would focus his feelings.

When he arrived in his apartment, he put his thoughts on paper as a sonnet, with an outpouring of passion aroused by that unforgettable day. He fell asleep at his desk after finishing the first draft. In the morning, he awakened with a stiff neck that eased with the realization that the day before had happened and was not just a pleasant dream. He had no desire to eat, hence he rewrote his poem then sat on his bed trying unsuccessfully to distract himself with reading. Yet all of his thoughts broke off and returned to counting the moments until he would see the lovely countess again.

Nature tends to strive for balance. Winters are dark, summers are light, autumns and springs fall between. Likewise, those who ignore the passionate side of their humanity usually take the hardest fall when love finally comes their way. So it was for Lionardo, whose awakened heart suddenly prompted him to abandon all for the sake of being with his beloved. Fortune had placed the two of them together and he knew he was helpless, save to follow that lead.

Chapter 13

The Bond Is Formed

Campania—1640

Lionardo obtained more coins of the Jesuits' bark from Don Ruggero, who noticed a marked elation in his former student's usually taciturn mood. Lionardo again promised to relate the details of his patient's symptoms to the kindly priest when time permitted, for he was in a hurry to return to the Carazutto palace where he spent most of his waking hours over the next week. He and Celestina monitored Diana, who had lost above seven kilograms in the short time since the ague had overtaken her. After starting the bitter tea, however, her fevers and chills had been suppressed, allowing her to gain strength and, as she improved, to vocalize her protests of the bitter drink. Despite the awful taste, the miraculous recovery also led to a return of Diana's strength that allowed her to walk around the room, heartening her caregivers and the baroness as well.

Celestina, Sophia, and Lionardo passed their days with Diana, reading stories from the *Decameron* and *The Tale of Tales*, sharing stories from their past, their views on religion and philosophy, and the ongoing war to the north. Lionardo kept a detailed journal of the treatment. He read each Latin entry aloud, and Celestina translated for Sophia and, as necessary, corrected his grammar. The connection between them felt perfectly natural to Sophia, for they seemed rightly matched in disposition and temperament. Likewise, Diana could see the bond developing, which tethered her own emotional attachment to the young doctor and allowed her to be herself without having to feign a bit of pretense.

On the thirtieth of July, following an afternoon siesta, they took Diana for a short walk in the garden. She was feeling stronger with each treatment, although by the time the exercise was completed, she needed a cool compress under a vigorous fanning to find some relief from the oppressive heat. Later that evening, a sentinel wind blew inland from the bay, announcing a long-awaited break in the weather. By midnight, a dramatic thunderstorm broke across the sky, followed by three more days of intermittent lightning and torrential rains.

Celestina would not allow Lionardo to leave the palace during the storm for fear, she said, that he might become ill. She had a room prepared for him in the servants' quarters where he would go to sleep after she had retired. And it was there that the folly of this affair first occurred to him.

Lionardo felt comfortable in the lower quarters, but the servants did not know how to relate to him. He slept with them, but he ate with the family. Was he of the servant class or, perhaps, a spy sent as a monitor? Their obvious discomfort registered in the back of Lionardo's mind like a nagging voice and gave pause to his ever-deepening devotion to Celestina.

After the welcome storm had passed, the muggy heat returned. By then, Diana was feeling well enough to suggest an escape into the countryside. The idea of spending time at one of the family's holdings in the mountains appealed to Celestina, and she asked Lionardo if he might accompany them to where the climate would be more conducive to her sister's recovery. Plus, she could show him some of her favorite places from her childhood and introduce him to her favorite cousin, Andrea Concublet. Lionardo accepted the invitation, on the condition that the baroness would allow it. Faustina approved of the plan, with the caveat that Signore DiCapua spent his nights in the servants' quarters at that castle. She would remain in the city to attend to matters delayed by Diana's illness.

The three of them and Sophia would move to the family castle in Sostegno. Faustina would join them later. All the necessary arrangements were made with the servants to depart early the following morning. Lionardo took his leave to prepare for the journey and walked directly to Don Ruggero's office.

The priest was impressed by the testimony to the near miraculous effectiveness of the treatment. "I have had no direct experience with using the bark," Don Ruggero said, "but I am not surprised by your report. I have heard similar stories of cures from many fathers who have travelled to the New World." Sensing the nervous energy he had observed in his former student on their last brief visit, the Jesuit then asked, "Is there something else you wish to tell me?"

Lionardo wondered as to the amount of detail he might relate to a priest who had taken the vow of celibacy. Their previous discussions about love had always been from a philosophical perspective. Romantic love? How could he broach the subject? "What do you mean 'something else'?"

The priest smiled. "I will be direct. Are you attracted to this countess?"

"The patient? No, no, no."

"Another, then?"

Lionardo blushed. At first, he tried to minimize what he said, but, like the bursting of a dam, his story gained momentum as it poured forth. He began by telling of the day he had first seen Celestina Carazutto in front of the hospital and then the pleasant surprise of going to her home years later with Doctor di Grazia.

"She was brave enough to question Maestro di Grazia about the *salasso*," he said. "And she was persistent in making me stand up for what I knew to be the only reasonable option for her sister. It seemed she could read my mind. She's intelligent, inquisitive, caring and . . . well . . . beautiful."

Don Ruggero realized that he was listening to a man swayed by the intense passion of his first love. He was happy to see Lionardo so animated. What concerned him, however, was the improbability of the romance. He knew enough about the strict class mores within Neapolitan society to appreciate the potentially painful path upon which Lionardo had embarked.

The priest thus employed his own diversion by reminding Lionardo of Democritus's belief that romantic love was a great hindrance on the road to enlightenment. "It was said that Democritus had his eyes plucked out so that they would not distract him from seeking the truth," he told the young man. "Of course, the story most likely is a fabrication, but the sentiment is valid." Don Ruggero paused to patrol the space in front of his desk, his eyes searching the wooden floor for remnants of courage as if hidden within the cracks. "I offer this advice out of concern that you might fall into a serious melancholy that could distract you from your calling. Remember, Lionardo, she is from a prestigious noble family, and daughters of wealthy barons serve two purposes to their families. Either they are used to strengthen the political ties with other noble families through arranged marriages, or they are sent to the convent."

"As always, I appreciate your advice, Don Ruggero," Lionardo replied. "But I must tell you that I cannot be as objective as Democritus when it comes to my feelings for Celestina. I feel elated in her presence, a sensation unlike any I have ever experienced and one that I cannot deny. She is my muse, my inspiration."

Lionardo paused, recognizing that he had said more than he should have. Such a passionate journey of the heart had been unknown territory to him. But, now that he had announced his affections, he summarized them with an even more exuberant and ultimately prophetic statement: "This is the first time I have been in love with a woman, Father. I welcome the passion that comes with it no matter the pain it might cause."

The kindly Jesuit rested his case. He gave Lionardo several more packets of the bark and offered his blessing.

* * *

The next morning, Lionardo arrived at the Carazutto palace before sunrise. By sundown, they approached Sostegno, their clothes and their skin caked with dust, and Diana exhausted from the long ride.

Lionardo was napping with his head propped in the corner when the excitement generated by the first sighting of Sostegno coursed through the carriage. He awakened and looked out the window. In the dimming twilight, he could see open fields outside a set of ramparts.

Within the walls, from that distance, only two structures could be defined: the Carazutto castle and the main church below it. The castle was perched atop the highest hill in Sostegno, with its façade staring over and above everything in front toward the valley below and its back protected by the steeper hillside behind. The rectangular shape with crenellated parapet and stark, austere façade betrayed its Norman origin. The sharp point of the church *campanille* rose to a height just below the base of the castle. Between the two structures lay the simple, stone houses of the peasants, indistinguishable in color from the earth.

They arrived at the south face of the palace before a grand, arched gate, protected by a set of massive doors, twelve inches thick, sheathed in iron. Inside was a spacious portico, large enough to garrison several carriages. Another set of less ponderous doors on the opposite side of this enclosed area opened into the living space. On the right half of this interior portal, a small slot had been cut, through which another guard posted on the inside could identify the petitioners and open a small door carved within the great portal.

Only a few windows sat within the other walls, leaving the inside of the palace in dark shadows. In the winter, this arrangement would be oppressive, but now, in early August it left the interior pleasantly cool. The main floor had high wood-beamed ceilings and cut stone pavement. Walk-in fireplaces sat in every room. To the left of the entry, a set of stone stairs, bisected by a runner of thick red carpet, led to the compact bedrooms on the top level, each with squeaky, parquet wood floors and a squat fireplace.

Over the centuries, renovations by earlier Carazutto barons had kept the castle in livable condition. Soon after they had married, Faustina had urged Carlo to finance another much-needed remodel. With the reversal of fortune that accelerated because of his failed livestock investment, that project never happened. Consequently, the privies remained primitive structures and the old furnishings had lately come close to tatters.

After dinner, Lionardo was shown his room in the servants' quarters in the basement. It was a small cell, just large enough to contain its furnishings: a single bed covered with a horsehair mattress; a triangular wooden desk nestled into the opposite corner with a firm chair that barely fit under the desk's legs; a ceramic wash basin and pitcher; and a small, wooden *armadio* for storing clothes. A double candelabrum was lit on the desk.

During the daytime, a narrow window cut high on the wall opposite the entry door would allow light to enter from the central courtyard above. There was a gaping crack in the whitewashed plaster that followed a direct path from the base of the window to the stone floor. Multiple side channels branched from this trunk like twisted limbs off a narrow tree. It was not a luxurious room, but its cooler, subterranean location allowed the occupant to escape the heat of summer.

Lionardo and Celestina spent their first few days attending Diana. Even though the fever had not returned, she had to suffer through another treatment with the bark and its usual side effects. Once the nausea and cramping had passed, they encouraged her to eat. The cook (the chef who had baked the *sfoglitelle* when Celestina was a baby) was retained whenever the family was there. Each morning he made a batch of the pastries that the three of them would enjoy for breakfast.

On the second day after their arrival, Diana remained at rest to regain her strength. By the third day she began walking in the courtyard. Soon, she was walking through the village, her pale cheeks taking on a healthy color and her mood improving with each excursion.

Lionardo decided to spread out the treatments with the tea to every four days; he carefully monitored Diana for recurrence of the symptoms. With Celestina's assistance, he continued to write entries into his journal, simply describing his observations. Without absolute proof, he avoided offering theories as to why the bark worked for fear of antagonizing the doctors of physick, who might then marginalize the effectiveness of the cure.

Nonetheless, there was undoubtedly something about the Jesuits' bark, some chemical constituent that eased the fevers of ague. Lionardo knew from his experience that, no matter how much the doctors of physick argued against the cure, the truth could not be denied, nor could its profound implications on the rigid system that they had for so long posited. The effectiveness of the bark supported Lionardo's strongly held belief that there was much uncertainty to the practice of medicine, and unlike Doctor di Grazia, his choice was to pursue the unknown rather than deny it.

The weather in Sostegno was hot, but the air was fresh, and at night, the temperature dropped to a comfortable level.

After dinner, Celestina and Lionardo would sit with Diana in the courtyard identifying the constellations or singing together, while Celestina strummed a lute. At one of these sessions, they talked about medical cures, and Lionardo professed his belief in the combined healing of the body and the soul. "Music animates the passions of the soul," he said, "and maladies can be cured in the process."

Diana concluded the discussion by announcing that, if this were true and Lionardo believed it, thence he should allow for their nightly singing as a substitute for further treatments with the bitter bark.

After a few days in the mountains, Diana was feeling well enough to suggest that her attendants tour the countryside as they had planned. Their excursions always departed in late morning, taking different routes to the same destination—a lake in the hills where Celestina's father had often taken her on fishing trips. She was a capable rider with a good memory of the directions to the small basin. Once there, they shared a packed lunch of cheese, bread, fruits, and red wine. Afterwards, they walked the shoreline.

On their fourth outing, as they strolled around the lake, Celestina recounted memories of her father. She missed him, she said. He was kind, fun loving and spontaneous—the opposite in every respect from her mother. She spoke of the tension that accompanied evening meals and how unhappy her parents seemed to be whenever they were together. "When you mentioned your belief in the connection between the mind and the health of the body the other night, I thought about my father's slow deterioration during his final years. When I was younger, we would all sing together after dinner. Father loved to sing, and sometimes he would get so carried away with the music that he would break into a dance with me or Diana or my brothers." She stopped to pick a yellow flower. "But near the end of his life, things changed. He would leave the table after eating little and retire to his study. I would find him looking tired and anxious, shuffling through his papers. When I asked him if he wanted to sing, he would usually say something like, 'Not now, Tina. Perhaps later. I must do more work.' And, of course, 'later' never arrived."

Celestina stared at the little wildflower with tears welling in her eyes. Lionardo took her hand. "Father became consumed with his investments," she continued. I had no idea of the problems, but after he died, mother told us that the results were disastrous. Looking back now, I think he worried himself to death." Celestina took a deep breath and said, "But that's enough of my story. What of your parents and your family, Lionardo? Tell me about them."

"I can't tell you much about my parents because they died when I was a child—within two years of each other. I loved them, yet I hardly knew them. Like you, I am the youngest in my family, with an older sister. After my father's death, I lived for a while with my Uncle Horace, my father's younger brother and his wife. They lived next to us in Bagnoli Irpino. I went away to school with the Jesuits in Naples when I was thirteen years old. The priest who gave me the bark was one of my teachers. He's been like a father to me."

"Will you return to your village?"

"Perhaps. I have established a small medical practice there and I have family there. And you? What are your plans?"

Celestina ambled toward a cluster of wild daisies growing in a field. She picked a handful and presented them to him. "I have no plans other than to help my sister get well and continue with my studies," she said. "Mother has been trying to arrange a match for Diana. She has avoided the subject with me, which pleases me since I cannot imagine marrying someone that I do not love, only to end up in an unhappy state like my parents."

They joined hands and resumed their slow pace along the path that skirted the lake until they came to a sandy area along the shore. Celestina sat and removed her boots. She pulled up the hem of her riding dress, tied it in front, and then walked into the water, up to her knees. Lionardo took off his boots, rolled up his pants, and met her in the cool water. Two, long-legged water spiders danced on the surface, creating ripples of reflected sunshine that gently coursed toward the sandy shore. Celestina reached for his hand. "What will you do then?" she asked.

"These days, I'm uncertain," he replied, trying to act nonchalant, as if unaffected by the warmth of her touch. "I could go to Rome to continue my studies or find a place in one of the academies, but I am from the Campania, and I am not inclined to leave." They walked slowly through the shallows. "In Rome, everything depends on who happens to be the pope," he said. "For support, one needs to remain under the protection of one of the cardinal princes, available at his beck and call, and subject to his whims and his fortunes." He nervously skimmed his free hand over the water's surface, creating another volley of iridescent wavelets. "Such an oppressive life does not appeal to me, even though it does offer the virtue of providing cover from the reach of the Inquisition. The advantages that come from a life dedicated to study and experimentation cannot be obtained without risk."

"Then will you return to Bagnoli?" she asked, leading him back to the sandy shore.

"Bagnoli Irpino is like your Sostegno—a small, isolated place, which could prove to be a blessing should I choose to devote my life to medicine and further study. However, I . . ."

Celestina interrupted him. "I remember a few days past, you were discussing philosophy, and you said that your goal was to find a place where you could pursue the ideal atomist life. It seems like Bagnoli Irpino is the perfect place."

"Well, yes, it is my ideal . . . or at least it was."

"Was?" she interrupted again, reaching with her long, delicate fingers for a piece of a leaf stuck to the back of his shirt.

"Until the past few weeks."

"The last few weeks?" she echoed.

"Yes, until your sister's illness."

"You mean, because of your experience with the Jesuits' bark?"

"Partly."

"What else, then?"

"Other things . . . other people."

"You mean Doctor di Grazia?"

He raised his right hand to his forehead to block the bright sun. "No . . . well, perhaps a little."

She moved closer to face him directly. "Who else?"

He felt a hot blush run up his neck and fill his face, distracting him from looking directly at her. "Countess . . . Celestina, please. I am not good at this."

"Not good at what?" she teased him. "Tell me. Please, Lionardo. Say it to me." She placed her hands gently upon his chest and tilted her head to intercept his oblique gaze and exact his answer.

He straightened himself, placed his hands on top of hers, and held her stare with a smile. "Celestina, you must already know. In my own awkward way, I have told you at least a thousand times."

"That is true, Lionardo. You have shown me much kindness. But you have never spoken the words."

"I have written them in my sonnets to you."

She drew closer to him. "Maybe. But I have never seen your sonnets."

"Because I was afraid of your response."

"My response?" she asked. "You have argued against the teachings of Aristotle and Galen, antagonized your professors and even the Holy Church, and you expect me to believe that you feared *my* response to your poetry?" She laughed, throwing back her head and chanting, "No, no, no and no!"

Lionardo felt another flash of heat climb up his back. He was lost with no idea of how to reply. Next to him, so close that he could feel her heartbeat, was this disarming woman whom he loved so desperately that he feared saying or doing anything that might cause her to retreat. In his confusion, he stammered, unable to string together a witty or even somewhat coherent thought.

She read the perplexed look on his face and continued the exchange in the same teasing manner. "But even if it were true, that you were 'afraid.' Well, that was then. Now you must tell me, dear Lionardo." Her smile disappeared as she stared into his eyes. "Say the words and I will give my response."

A sense of certainty swept over him, a realization that all would be right in the profession of his love for this woman who was so different, yet so fundamentally like him. She had led him to the edge of this emotional precipice, from which there was no retreat. He let go of her hands and encircled his arms around her, pulling her body into his. "I love you, Celestina Carazutto, and I never want to be apart from you. I cannot imagine my life without you."

"And I love you, dearest Lionardo. You are my hero and I wish to share my life with you."

She closed her eyes and met his lips in a short hesitant kiss that quickly evolved into a yearning that had been seething inside each of them. Celestina momentarily broke the embrace to lower herself into the sand, drawing Lionardo down to her side. She wrapped her arms around his neck and kissed him longingly, all the cerebral conformity of their lives swept aside by the intensity of the moment. They were inexperienced lovers, fumbling through their desires, simultaneously both embarrassed and aroused. But their awkwardness soon gave way to the inevitability that had drawn them together.

Chapter 14

A Friendship Gained and a Love Lost

Campania—1640

In the afterglow of that surprising day, the two lovers revisited that singular moment when their emotions had led them into such passion. During the next week, whenever the opportunity came to steal away quietly and share their affection, they continued doing so. Lionardo adjourned to his small room in the servants' quarters late every night after they parted and awakened at the first light of dawn, anticipating another day together. Along with his medical journal, he kept a diary, in which, in the quiet of his small room, he added more love sonnets to Celestina. Somewhere in the back of his mind was the now-distant realization that he had abandoned his practice by nearly a month. He had been a determined scholar with his energies directed towards a definite goal. Yet he now found contentment with the notion of being at Celestina's side, enjoying the moment, with little concern for anything else other than the continuing care of her sister.

Lionardo and Celestina carefully monitored and recorded Diana's steady improvement. No further episodes of the fever or the rigors came to her, only the belly pain she suffered with the treatments. Except for those times, her appetite was good, allowing an accumulation of strength such that she could walk without a pause for over an hour. Celestina insisted that Diana take a *riposo* every afternoon, not just for her sister's health, but also somewhat selfishly; it presented the opportunity for the two lovers to spend time alone.

During the first week in August, the Marquis Andrea de Concublet, a cousin of the Carazutto sisters, arrived at the castle along with two of his servants. They had ridden for three full days from Andrea's home in Arena, near the toe portion of the Calabrian boot. They came on horseback since the Marquis Concublet preferred riding in the open air to the confines of a carriage.

The origin of his titled lineage was from a German principality, an earlier ancestor having been a trusted adviser to Emperor Charles V. His father was the powerful *Scrivano di Ragione dei Regno*, the official monitor and recorder of the finances within the kingdom, a position that would be inherited by his son upon the father's death. Andrea was a vigorous, well-built and well-established gentleman in his late thirties, with a warm demeanor that frequently carried him into a deep laugh. He possessed a kind regard for his cousins, with whom he playfully teased. They obviously thought him quite dear.

Lionardo was likewise taken by Andrea's affections and could see that this son of a noble baron would also make quite an impression in any athletic endeavor. They both enjoyed the outdoors and, along with Celestina, would ride throughout the countryside. Their quotidian adventures would then become the starting point for conversations that would commence after Diana had retired. The subject reflected a particularly relevant principle previously expounded by this or that philosopher, upon which the three of them would offer their own interpretation. The two men quickly realized a common approach on a variety of subjects, which drew them into a warm friendship that gladdened Celestina's heart.

Like Lionardo, Andrea had been influenced at a tender age by a teacher whose imprint was indelibly left on his character.

In his case, that teacher had been his grandfather, the Marchese Scipione, a close friend of the famous Dominican monk Tommaso Campanella. The marchese had been accused of protecting the monk during the Calabrian Revolt in 1599. In punishment, the grandfather had been confined to his castle, where he carefully directed his young grandson's education, assuring a healthy exposure to writings deemed offensive by the office of the Index. Scipione was a freethinker whose son outwardly towed the line, while his gifted grandson carried forth a thoughtful and often rambunctious life in keeping with his grandfather's principles. Andrea was unlike any noble that Lionardo had ever met.

On the tenth of August, the palace cook concocted a rich cream *torta*, which was eaten at a party given to Lionardo in honor of his twenty-third birthday. After darkness had arrived, everyone—the servants, cooks, stable hands, and even Diana—gathered in the courtyard with several bottles of wine to watch the celestial fireworks, the traditional hot tears of San Lorenzo, streak across the clear ebony sky. Around midnight, after a particularly brilliant flare crossed from horizon to horizon, the effusive Andrea rose to his feet and announced in a thick Calabrian dialect, *"Per San Lorenzu 'a nucia spacca ammenzu."* ("For San Lorenzo, the night is split in half.") He continued: "And on this beautiful night in which the heavens have become divided, I propose a toast to Lionardo on his birthday. Drink up, all of you, for this is a blessed and happy night." Indeed, those felicitous and loving days were, perhaps, the happiest of Lionardo's life.

The joyous mood ended quite suddenly, however, with the arrival in mid-August of the Baroness Carazutto. Instinctively, Lionardo assumed his formal position as physician to Diana, unable to express himself openly to Celestina or Andrea in the manner to which he had become accustomed. He felt a coldness emanating from the baroness that rippled uncomfortably among the other family members whenever they gathered. And even though Celestina did her best to conceal her affections, the baroness noted the subtle gestures from her daughter whenever she was around the young doctor. Faustina could not deny the great improvement in Diana's condition, and she expressed her deep appreciation for Lionardo's help. But with the recovery, the baroness felt comfortable discharging him and having Celestina administer the bark, at least until they returned to Naples. Hence, Andrea decided it was time to depart and he offered to accompany Lionardo back to Naples.

A return to reality meant that Lionardo would be leaving this bucolic paradise and separating himself from his love at a time of great confusion for him. Thus was his true status with Celestina Carazutto again made plain, reminding him of the futility of such a love, as Don Ruggero had warned. On the morning of the twelfth of August, Lionardo and Celestina parted in a cordial way in front of the castle gate, while the baroness observed the separation from the heights of her palace. Despite their intense feelings for each other, they were forced to carry on in a formal manner, having judiciously expressed a tearful adieu in private the night before, Andrea Concublet providing the necessary diversion of his aunt's attention.

Lionardo rode from Sostegno with Andrea Concublet and his two servants. They stretched their journey to four days, stopping at various hot pools and mountain lakes. The weather throughout was perfect for an outdoor excursion—the days warm, the star-filled nights clear and sprinkled with comets. The time spent together in the enjoyment of nature's bounty forged a friendship and united their destinies. This was especially meaningful for Lionardo, who felt liberated to share his feelings with someone who understood his ideals, even if there were differences between them. Andrea was fifteen years older, of noble lineage, and much wealthier. He had considerably more life experience than his new friend, whom he treated like a kindly older brother would a younger one.

Andrea's biggest concern was to help his companion understand the complicated mores of noble society. He realized that Lionardo was in love with Celestina, and he tried, like Don Ruggero had, to politely caution him as to the many difficulties inherent in the relationship. But love, especially first love, recognizes no boundaries in its reach for the other, and despite his sudden eviction from Sostegno and the advice of his new friend, Lionardo still refused to accept the obvious. Realizing the depths of Lionardo's feelings, Andrea vowed in his heart to be his faithful protector.

Lionardo remained in Naples, lovesick and confused, knowing that he should return to his responsibilities in the Irpino, but immobilized while awaiting word from his beloved. A week after his return to the city, he received a note from Celestina telling him that she was back from the countryside and asking him to call upon the Carazutto palace the next morning.

When he arrived as requested, the two lovers could barely restrain the embrace each longed to give. On the way into the garden, Lionardo scanned the hallway, thence opened Celestina's hand and kissed her palm. She paused, met his smile, and lightly touched his face.

It was a pleasant early autumn day under the pergola where they sat. Celestina told him that she had continued administering the coins of bark to Diana every fourth day, and that there had been no recurrence of the fever. The abdominal cramping that came with the treatments had become so bothersome that Diana was willing to risk a return of the fevers. Thus, she explained, it would not be necessary for him to obtain more of the Jesuit's bark. Lionardo assured her that there was no one who could advise them as to the need for further treatments. He remained at their service should the need arise. "At least we could settle this one issue," he said. "As for the future, I postponed my decision until seeing you."

Celestina reached for his hands with a downward gaze. "Lionardo, I love you dearly." She answered. "Nothing would give me greater pleasure than to be with you all the rest of my days. I hope you realize that."

"Yes, I do," he responded sensing the hesitancy of her statement.

"I asked Diana for her opinion, and she assured me that our mother would never allow our marriage." She hesitated as a quiver stole her usually steady voice. "She reminded me that our family actuates these arrangements through a formal process, which we would have to usurp. Power, money, political ties, covenants between families—these are the considerations they usually entertain in holy matrimony. Love does not enter the picture."

"It pains me to see you so sad, my love," he said.

"It pains me more to know that I have occasioned this sadness in you. I was the one who initiated the affair, so taken as I was by the moment. But you must forgive me, for I have never felt as I do, my love."

A smile spread across his face. "I admit that you did initiate things, but I must also say that you were forced to do so by my utter lack of courage, for indeed it was also my fondest wish." He looked down at their coupled hands. "There is no need of forgiveness, unless it is I who request it from you, for I am also the first time in love, with no experience in how to proceed." He straightened himself, rearranged his hands around hers and looked into her eyes. "It seems we have but two choices, dear Celestina, and both bring great difficulty. The first is that an intermediary or I present to your mother the possibility of our marriage. It will be explained that I do not wish a dowry, that the ceremony will be small and private, and that I will provide an *antefato* as she might request."

"And the second is?" Christina asked.

"And the second is the one which I prefer. That is that we make our marriage vows privately before my Jesuit friend, Don Ruggero, and then depart the city. We will find a place, perhaps in the Irpino, perhaps elsewhere, where I can continue my medical practice, and we can raise our family. We shall have a comfortable house in the countryside with a small plot for a garden, good stoves well stocked for warmth, and a library with our desks facing each other and the walls lined with books. And there, God willing, we will teach our children and our children's children what has come to us as wisdom."

Celestina squeezed his hands and kissed him on the cheek. "Let us sleep on your suggestions, and we will talk tomorrow, my love."

The following morning, Sophia led Lionardo to a garden gate in the palace where Celestina waited. Her eyes were red and ringed with a blush. Her shoulders were sloped round, as if a great weight were pushing upon her. She kissed Lionardo, thence held him in a tight embrace. Each leaned their head upon the other's shoulder as they stood together. His first consideration was to turn and depart the way he had arrived to spare her the painful disclosure. But then, he thought of the time before they had met, how they were both content with their lives. To love, he thought, is always a risk.

They took a seat together under the pergola. She covered the back of his hands with her delicate palms, a warm bandage for his bruised spirit. "We do not have much time, my dear, Lionardo. Diana and I spoke with our mother last night and she announced her intention of having the both of us join the convent of San Gregorio where our aunt is the Mother Superior. My future was decided after my father's death. Apparently, I was always intended for the convent. If I were to disobey her,

I would be abandoning Diana. Our mother would never cease making life miserable for her, for me, and for you through her powerful connections."

Lionardo felt faint as a sudden weakness gathered throughout his body. His stomach knotted just as it had years earlier when he had seen the doctor's carriage tethered to the Gavitone fountain. "And when is this to happen?" he asked.

"Soon," she responded lowering her head. "Very soon. Since Diana's illness, all proposals have ceased. Three families had been competing for her hand until the night that she collapsed at the ball. The word spread quickly. No one wants to take a woman with ague, no matter how appealing the name. Too many other families are looking to marry their daughters currently. Too many other choices."

They sat in silence. Celestina finally excused herself and ran through the garden into the palace. A door slammed. He could hear her retching. The pain he was feeling no longer registered, as it quickly dissolved into an intense feeling of guilt for the anguish he had caused.

Celestina did not return. Instead, Sophia came to relay the message that her mistress was too upset to carry on presently, and that it was now necessary to show him the way out. Lionardo followed Sophia to the garden gate and, as he departed, she told him that Celestina would contact him as soon as possible.

A week passed without news. In the interval, Lionardo suffered from a complete immobility of purpose. He slept poorly, ate little, and felt a constant ache in his gut. His world had shrunk to four surrounding walls, which he rarely left. Friends would call, but he remained silent behind a locked door. His only solace was writing sonnets to Celestina. Often, he would spend hours in search of a single word or a more lyrical phrasing in the vague hope that, somehow, it might change the unbearable reality.

Then one night he had a dream in which Celestina came to him. She told him that she would always love him and asked him to honor her by rededicating his life to his calling. The next morning, he walked to the Carazutto palace and anxiously rang the bell. Sophia intervened to say that Celestina was forbidden to see him. If he did come, she was to present the countess's apologies for not contacting him. The two sisters would be leaving for the convent the next week, she told him. Diana was feeling well enough. Celestina was completely distraught.

Sophia began to cry. Lionardo took her hand and asked if she would kindly pass on a message to Celestina. "Tell her that I consider myself the most fortunate of men to have known her. That I will always love her. Tell her, Sophia, please. Tell her that I will forever be devoted to her and remain at her service. Should she ever need anything, she must not hesitate to call upon me."

Sophia agreed to transmit the message. Then, as they said adieu, she told Lionardo that Celestina loved him dearly. "She asked me to relate to you that she would hold the time the two of you spent together as the happiest days in her life."

And so, a heart-broken Lionardo DiCapua turned and walked from the *palazzo* of the Carazutti, not knowing if he would ever see his love again.

Chapter 15

Back to Bagnoli Irpino

Bagnoli Irpino—1640

When Lionardo DiCapua returned to his life in the Irpino, the Thirty Years' War was well into the third decade of hostilities, while the war for independence from Spain by the United Provinces of the Dutch Republic was in its eighth. Several Italian nobles served as officers for the Spanish in the Dutch war, including Celestina's brother Giulio. He had remained attached to what was the remnant of a once-proud force of nearly ten thousand Italians, originally assembled by the Spanish Duke of Alva in the latter half of the sixteenth century to cleanse the Netherlands of heresy.

Soon after Alva's initial arrival in the north in 1567, English pirates and the local collection of ragtag sailors (known as the "Beggars of the Sea") began intercepting provisions and monies destined to support the duke's splendid army. The Beggars also raided unprotected towns along the coast, effectively isolating Alva and buying precious time for the relentless William of Orange to gather his army. As a result, the Dutch won a critical victory at the Battle of the Downs, which took place in the English Channel near the end of October 1639. More than seventy Spanish vessels were destroyed, and more than 15,000 Spanish-sworn sailors were killed.

This devastating defeat, which rivaled the earlier destruction of the great Armada in sheer loss of ships and lives, was another major blow to the disintegrating Spanish Empire. The Spanish were still squeezing provisions and conscripted men from the duchy of Milan and the kingdom of Naples, but their inability to resupply their floundering army led to a retreat from the war with the United Provinces. Giulio's Uncle Pietro was reassigned to support the Spanish army in its ongoing fight with the French to the southwest as part of the simultaneous Thirty Years' War. When he departed the United Provinces, his posting was not firmly established. In the confusion, Giulio seized the opportunity to satisfy his need for martial action that he had long desired, and which indeed had now become a reckless obsession. He volunteered to lead a rear-guard force to protect the Spanish army against the Dutch, who continued to harass its flanks as it retreated to the southwest. Without his distracted uncle's oversight, Giulio was placed in charge of a small cavalry force, which supported a contingent of conscripted Italian foot soldiers assigned to do battle with the Dutch along the periphery.

In one of those infamous skirmishes, memorable only to the survivors and the families of the vanquished, Giulio led a gallant charge into a clearing in pursuit of what he thought was a small band of the enemy. The narrow field was edged by a thick forest of grand firs, behind which was a larger company of Dutch mercenaries mounted and on foot, waiting to spring the trap. Driven by a rash disregard for his life, and impelled by the exhilarating energy of the chase, Giulio thrust his sword forward to lead the attack. The enemy's sides collapsed around him, yet he continued to pursue his foe, slicing and stabbing at his opponents. His heroism, however, would not be decorated, for he and all his comrades were cut down by the overwhelming force of the enemy.

Giulio died from a ball of lead shot that exploded his hand-some young face and propelled him into an inglorious fall from his mount. The desperate civilians who gleaned his fancy uni-form and sturdy boots left no other identifiable signs of his elevated status. He was buried in an unmarked grave near the edge of that unnamed field, the victim of an anonymous battle on the losing side of a now-forgotten war. By the time the news of his death arrived in Naples, the Carazutto sisters were already in their habits at San Gregorio and Lionardo DiCapua was back in Bagnoli Irpino.

* * *

Experience had taught Lionardo that adversity could be a crip-pling blow or a reinforcing gift. The death of his parents was a tribulation that still brought sadness. Yet, if they had not died, he might never have left his village in the first place, nor experienced the intellectual thrills that so enlivened him. At the same time, had he not gone back to Naples, he never would have been reacquainted Celestina. Time alone would have to ease his pain. In the meantime, he would carry a pride of purpose and the atomist desire for knowledge—plus the Stoic ideal of simplicity—into the next phase of his life.

Soon after he was settled, he wrote a long letter to Andrea Concublet, explaining what had led to his decision to return to his ancestral home and asking for any news he might have about Celestina and her family. Since Andrea had many well-con-nected friends, Lionardo also asked him how he might discover the whereabouts of his friend Luciano. Concublet replied with the news of Giulio's subsequent death, and the melancholy that had come over the two sisters. Andrea ended his missive by encouraging Lionardo's intellectual pursuits. Andrea also prom-ised to visit Lionardo in the Irpino, and when he did, he carried the news of Luciano's fate.

The young man had been sent to the Dutch Republic to fight in the infantry against the United Provinces. He and several others were mortally wounded in a skirmish while protecting the retreating Spanish army. He was buried in an unmarked grave somewhere alongside Giulio Carazutto, who was captain of the Italian contingent. When Lionardo passed on this information to Luciano's mother, a deep melancholy overcame her. She took to her bed, announcing her desire to die; her wish was granted within a month.

Thus, the years passed for Lionardo DiCapua by working, studying, experimenting, and teaching a small group of young men, including his nephew, Fabio Gargano, who was attracted to his uncle's intellectual pursuits. DiCapua's philosophical teachings, being what they were, inevitably spilled over into politics. During this charged and changing time, his ideas challenged the unbridled and oftentimes brutal actions of the local aristocracy. Bagnoli Irpino was part of the Kingdom of Naples and, as such, became much affected by the financial crisis of the Spanish monarchy, whose ongoing wars in the north left them in desperate need of men, money, and goods. The archaic feudal system that existed within the kingdom gave free reign for local barons to strip their regions of the necessities of war and, in the process, take their own share. The upshot of all this would evolve throughout the 1640s in the provincial towns and villages—as well as in the capital.

Chapter 16

A Piece of History

Bagnoli Irpino—1643–1645

At the time that Lionardo returned to Bagnoli Irpino, Ferdinand Mayorga was the feudal lord. He represented the new aristocracy, which had grown out of the Spanish government's economic policies of selling titles and offices to those enterprising individuals of Neapolitan, Genovese or Iberian stock who had become successful financiers or bureaucrats.

Ferdinand Mayorga was the minimally Italianized nephew of Ferdinand of Majorca, Spain, who had served as secretary of state for the kingdom until his death in 1598. This well-connected uncle had prime access to the properties of Italian barons suffering from the recurring economic difficulties of the time, and he took full advantage of his position to secure financial wealth for himself and his family. In this manner, the young Mayorga became the duke of Bagnoli Irpino. He married a Spanish woman named Donna Sansicia and brought his bride to his estate. They had a daughter, whom they named Eleanora. This was the high point of the duke's life, although it would hardly be viewed as an auspicious occasion for anyone residing under the rule of the Mayorga family.[1]

This duke had attained his well-endowed estate by questionable acts of nepotism and probable murder; taxed his subjects to excess; helped himself to an inordinate share of their goods; extorted their lands; and kidnapped the young men to fight in the Thirty Years' War. As such, he did not garner support from Lionardo DiCapua.

As a respected physician in the town, Lionardo's anti-Galenist ways and the low regard he held for the duke eventually came to the attention of Mayorga. The duke did not appreciate a man who stood against him, and he set about making contacts in Naples to discover DiCapua's vulnerabilities. Through connections within the upper echelons of government, word of this reached Concublet in late 1643, and he arranged a meeting with his young friend in Avellino, the provincial center, three hours' ride to the northwest from Bagnoli Irpino.

* * *

Andrea Concublet was returning home to Arena after a visit with his father in Naples. Aware of Lionardo's need for protection, he dispatched two of his father's servants to accompany DiCapua to Avellino, where he had planned an excursion into the nearby mountains. The two friends, along with four servants and an acquaintance of Conclubet named Francesco from Benevento, met at the home of an apothecary in Avellino, and then they departed for the mountains to ride, fish, and hunt for birds.

Andrea took the opportunity to caution his young friend of the rumors that had lately come to him regarding Mayorga's inquiries. Lionardo's arguments against Aristotle and Galen, and his writings known to reflect his unorthodox opinions on physick had been the subject of the investigation. Ecclesiastical authorities had been consulted.

Andrea, being of a strong persuasion against unscrupulous nobles like Mayorga, understood DiCapua's disgust for the duke. However, he knew of the Mayorga penchant for indiscriminate violence, such that he feared retribution against his young friend. The Mayorga family had been a great supporter of the king, thus the duke remained a favorite of the viceroys. If Mayorga decided to act, he could do so without fear of official retribution, and ultimately any crime, even the most vicious, could be buried in the Neapolitan courts. Concublet impressed upon Lionardo what these trails of gossip signified and where they might lead. It was agreed that if Lionardo ever felt imminently threatened, he was to depart from town as quietly as possible and ride north to Avellino, and then contact the apothecary who would immediately provide protection until Francesco arrived from Benevento. Concublet would dispatch more help as needed.

Andrea also brought the latest word of the Carazutti family, much of which was unpleasant. It had happened in June that, while in the middle of having intercourse with his wife, Giacomo came into a sudden spasm wherewith his breath failed him; he died while in the act. Imola fell into such a state of apprehension that she moved back to her family's home in Naples, forsaking the *feudo*, its castle, and all the belongings. Having lost both of her boys, Andrea's aunt, the Baroness Faustina, was terribly despondent. As for the Carazutto sisters, Diana (now Sister Maria Niccola) suffered from periodic relapses of the fever of ague, and Celestina (now Sister Maria Fiametta) was finally adapting to her new life. Since the convent was cloistered from outsiders, Andrea had not actually seen either of them for four years—at least, that is what he told his curious friend.

* * *

The winter of 1643–1644 was a particularly busy one for Lionardo. Amenta later wrote that, at the insistence of his friends, Lionardo assembled his writings into a collected format "to let the beauty and wisdom of his prose and poetry shine in published form for all to see." Hence, in addition to his regular schedule of medical work and experimentation, he worked on editing his writings and contacted some of the publishing houses in Naples. He planned to have his work published the following spring of 1644. He balked when the time arrived since he could not trust the publishers to perform the necessary editing. He needed to take them to Naples himself.

In June of the same year, the duke's daughter, Eleanora, was married to Luigi Strozzi, a nephew to her stepmother. At the feast, the duke announced that Duchess Eleanora would be granted control of the *feudo* within a year. The people were hopeful that under her leadership a more conciliatory relationship might be established. The duchess inherited the leadership of the town in 1645, but the anticipation of a more enlightened and sympathetic ruler quickly disappeared when Eleanora soon exceeded her unscrupulous father in cruelty to her people. The duke, it seemed, had taught her well.

* * *

At this time—near the middle of the seventeenth century—Bagnoli Irpino was one of more than 1,500 enfeoffed *'universita'* (communities) in the Kingdom of Naples, in which more than 75 percent of the population lived. The religious revolutions that had occurred in the northern countries never developed in an overwhelmingly Catholic southern Italy.

Campanella's Calabrian revolt at the beginning of the new century had been a complete disaster, and an archaic feudal system had persisted, particularly outside the capital. Living in the countryside usually meant living in a *feudo* (fief), a political entity that was like those that existed during medieval times, especially for the peasants. The kingdom was a highly feudalized society, even more so than the mother country of Spain. Power was divided between the overarching Spanish monarchy—represented by the viceroy in Naples—and the old and new aristocratic barons, whose local power secured the system. The leaders of the Catholic church vacillated in their support of these two controlling forces.

The old Italian aristocracy retained its political integrity, for they were looked upon by the peasants as leaders possessing the legitimacy lacking among the foreigners. Some of the old Italian families, like the Concublet, were of a strong persuasion to look after the welfare of their people in the mode of a benevolent *padrone* (owner). Just the same, during the two centuries of Spanish dominion, the economic and social development of the south was intimately linked to events and decisions that emanated from the Iberian Peninsula. The newer barons retained a strong connection with the Spanish monarchy and each group used the other to enforce control, whereas the older Italian families by turns joined with the Spanish or resisted them.

One of Eleanora's first official acts as duchess was to refuse to renew the *Capitoli* between herself and the townspeople, who were the formal core of the carefully structured hierarchy that defined a *feudo*. Thus, the duchess essentially revoked the contract that was the basis for the way she would interact with her subjects—something that not even her despotic father had dared to do. Yet, despite her revocation of the *Capitoli*, she demanded a continuation of her family's privilege to tax her people in money and goods, and she used her soldiers to intimidate her subjects and enforce those prerogatives.

The townspeople could find no response to this usurpation, for they were like the submerged pillars of a bridge, providing the necessary support for those above them to pass over. They lacked the connections and political savvy to challenge their baron.

Between the helpless peasants and the aristocracy was the small bourgeoisie class comprised of shopkeepers, lawyers, physicians, and artisans. This stratum of society in Bagnoli

Irpino, as well as throughout southern Italy, remained small and ineffectual in the exertion of political power. The only recourse was to appeal to the Catholic church, and when the town council of Bagnoli Irpino asked the local bishop to intercede for them with the Duchess, he posed diverting arguments and, in essence, removed himself from the fray. Hence, the hope of the people for a more enlightened ruler was quickly destroyed, and they soon hated their duchess more than they despised her father.

Lionardo was likewise vocal in his anger, seeing Eleanora's arrogant actions as a blatant and unnecessary abuse of power by a selfish and vacuous aristocrat. He shared these ideas with his friends and wrote them down in an essay that was included in his collected writings, which he hoped to have published soon. Having seen many typesetting errors in the texts of other writers and poets, Lionardo felt it was important to inspect the final setting to correct mistakes before the work was released.

Thus, by late spring of 1645, Lionardo had decided to take his writings to Naples and oversee their publication. While there, he would visit friends and call on the convent of San Gregorio to give his sincerest and long delayed regards to the subject of his sonnets.

Early one clear May morning, he left Bagnoli Irpino travelling alone on horseback and carrying his manuscripts, along with enough money to pay the publisher. He followed the trail downhill for some distance outside of town. The path flattened and then wound through the forests. Finally, Lionardo came to an old Franciscan monastery, said to have been started by the much-traveled Francis of Assisi himself. Continuing onward through the flatlands, Lionardo arrived at an area called *Cruci di Montella',* a few kilometers from Bagnoli not far from where it crossed to the next town of Montella.

Lionardo rode around a blind bend and traveled directly into the snare of a band of masked brigands who spoke in a dialect from the Abruzzo. They forced him to dismount and demanded his money, his cape, his boots, and the pouch containing his writings.

Fearful at first for his life, Lionardo quickly came to a sobered intention and tried to bargain with the thieves. His clothing, the horse, and the money were useful to them, he said, but the manuscripts in his leather pouch were meaningless. To prove the point, he removed a random page from the poetry folio and handed it to the leader of the group. This action only succeeded in turning the brigand's somewhat playful posture into outright anger, for it became obvious that he was unable to read. He tore the page and threw it angrily to the ground. Thence he cocked his pistol, taking aim at Lionardo, as did the rest of the band.

Lionardo removed his cape, his boots, and his wallet, placing them next to his horse as advised. He held on to the satchel and, once again, tried to bargain with them. He promised to deliver more money and another horse to a place of their choosing without notifying the authorities if he could keep his writings. "These are merely tracts of my own musings," he tried to explain. "They are worthless in value to anyone but me."

The leader, however, would not be deterred in his mission. He dismounted and walked toward his prey with his pistol pointed at Lionardo's heart. He grabbed at the pouch; Lionardo held firm. The thief raised his gun directly into Lionardo's face. "I can assure you, Signore," he began, "that I have killed many men before you. If there is a God in heaven, he has already damned my soul to the eternal flames, such that if I kill you, the devil and his kin will truly rejoice. Now, let go of this pouch and I will spare your life."

Lionardo refused to relinquish his writings, causing the thief to pause and study his captive with eyes tinged with vengeful fury. Then he continued to speak slowly. "Hear me well, Signore! If you do not let go, I will dispatch your soul to wherever it may fly, and I will then rip this pouch from the clutch of your dead hands." He placed the barrel of the gun directly onto the center of Lionardo's forehead.

Realizing the futility of his situation, Lionardo finally released the satchel. As the leader returned to his horse, two of his accomplices dismounted, one taking the reins of DiCapua's horse, the other taking the rest of the booty. They mockingly advised him to return home before his unshod feet led to serious illness. Thence they rode off in the opposite direction from Bagnoli, sarcastically imitating his sorrowful pleas.

Lionardo picked up the one torn poem and made his way back to Bagnoli, as if a stupor had left him insensitive to the pain in his bare feet. All his accumulated manuscripts would most likely be thrown to the wind or used to start a campfire. What a cruel hoax to have his writings stolen by a band of illiterate thugs! His most lyrical prose, his philosophical musings, his essays and critiques, his scholastic lessons, two tragic plays, some comedies, a sylvan fable—all of them lost. And most egregious, more than two thousand love sonnets to Celestina (save one) taken from him forever, just as she had been.

One can only imagine the depth of his despair and, likewise, be assured that phrases and scenes would come back to haunt Lionardo with their beauty and insight. Yet, the passion that created the love sonnets had faded. He would write no more sonnets, no more plays, no more fables. All those feelings would remain inside him. For the rest of his life, Amenta wrote, Lionardo confined his writings to the subjects of philosophy, natural science, history, and medicine.

Considering that the loss of his writings was such a huge wound to Lionardo, it's surprising that Amenta presents only a brief description of the thievery in *La Vita*. Left open are questions, such as why Lionardo traveled alone without an escort given Concublet's warning and the known fact that brigands worked the roads throughout southern Italy. And why would they care about his writings? To Amenta, the robbery was due to Lionardo being in the wrong place at the wrong time. Or, as he said, "Lady luck had been so contrary to Lionardo and had been his enemy."

But in a short history of the village, written sometime later, the unknown author raises the possibility that Lionardo was not a victim of the bad luck that Amenta implies. Instead, there is a vague reference to the perpetrators as people who knew Lionardo well: "But envy, that passion of vulgar and base spirits, unable to lift itself to the state of virtue, pulls the other to its own level, and looks with an evil eye on the glory acquired by DiCapua." No explanation is added. No names are mentioned. Yet, the message is clear: Someone planned his misfortune and used the brigands to cover their trail.

* * *

Just as Andrea Concublet had cautioned him, the forces of authority were of a strong persuasion to sanction control over their dominions, and Lionardo had become a vocal critic of the ruling Mayorgas. Suffice it to say that news traveled fast in a small town. Lionardo's plans to publish his controversial writings would have become noteworthy throughout the village. People who despised the author and heard of his decision to publish could prevent him from reaching Naples.

The drops of water that fall on one's head from a leaky roof seem to originate from a spot directly above the recipient. Finding the true source of the problem, however, can lead to a location far removed and hidden from sight. In his heart—and by the concerted action of the thieves that regrettable morning— Lionardo also sensed that the source of his trouble originated as a side channel, loosely connected to the thieves, although he could not find proof of a conspiracy. With time, however, the truth would be made known to him.

NOTES

1. What I have learned about Ferdinand Mayorga is quite unflattering. He was not the benevolent *padrone* who looked after his people and bonded with them in the process. Nor was he the best example of Christian virtue. He was, instead, feared by the peasants and hated by his servants. The beatings he administered to his wife, Donna Sansicia, became so awful that her mother attempted, in vain, to kidnap her and take her back to Spain. When the wife died suspiciously in 1632, the duke inherited all her money, and within a year he married a Roman woman of noble lineage named Anna Strozzi. She came to live with her new husband and her stepdaughter in Bagnoli.

Chapter 17

Revolution in the Kingdom

Campania, 1647

As the Thirty Years' War approached its violent and impoverished conclusion, central Europe had become a wasteland. To
the north, England had managed to remain mostly above the
continental fray, while its own religiously inspired civil war
was still brewing. To the south, the Kingdom of Naples was
being bled of its treasury and its goods, and many a peasant had
been forcefully conscripted. Fortunately, the physical holocaust
incurred by the German Principalities and Bohemia never came
to southern Italy.

In the penultimate year of the Thirty Years' War, 1647,
another blow was struck against Philip IV and his cousin, the
new Hapsburg emperor, Frederick III. Following the revolts that
had begun in Portugal and Catalonia at the beginning of the
decade and the insurgency in Palermo, Sicily, in 1646, the Kingdom of Naples exploded in mass uprising. Each of the rebellions
seemed to be an isolated event not linked to the others by planning or coordination; yet the earlier insurrections undoubtedly
provided inspiration for the people living within the Kingdom
of Naples. This was especially true with the revolution in neigh-
boring Palermo, where the people obtained tax relief and were
granted a general amnesty by the viceroy.

The events leading up to the revolt in Bagnoli Irpino offers one example of the resentment felt by the citizens. The circumstances were unique to that town, yet, when multiplied by similar experiences in hundreds of locales, one can understand why the kingdom came to a full-scale uprising.

After Duchess Eleanora refused to renew the *Capitoli* in 1645, she continued to provoke the animosity of the townspeople. When the duchess heard rumors of a woman speaking unkindly of her, she sent soldiers to arrest the offender. The woman was the widow of a respected lawyer in the village, and her accusations concerning the Duchess reflected the general feeling of her fellow citizens. The insensitive Eleanora wished to make an example of her subject, so she placed the widow backward on an ass—a highly symbolic gesture usually reserved for the crime of heresy—and paraded her through the town while being flogged nearly to death. The animosity created by this unnecessarily brutal act compelled the locals from animosity to outright hatred of the duchess.

Unfazed, Eleanora continued to disregard her subjects and pushed her agenda to the brink in the early spring of 1647. The Mayorga family owed an old debt to the town, one that they had agreed to pay at some future time. After the shaming of the widow, the town council decided to call in the loan. Negotiations ensued until the end of March, when Eleanora summarily announced that she had unilaterally voided the loan, claiming that her family owed nothing to their fief. In response, the usually languid populace listened to loud speeches of protest, thence rioted in the squares while the guards, out of sympathy for the rebel cause, made no effort to quell the chaos.

At the end of July 1647, the town council announced that, since there were no formal agreements with the Mayorgas, the fief had been dissolved and the "Republic of Bagnoli Irpino" was proclaimed. Lionardo DiCapua and his nephew, Fabio Gargano, wrote the charter that created the new Republic. Unfortunately, this document was lost in the ensuing chaos. But based on word of mouth from people who read the declaration, it was a compelling statement suffused with DiCapua's neo-stoic and atomist ideals. It was unusual for literati to participate in political events in the kingdom, and Lionardo must have understood the danger in doing so. Yet he pursued his anti-aristocratic beliefs, using his mind and his pen rather than a sword, for the benefit of his fellow citizens—even at the cost of eventually having to flee Bagnoli for fear of his life.

The varied impulses that led to the crisis in the Irpino were similar, although not identical, to those that brought revolution to the streets of Naples. The common problem throughout the kingdom was financial debt, with actual expenditures at twice what came into the treasury. Most of the money was spent on the wars and servicing the debt. Orders from Spain demanded more soldiers and more money for the navy. The Genovese merchants who were financing the debt had to be paid, and more grain and gunpowder were needed as well, forcing the viceroy to meet the demands for war by peddling whatever he could for the best price he could obtain. Offices, titles, lands, and the collecting of taxes (the tax farmers) would go to those who could pay for them, thus, accelerating the deterioration of the economy.

As the kingdom edged closer to the financial abyss, resistance to conscription intensified among the peasants. Many southern Italians ended up fighting the French in Milan or the rebels in Portugal, with whom they had much in common. People questioned whether they were truly defending their kingdom or merely pawns being used to defend a perpetually absent foreign king, whose allegiance they questioned. As the wars and revolutions dragged on, the methods used to seize the conscripts from the provinces became harsher, as was the case for Luciano and other men in Bagnoli. These tactics led to riots in some of the villages and further erosion of the tax base and supply of goods, as the departure of the younger men meant that many of the fields were left fallow.

Continued fiscal imbalances led the Spanish to levy more than twenty-five new, indirect taxes on the cost of goods, which were leased to the tax farmers. The city sat like a pile of desiccated timber waiting for an incendiary spark and a hot wind to burst into flames. The seemingly minor spark that set off the revolt in Naples was a tax (*gabella*) levied against the sale of fruit, such that what began as a citizens' protest against this one *gabella* quickly escalated into a general insurrection all across the city. One of the more interesting facets of the revolt was that its leader was not a disaffected military man, a politician, an academic or even a merchant. Instead, fortune had placed an uneducated peasant as the *Capopoppoli,* a fisherman originally from Amalfi by the name of Tomaso Aniello, known in the Neapolitan dialect by the contraction "Masaniello."

Chapter 18

The Revolt of Masaniello

Naples—1647

Thanks to an eyewitness account written by Alessandro Giraffi, the events of the most dramatic part of the Neapolitan revolt (the first ten days) were recorded in an eloquent and—in keeping with the times and the locale—somewhat sensationally baroque style.

The uprising began on Sunday, July 7, 1647. The mostly unknown but determined Masaniello rallied the people through his skillful propagation of slogans against the *gabella*. He directly confronted those who tried to collect them at the central *Piazza del Mercato,* where much of the fruit and other foods were sold. The tax house within the piazza was burnt to the ground, thence the gathering crowd of thousands scattered across the city to torch the other tax houses as well as the collection sites of the tax farmers. Afterwards, they headed to the Royal Palace, easily broke through the German and Spanish guards, sacked the rooms, and threw the furniture out through the windows. Then they pursued the Viceroy Duke of Arcos, who diverted the gathering by throwing a few handfuls of coins into the crowd, thence narrowly making an escape in his carriage.

When night finally gave way at the break of dawn, the mob did not pause in its passions. They overran other contingents of soldiers at various armories and stole the weapons.

They emptied the prisons, burnt the flour customs house to the ground, and burnt the shop of a seller of pikes, inside of which was dry gunpowder that exploded, causing numerous deaths and scores of wounded. Included in the deaths were Sophia, the Carazuttos' servant, and her husband, who were standing nearby when the explosion occurred. She had left her son, Rosario, with a neighbor.

The next day, Masaniello obtained concessions from Viceroy Arcos to remove some of the more odious *gabelle* and increase the size of the loaves of bread without increasing the cost. The demands of the people, as expressed by Masaniello, then expanded into equal representation on the Collateral Council and the removal of all *gabelle*. Intellectuals, artists, and many low-level religious people supported these goals as the movement expanded to more than just a revolt of the peasants.

Hearing of these successes, armed men and women from the nearby provinces poured into the city, swelling the ranks of the mob to around 150,000. They developed a list of more than sixty ministers plus the names of people who were tax farmers or had cooperated in any way in the taxation of the people. Their houses were systematically burnt.

Elsewhere in the city, several cannons were seized and set up at strategic points, and thousands of muskets were distributed to the people. The archbishop became concerned that the city and, indeed, the entire kingdom were in danger of being destroyed by the popular fury. He petitioned the Duke of Arcos and they met Masaniello—wearing a silver suit and a white hat with a long, white plume—at the palace, where they agreed to remove all the recently imposed *gabelle*. After the meeting, they stepped onto a balcony to announce the capitulation, and the viceroy presented Masaniello with a heavy gold chain and placed it around his neck. Masaniello promised to turn the control of the city back to the viceroy soon after the agreed upon terms had been read to the public on Saturday, July 13, in the cathedral. Two days later, Masaniello reneged on his promise.

People on both sides of the insurrection soon became concerned by what the increasingly megalomaniacal man might do. Thus, a secret conference was called among all the principal characters while Masaniello was boating in the bay. He was arrested and placed in prison upon his return. On the tenth day, after making a rambling, incoherent speech in the crowded cathedral, he was shot and decapitated, with his head paraded around the city on a lance. But the revolt did not end with Masaniello's death. For nine more months the unrest continued.

At the beginning of October, the Spanish fleet arrived under the command of Giovanni d'Austria, King Philip IV's son. The attack on the city occurred on the fifth of October, and after a bloody battle, the Spanish managed to regain only part of the city. Six weeks later, the French, under Henry of Lorraine, arrived and took up with the insurgents. He was such an embarrassment to the French government, however, that they sent a small fleet in mid-December to kidnap him. Henry somehow escaped and returned to the city, where he further fractured the insurgent cause. In the final scene of this Baroque opera, the Spanish ambassador in Rome coordinated the effort to remove Henry, and on the sixth of April 1648, following two days of heavy fighting, the Spanish regained control of the city.

* * *

Interpretations on the effectiveness of the revolt vary. After the initial explosion against the taxes had been released in the first ten days, Masaniello's revolution did not fade away. When it finally ended, the agreement reached with Arcos's successor, the Viceroy Count of Onate, satisfied some of the demands for tax relief made during the conflict. But of greater consequence was the fact that Viceroy Onate agreed to include the peoples' organizations in the restructuring of the tax economy—an exceptional notion for this time in European politics.

Undoubtedly, this taste of freedom—however small it might have been—affected many aspects of Neapolitan life. In the last half of the seventeenth century, Naples would see a flowering of cultural, literary, and scientific progress that connected the city and its luminaries to other intellectual movements happening in other centers throughout Europe, particularly in England. At the same time, because the crown had to make allowances to the nobles as well, the control of the nobility over their titled fiefs in the countryside was strengthened. Those concessions would have a major impact on the immediate future of Lionardo DiCapua and his partisans in Bagnoli Irpino.

* * *

The end of the revolt in the Republic of Bagnoli Irpino came when the Spanish troops arrived following the cessation of hostilities in Naples. Amnesty was granted to those who would submit to royal control; however, Duchess Eleanora sought revenge against the leaders of the uprising, especially Lionardo DiCapua and his nephew, Fabio Gargano. They were accused of multiple crimes, most of which Lionardo was able to shed, save for the most serious of all the charges: a double homicide of two loyalists that had occurred in the village in March 1648. DiCapua had nothing to do with the murders, yet the duchess pursued the case aggressively, such that Lionardo realized his life would be endangered should he stay in the village to fight the false charges.

Hence, he pursued the plan that had been conceived with Andrea Concublet a few years earlier, and he secretly fled to Avellino. The apothecary had heard of DiCapua's plight and was expecting him. He protected Lionardo, as promised, until Francesco arrived later that evening. Riders were also sent to

Naples to request direct assistance from Andrea Concublet. That same night, Francesco took Lionardo to nearby Benevento, which was in a foreign country under the domain of the Papal States, four hours' ride north from Avellino.

Chapter 19

Exile

Benevento—1648–1650

Lionardo DiCapua would remain in exile in Benevento for more than one-and-a-half years, during which friends and family of "the Dante of our time" (Amenta's words) would work to remove the charges against him. Concublet sent four, armed men to assist Francesco, who remained ever vigilant in his role as guardian of Lionardo.

"Cesco" as Lionardo called him, was a stocky man of medium height, in the latter part of his fourth decade, with the dark skin, oval eyes and black hair that betrayed an Arabic influence. He seemed to be a step ahead of those around him in the constant preparation of a plan for what might come next and how he might react to it. He had a nervous habit of clearing his throat frequently whenever he spoke, and his movements and expressions could change suddenly, often leaving people who did not know him confused and uncomfortable. Locri was his home— a coastal town along the lower tip of the toe in Calabria that once had been part of *Magna Grecia;* it had incorporated successive waves of invaders ever since. His father—who had met Andrea's grandfather, the Marchese Scipione, during the Calabrian revolt—had introduced him into the service of the Concublet family.

Francesco's real name was Vincenzo. He changed it while in a Dominican monastery in the Abruzzo, where he had spent four years learning to read and write Latin and imbibe the legend of Campanella. Being a man of action desirous of helping others in a more material way than the priesthood might allow, he left the monastery while still in the novitiate to join a group of *briganti* in the Abruzzo.

In time, Francesco came to the realization that the *Capo* was a mere mercenary who covered a vicious character and a cold heart with high-minded talk. The ex-monk escaped from the band and, at the behest of his father, contacted Andrea's father who, despite Francesco's recent history, saw in him a bright man with good intentions.

Notwithstanding his decent motives, however, Francesco had a problem. He could not remain in Naples where he was known as an outlaw, and he could not return to his home in Calabria for fear of being tracked by his former group of brigands. Hence, the Marchese Concublet sent him (under a pseudonym) to Benevento, a city in the Papal States and the closest principal city outside the kingdom where, with his knowledge of Latin, he could represent his master at the Papal court. There he remained a reliable servant for more than eight years.

Lionardo stayed with Cesco and the guards at a home owned by the Marchese Concublet in Benevento. The vigilant Cesco asked that his guest not leave the house without the accompaniment of at least one, and preferably two, armed men. Otherwise, he was free to do as he wished, which for Lionardo meant establishing a small laboratory in the *cantina* and having a well-lit site for reading since, as Amenta wrote, he was of the habit of reading for ten hours a day. Cesco provided his charge with books, writing materials, and the occasional dead animal for anatomic studies. He also provided all the meals since he was an accomplished cook.

One night early in Lionardo's exile, following a filling dinner of wild pheasant and greens, he and Cesco sat around the fireplace having a conversation typical of the idle chatter of acquaintances who had yet to become friends. After a few glasses of wine, Lionardo asked his host a question about his connection with Andrea. Thus began the unfolding of the details mentioned above (in much more detail) over several hours, aided by multiple glasses of wine. Francesco assured his guest that bands of the brigands were still active throughout Italy, either as individual criminals on their own or, more commonly, in the service of a well-to-do protector.

"Do you know any of them?" Lionardo asked.

Cesco cleared his throat. "I have contacts who know them."

"Perhaps you might know of the band that robbed me three years ago?"

Cesco told him that he had had heard of the incident and inquired soon after the theft had occurred. "What I can tell you with certainty is that the brigands were from a gang centered in the Abruzzo. They were known mercenaries with contacts throughout the south." He cleared his throat. "Your job had been arranged and paid for in advance, yet I have not been able to confirm the source of the money; it was delivered by intermediaries."

"If I put up the money to an extent you might suggest, would you again check with your contacts? I was on my way to Naples to have my writings published. I don't care about my horse or the money, but if possible, I want my writings back."

Cesco assured him that his money was unnecessary because the offer had been made by Andrea Concublet and was still in effect. He smiled, then quickly frowned. "I'm sorry for your loss and that you had to learn the hard way that you never should have gone on your own. I am confident that we will eventually discover the source. The large band was made up of many smaller groups. The bandits who robbed you had just joined and wished to prove their abilities to the bigger group, hence their bond of secrecy was tight." He paused to sip from his glass. "But remember, my friend," Cesco continued, "these things change over time. These men are criminals and, among criminals, allegiances that create the chain of secrecy always fade in time. Hence . . ." he coughed, ". . . they can be broken by offering ducats to the weakest link."

* * *

While he remained in exile, Lionardo's friends and family worked to disprove the allegations by the Mayorgas at the higher jurisdictional level in Naples. Contacts had been made with Francesco D'Andrea, the brilliant young lawyer who recently returned to Naples. He had also studied natural philosophy under Marcaurelio Severino and was known for his reformist tendencies. D'Andrea, originally from Amalfi, gained the confidence of the viceroy through his adept arguments made in the royal court at Naples. He served as the viceroy's representative in the city of Chieti in the Abruzzo and remained there through the revolution of 1648. Upon his return to the capitol, his influence continued within the legal-political circles, despite accusations that he had supported the rebels against the aristocracy while in Chieti.

In Benevento, around the sixteenth of December, word arrived of D'Andrea's success on Lionardo's behalf, and he was advised to prepare for his return to Bagnoli. Cesco and the guards would accompany him, leaving Benevento in plenty of time for a *festa* to be held in Lionardo's honor. The night before they departed, Cesco served a celebratory dinner for Lionardo and the four guards, featuring *cinghiale* (wild boar) that he had killed earlier in the week and spent three days preparing in the traditional manner. Toasts were made throughout the meal, and Lionardo presented Francesco with a poem, since lost, in which he made a play on the words "Cesco" and "*cieco*," the word for a blind man. The *cieco* was Cesco who, though blind in his loyalty and friendship, was made aware of things before all others using his other keen senses.

Francesco thanked his friend and then handed him a present. It was a scroll rolled and tied with a scarlet ribbon. Lionardo opened it to find just two words, beautifully scripted: *"Era Mayorga!"* (It was Mayorga!)

Lionardo DiCapua returned to Bagnoli Irpino in triumph on the twentieth of December. A procession met him at the old gate and accompanied him to the main piazza, where speeches were given and laurels presented. During the celebration, Lionardo was given the sad news that his nephew Fabio Gargano had not been as fortunate in shedding the charges as Lionardo had been. Fabio had been accused of protecting brigands, and he was given an enormous fine that was well beyond his means or that of his family. Consequently, all his goods were confiscated, and he was forced to flee to Naples to escape prison. He would remain there until his death in 1670 without ever having the chance to return to his hometown.

Eleanora was officially restored as Duchess in 1652. Much to her dismay, Lionardo pursued Fabio Gargano's acquittal in Naples and formed a political party whose partisans were elected to run the new city council, although Lionardo would not be among them. Having received the confirmation of the Mayorga complicity in his theft from Cesco, and realizing a calling that was much bigger than a local fight with the Duchess Eleanora, he came to the decision to leave Bagnoli Irpino and return to Naples.

During his exile in Benevento, he had often considered the loss of his love sonnets and, more so, the loss of Celestina herself. Thus, he prepared to face his past and return to the city. The irony inherent in that realization did not escape him, for despite the pain it caused, he could thank the Mayorga for helping him find the strength to make the move that he knew was necessary. His family and friends were saddened with his decision, especially Uncle Horace who seemed to have aged greatly during the ordeal of Lionardo's exile.

For his part, Lionardo felt a mixture of sadness and excitement as when he had first gone to Naples twenty years earlier. To stay in the Irpino would have limited his opportunities to advance his knowledge and promote the kind of new thinking necessary for greater understanding of the natural world. Overall, the years spent in his hometown had been a productive preparation for greater things to come.

And so, in the late spring of 1650, Lionardo DiCapua left Bagnoli Irpino and moved to Naples. As he settled in, he reestablished his contacts with many of the literati known from his earlier days. His first maestro, Don Ruggero, weakened by the disease that had lingered since his time in the New World, had died in 1648. However, his second great teacher, Marcaurelio Severino, was still in the city and was anxious to renew their friendship. Lionardo promised himself he would not try to contact Celestina, although he would continue to seek updates whenever he saw Andrea Concublet.

Concublet's father had died in 1648 after the revolution, leaving Andrea to receive the title of his ancestral lands as Marchese di Arena. He also inherited the position of *Ragione del Regno* for the viceroy. Hence, he was now spending nearly all his time at his palace in Naples.

Chapter 20

Return To Napoli

Naples, 1650

While Lionardo was in exile in Benevento, the Peace of
Westphalia was signed in October 1648, ending the Thirty
Years' War—or at least that part of the war between the
Spanish-Hapsburg side and the Protestants. Hoping to weaken
French influence, Spain signed a separate treaty with the Dutch
that granted their independence after eighty years of war. As a
result, the angered French refused to sign a treaty with Spain,
and their war would continue for eleven more years. A war
interwoven within a war upon an even grander war—so went
the seventeenth century.

The Thirty Years' War marked a continuing decline in the
prestige of the old Hapsburg Empire, with the French Bourbon
dynasty securing the greatest gains. Indeed, Catholic France,
whose political aims exceeded their loyalty to Rome, saved the
Protestant Reformation.

The Treaty of Westphalia brought to a dramatic close the
religious struggles that had thrown Europe into chaos since
Luther had denounced Catholicism. The enormous devastation
of a war in which more than ten million people died, lands and
fields were devastated, thousands of villages were deserted,
famine and disease persisted, and the survivors were left on the
margins of existence was sad testimony to religion run amok.

Political leaders had used religious faith to further their own agendas. Once unleashed, those passions left a swath of death and destruction unseen in the history of European warfare.

On the positive side, the skepticism generated by the brutality opened the path for a more enlightened way. This new thinking, which had begun so tentatively in the early sixteenth century, accelerated the advance of reason over authority. In the Italian peninsula, some of the most intense activity occurred in the northern cities of Florence, Bologna, Padua, Venice, and Pisa. Southern Italy, likewise, began to flower with new ideas, particularly in Naples; a core of progressive thinkers began to assemble, advancing the notion of open inquiry based on careful observations. Their willingness to present their theories in a general forum was completely foreign to the feudal south. It would take decades to dismantle that heritage.

During that time, the hierarchy of the Catholic Church, the Spanish government, and some of the aristocrats would continue to resist change such that anyone who advanced the new ideas faced the possibility of retaliation. Thus, it would take more than an inquisitive mind to further scientific principles. Progressives would need to be cunning and courageous, for the fate of Giordano Bruno, Tommaso Campanella, Galileo and others had clearly demonstrated that an individual could not take on such reactionary forces and survive. Safety was to be found in numbers. The effort was risky, but the camaraderie and intellectual excitement of exchanging ideas with people who shared an interest in the arts and sciences was worth the gamble. Consequently, throughout Italy, creative academies flourished.

Music and theater academies were established in Venice, Siena and Bologna, and artistic and literary academies in Bologna, Florence, Rome and Naples. Overall, during the seventeenth century, in over two hundred Italian centers, more than eight hundred new academies opened. Even more than the universities, they were the breeding grounds for the ideas that would lead to a new enlightenment. The newest to form were those that concentrated on scientific issues: the *Cimento* in Florence, the *Lincei* in Rome and, in time, the *Accademia degli Investiganti* in Naples founded by Tomaso Cornelio and Lionardo DiCapua.

* * *

Lionardo departed from Bagnoli Irpino and arrived in Naples in the spring of 1650. Upon his return to the city, he contacted Marcaurelio Severino and rekindled their friendship. They agreed to meet regularly and to review and edit any works of natural philosophy that each of them produced. Lionardo also renewed his friendship with Tommaso Cornelio who, likewise, returned to Naples in late 1650.

In the intervening fifteen years since they had parted, Cornelio had completed training in medicine from 1637 to 1643 at the University in Rome. He was also fortunate to meet Marcaurelio Severino and observe him performing anatomies. The two became friends and exchanged letters during and after Tommaso's medical training.

After Rome, Cornelio devoted his time studying the Galilean method with a small group in Florence that included, among others, the noted physicist, Evangelista Torricelli, the inventor of the mercury barometer. Always a retiring person, Tommaso spent a quiet year writing poetry and seeking solitude and knowledge in Bologna. By the middle of 1647 he considered returning to Naples, but Severino dissuaded him from doing so because of the political unrest brewing within the city.

Earlier, Cornelio had tried to convince Lionardo to travel with him to the intellectual centers on the continent. Tommaso was attracted by the teachings of the great thinkers in Italy, France, Holland, and England, as was his good friend. However, Lionardo balked at going, Amenta tells us, "Because Cornelio was gifted with a much greater spirit than that of Lionardo and was also of a stronger constitution and more eloquent."

And while there is truth in this assertion, again it is incomplete. At that time in their lives, Tommaso, who had always been physically stronger than Lionardo, was likewise more comfortable with strangers. After completing his studies at the university, he had travelled to Rome and Florence, which expanded his world beyond the narrow confines of southern Italy and created the desire to travel beyond the peninsula to elsewhere on the continent.

Lionardo always lived in the Campania, and he felt uncomfortable leaving his home and his friends. This may have been due to the traumatic losses he had suffered earlier in his life. Maybe the fear of another episode with the *briganti* or, perhaps, some other unrealized trepidation weighed on his mind.[1]

Some people are travelers, born under a wandering star. They seem constantly out of place in the land of their surroundings as if they happened to come there by some accident of fate. An inner force that perpetuates the search for a precinct far removed from the familiar drives these restless souls. And even though others might often ascribe this ceaseless activity to mischievous or even scandalous motives, in truth, many are not running *from* their station in life so much as *to* it.

On the other hand, people like Lionardo DiCapua are content to remain in and around familiar territory their entire lives. They have found their place within their surroundings; hence, they have no reason to look elsewhere. Thus, Lionardo commended the idea of travelling to Tommaso, but refused to accompany him on the journey. His one request was that his friend would return to Naples with as many good books as possible, especially in medicine, philosophy, and mathematics, without regard to cost.

＊＊＊

While Tommaso spent time in various northern cities, Lionardo devoted himself to rereading Hippocrates, Galen, Plutarch, and Diogenes Laertius. When Cornelio returned from his tour in the winter of 1650, he brought with him the writings of Francis Bacon, Thomas Hobbes, Robert Boyle, Thomas Willis, Pierre Gassendi, Rene Descartes, and Galileo, among others. Thus, after Tommaso returned, Lionardo devoted several more months to reading the new ideas and comparing them to the classics. Thanks to his intense study, he decided to bring together scholars capable of speculating on various subjects so that, as Amenta would write, "Without regard for the authority of men, and only with the escort of open thinking and of reasonable opinions, they would discover the causes of all natural things."

Cornelio and DiCapua were familiar with the literary academies in Naples—like the *Oziosi*-and they considered it worthwhile to use that model for freethinking discussion on scientific ideas. They knew that such an undertaking could raise the ire of the Neapolitan authorities; hence, they set up a small informal group in Cornelio's home. They were joined at times by the brilliant Giovanni Alfonso Borelli and philosopher/physician Sebastiano Bartoli, a close friend of Lionardo. The lawyer, Francesco D'Andrea also participated, as did Marcaurelio Severino, the influential, common connection between them all.

By 1653, Francesco D'Andrea used his political connections with Viceroy Onate to secure a place for Cornelio and DiCapua on the faculty at the University of Naples. (Remember that the university had been established as an independent corporation run by the Spanish crown in the person of the viceroy.) The University of Naples, like most of the universities in Europe at the time, was not an institution that expected or encouraged innovative ideas. However, proponents of the new ideas were not excluded from university chairs; private teaching in the independent colleges within the university was possible, and a student could obtain a degree from one of those colleges without necessarily attending the university.

Cornelio's first appointment was in mathematics, then medicine and astronomy. Lionardo presented instructions in the emerging field of chemistry to the medical students. Galileans like the renowned Borelli had helped separate chemistry from its links to both the quacks, who made uncontrolled medicines, and the alchemists, who were often enlivened by the greed for gold more than science.

The subjects and techniques of DiCapua's lessons were provocative, and they generated a great deal of discussion among the students and, eventually, among the practicing Galenists, some of whom remembered his earlier years in Naples. Lionardo empathized with Paracelsus, admired Von Helmont, and emphasized the Galilean and Cartesian methods, while mixing and presenting all with atomist philosophy.

Cornelio's classes reflected the same investigative approach. These two innovators brought an air of excitement to the staid curriculum, which also raised the intensity of debate as they made inroads among the new graduates. The theories being discussed connected the innovators with scientists, mathematicians, and philosophers across the continent. In England, where the physician training programs had been modeled on the original ideas of the *Incurabili*, British reformers had been proposing the acceptance of chemistry instruction as well. Great advances in the subjects of anatomy and physiology were occurring on a regular basis, such that a sense of new possibilities in medicine had arrived across Europe.

Despite this success, the well-established Galenists reacted strongly to the inherent threats of the innovators' methods and teachings. But Cornelio and DiCapua found protection in

D'Andrea's relationship with the viceroy.

Severino, on the other hand, had been the target of the authorities whose animosity toward him had festered for years. His connections to Campanella were again raised in public. He was accused of atheistic beliefs, and accusations circulated that his anatomic methods included necromancy. The power of the religious and political authorities was intentionally activated by these charges, leaving Severino open to persecution. Consequently, after a lifetime of brilliant teaching to his students and devoted treatment to his patients, Marcaurelio Severino was deprived of his position at the University and given a heavy fine that forfeited much of his savings. Worse still, he was forced into intellectual exile apart from the world to which he had been so devoted.

The unjust treatment of their mentor angered, yet did not intimidate Cornelio and DiCapua. On the contrary—and with their maestro's support—they came to an even stronger persuasion to challenge the Aristotelian-Galenists and to call for open discussion of the ideas that they and other progressive doctors were espousing.

Through their persistence, these new teachings gained a foothold of acceptance among physicians throughout the first half of the 1650s. With each success, the new ideas continued to advance until the beginning of 1656. At that point, the two innovators, along with their adversaries, were confronted by a mutually implacable foe of such extraordinary power that it swept through the kingdom, impartial to any argument or any philosophy.

NOTES

1. During my research, I came across an older relative of Lionardo who told me that most of the males in the family, as far back as she could remember, spent most of their time close to home. They were good family men who preferred interacting with their children and studying rather than socializing with friends or traveling abroad. Thus, it could be that Lionardo carried a predisposition for such a life.

Chapter 21

The Plague In Naples

Naples—1656

Rosario left his home at the San Gregorio convent and arrived
at the Duomo early in the afternoon of Saturday, May 3, 1656.
The first Saturday of May was the day that the Neapolitans
traditionally celebrated the arrival of the body of San Gennaro
to Naples. Gennaro was the legendary bishop of the city of
Benevento who was beheaded by the emperor Diocletian around
the year of our Lord 305. The remains of his body, plus two
ampules of his blood, had been brought to Naples in 1497, and
since then he had been hailed as the patron saint and protector
of the city.

Three times a year the people would gather in the *Duomo* to
witness the miracle of the liquefaction of the congealed blood. A
rapid conversion was a good omen. A delay or failure indicated
grave misfortunes. To speed the process, several old women sat
at the front of the church intoning prayers and, if necessary,
insults to the saint. When Rosario arrived, these *Parenti* of San
Gennaro were angrily addressing the saint in their dialect, for
the blood was still congealed.

Normally, there would be an impressive procession that
would carry the relics to the Church of Santa Chiara where they
would be exhibited for eight days. But the procession could not
begin until the blood liquefied. Over the next several hours, the

archbishop repeatedly inspected the ornate gold shrine that held the ampoules, hoping to lift it before the crowd in confirmation of the miracle. Each time this day, however, he would return to the sacristy where his increasingly nervous retinue waited. Meanwhile, the *Parenti* wailed louder as a palpable sense of foreboding spread among the faithful.

By late afternoon, some of the people began leaving the cathedral, pushing their way through the thinning crowd outside. Rosario stayed until early evening then returned to the convent. At daybreak, the peeling of the *Duomo* bells awakened him, announcing that liquefaction of the blood had occurred. Mother Superior again sent him to take part in the ceremony and report back on what he had seen. During the procession that followed a solemn High Mass, he overheard people recounting stories of numerous deaths in their quarter.

Over the next eight days, the relics were customarily displayed, but the delay in the liquefaction had impressed on the collective spirit of the city the belief that something horrible was coming. By the middle of May, hundreds of people were dying each day throughout the city. The archbishop called for a procession of repentance to propitiate God's anger caused by the sinfulness of his people. The relics of San Gennaro, Santa Irena and other protectors of the city led thousands of people through the streets. Within a week, officials announced that the cemeteries were full, but the deaths continued, reaching over five hundred each day by the end of May.

* * *

In January 1656 the plague came to Naples. How it came there is not fixed, although the commonly held view is that it arrived when a flotilla of ships, carrying soldiers to Lombardy, made its way into the Bay of Naples. On board one of the vessels was a Neapolitan named Masone, who had been a captain under Masaniello during the great revolt. It happened that first Masone, followed by his servant, then followed by Masone's mother, died of a mysterious disease. The servant was from the *Vicolo Rotto*, the same poor alley in which Masaniello had lived, and it was in that quarter of the city that most of the early deaths occurred. The Spanish governing elite quickly announced the obvious connection: this disease was God's wrath belatedly being leveled against a people that had rebelled against its legitimate sovereign.

"No!" proclaimed physician, Giuseppe Bozzutto. "These are the first fatalities of an epidemic of *peste*." The petechiae and the buboes on the victims, he argued, were the classic signs, and he implored the civil leaders to quickly establish isolation procedures to stop the spread.

The response of the authorities was swift. Doctor Bozzutto was the one person officially segregated from the public when he was placed in jail for proclaiming false rumors. He died there mysteriously soon afterwards.

As the contagion spread further, the viceroy ordered that all dogs and cats be killed. This was in keeping with the theory of the poisonous effluvia or "miasma" that sticks to and is thus transmitted on rough surfaces like animal hair.[1]

When the animal killings failed to stem the epidemic, the French conveniently became suspect. They were rumored to have placed poisonous powder in the holy water fonts of the Spanish chapels and churches. Other foreigners and any Jews living within the confines of Naples were also accused. Some of these poor souls were slaughtered and their bodies thrown outside the walls. Those who were spared were expelled from the city, most likely to their benefit. But despite all these extreme measures, the vicious pestilence raged, prompting the suspicious Neapolitans from the poorer quarters to proclaim the "true" cause: It was the Spanish themselves, they said, trying to rid the city of its indigent underbelly.

Not until the twenty-third of May (nearly three weeks after the delayed liquefaction of San Gennaro's blood), when all those who could be blamed were and all other presumed possibilities had been exhausted, did the authorities finally admit to the existence of the disease. And even then, the naïve Viceroy Count of Castrillo insisted it was a *"Morbo Corrente"* (Usual Disease), one of the many febrile illnesses that periodically struck the poor sections of the city.

The social pressure applied by city leaders was intense, particularly from the commercial and political interests that stood to lose enormously should a contagion be declared the *peste* (plague). The wealthy Tuscans and Genovese, through their advanced Magistracies of Health, would place a quarantine on the city. All exports would be forbidden; no imports would be delivered to the bay. Given those far-reaching economic consequences to the city, Neapolitan physicians, who reflected on the plight of Doctor Bozzutto, were not about to argue the point, proving once again that humans have an extraordinary capacity for self-delusion.

It took more than four months for the civil administration of the city to establish a *Deputazione di Salute* (Department of Health) to coordinate the response. By then, about 150 people were dying per day. The various quarters of the city had a physician and a barber-surgeon assigned to them; but from the outset, they had difficulty obtaining the assistance and support of the all-important religious authorities. The clergy blamed the pestilence on a God angered by the evil ways of His people, and by the fact that the government, for purely economic reasons, had recently reduced the number of religious holidays.

Over the feeble protests of some of the *Deputazione di Salute,* church leaders insisted on processions and masses of atonement. For forty days in a row, Cardinal Filomarino implored the faithful to take part in the ceremonies. Statues of the virgin and relics of the saints led the marches. Prolonged litanies were recited, the priest chanting the holy name, the marchers begging for intercession:

Santa Maria!
   Ora pro nobis! (Pray for Us!)
Santa Irena!
   Ora pro nobis!
Santo Gennaro!
   Ora pro nobis!
Santo . . . etc.

The cause of the terrible disease was and, as of this writing, remains unknown. Yet it mattered not from whence it came, for indeed it came into Naples. Finally, on the second day of June, a true epidemic of the *peste* was proclaimed. By then, thousands of people were dying every day. Letters from eyewitnesses exaggerated the toll to as many as 40,000 people a day.

These claims apparently traveled far and wide, making their way even to England as recounted by Daniel Defoe in his *Journal of the Plague Year.* Defoe mentions the bills set up in London meant to summon people to the lodgings of the advertiser to obtain advice in case of infection during the great London plague of 1664. One of them proclaimed, "An Italian gentlewoman just arrived from Naples, having a choice secret to prevent infection, which she found out by her great experience, and did wonderful cures with it in the late plague there, wherein there died 20,000 in one day."

The peak number of deaths, according to the account of the government, was about 5,000 per day in July. But whether it was 1,000 or 5,000, the dead quickly filled the cemeteries and overwhelmed the devastated city. Since cremation was an unacceptable alternative by the Catholic church, heaps of rotting bodies accumulated in the streets and eventually were buried in mass graves in the great piazzas and squares. According to one eyewitness, Carlo Celano: "I saw with my own eyes on the Strada Toledo, where I live, the pavement strewn with so many cadavers that any carriage which passed into a palazzo was unable to pass without going over baptized flesh."

Meanwhile, many of the most emotionally affected resorted to extreme measures of penance. They paraded through the streets, flagellating themselves to the extent that pieces of bloody flesh torn from their backs by the metal barbs of their whips were scattered among the mesmerized crowd. In the year of our Lord 1616, forty years before the epidemic, a monk named Orsola Benicasa had predicted the disaster. He said that the city could placate God only by building a hermitage on the Vomero hill. As a result, during the plague, people began carrying materials and preparing the site for construction, including the viceroy who was said to have excavated twelve large boxes of dirt himself.

Yet no amount of religious fervor, via prayer or supplication, could stop the awful disease. Fearing the worst, Cardinal Filomarino ordered his priests to stay with their people and aid them. Thence, he shuttered himself in isolation at the Monastery of San Martino. The viceroy and the Collateral Council soon followed the lead of the cardinal.

Anyone ill, regardless of their position, was confined to their home under penalty of death. Among the lower classes, the relatives were segregated into the wards of the *lazeretti* or "pest houses" established throughout the city. There, they would die or face containment for weeks on end. The dead and dying were thus often abandoned in their homes to face their mortal end alone without the means to obtain their bread or anyone to give it to them. As the epidemic progressed, the deputies, physicians, barber-surgeons, and nurses that cared for the sick also died, causing a continuous turnover of leadership among the health authorities and hence more mayhem. A thriving business in tomfoolery was the result.

Quacks, mountebanks, conjurers, cunning men and women, claiming expertise in medicines and remedies, advertised their wares and methods to the people. Potions and pills of uncertain content and amulets to ward off the disease were particularly sought. Astrologers and fortunetellers did a brisk business describing the mischievous influence of a certain conjunction of the planets, or predicting the future, or calculating the fortune based on one's nativity. Fear was the predominant passion. Those who extorted it gained financially.

Early in the epidemic, thieves and robbers broke into abandoned homes to steal from the dead. There was a shortage of officers to enforce law and order, making it easy to get away with theft. Aside from this one devious segment of the economy, commercial enterprise came to a standstill. As predicted, the ever-vigilant Tuscans ended trade with the Neapolitans. Other regions followed. All the important infrastructures of commerce were undermined. Even the prostitutes were forbidden, under the threat of death, to practice their trade. The viceroy exempted all tax debts, although not necessarily out of a sudden kindness. He had little choice since no agency was bold enough to attempt collection.

Indeed, all segments of the city were infected. The poorer sections were stricken first, and the contagion then spread to the homes of the few aristocrats remaining in the city by servants from the squalid quarters. Interestingly, it was said that, among the survivors, most were poor. Thus, the privilege of the rich consisted of the fact that they might avoid the plague, while the privilege of the poor was that, once infected, they might survive it.

The pestilence was at its height in the warmer months, but whether in winter or summer, there tended to be two presentations: those with and those without the tokens. A medical report from the epidemic that struck Rome about the same time as the Neapolitan contagion summarizes the symptoms of those with tokens:

> Onset is marked with very high temperature, very severe headache, bilious vomiting, sleepiness, occasional diarrhea, and cloudy, dark urine. If the above-mentioned signs did not appear on the first day, they did not fail to appear on the second. Quite often on the second day delirium also supervened. In many patients, buboes and carbuncles appeared with the first attack of temperature. . . . In other patients, buboes and carbuncles appeared on the second, third or fourth day.

Those with the tokens were said to have *"vera pestis"* (true plague), or "pestilential fevers" or "putrefactive plague." Physicians and barber-surgeons learned from experience, however, that the plague could present with a cough, without the tokens. Those victims with pneumonic symptoms were frequently dead within a day, sometimes without exhibiting fever, perhaps because death came so rapidly the body did not have time to react.[2]

* * *

On the second Sunday in May, during Compline at the San Gregorio Convent, one of the sisters passed out with fever. The next morning the Mother Superior met with Rosario. "Gather all your belongings," she told him, "and prepare to leave Naples, perhaps for good."

"And what of you and the other sisters?" he asked.

"You know that we cannot break our rules. We cannot leave our cloister."

Many of the aristocratic families had already abandoned their palaces to return to their ancestral fiefs in the countryside. Thus, Mother Superior sent a desperate dispatch to her brother-in-law, Andrea Concublet, Marchese of Arena. He agreed to house Rosario, along with a younger boy who also lived at the convent, for the duration of the epidemic. A carriage was arranged, maps were reviewed, provisions were gathered, and contacts were initiated along the way from Naples to Arena. By Friday of that week, the first sister was dead. The following day Rosario and the boy, Guglielmo, left the city. It was a tearful goodbye.

Mother Superior, along with her two nieces, Sister Maria Fiametta and Sister Maria Nicola, hugged and kissed the young Guglielmo repeatedly. Then Sister Fiametta knelt before him, holding his hands. She looked into his eyes, "I know you must have many questions," she said. "I promise to answer them when we are together again."

"Will we be?" The boy asked.

"Of course, we will. Be a good helper to Rosario and listen to what the marchese tells you. He is a very wise man, and he knows what's best."

Mother Superior reviewed the directions and the plan a final time with Rosario. He thanked the three nuns for all that they had done for him since his mother's death, and he promised to look after the boy while they were away from the convent. Just before leaving, he hugged Sister Fiametta one final time. They held each other in a long embrace, punctuated only by sobs, her head resting on his shoulder. "Thank you, dear sister," he said, "for everything you have done for me, everything you have taught me."

She had fulfilled her promise to his mother, raising him

as if he were her own, teaching him to read, to play music, to learn about herbs and plants and, the greatest gift of all, to love learning. Rosario then uttered the words without conviction in his voice: "All will be fine," he said. "We will be together again soon."

"Yes, we will." She handed him a letter. "If I succumb to the *peste*, please deliver this to the signore listed. He is a guest of the marchese in Arena."

Rosario agreed and kissed her hands before leading his younger charge through the courtyard gate. Once outside, he and Guglielmo climbed into the carriage and rode down the street toward the *Capuana* portal and the road to the southeast.

NOTES

1. And even until this time, the theory of the sticky miasma remains the most accepted cause for pestilence, although I, like DiCapua, feel that the theory is incomplete.
2. These words that I write, more than seventy years after the tragic event, may serve a little to describe that dreadful time. But words alone cannot give a true accounting, except to say that it was a seemingly endless unfolding of horrors. Death and the gripping fear of it were everywhere. Those who survived were left to wonder why.

Chapter 22

In Arena

Arena—1656

Rosario and Guglielmo spent five full days traveling along the main roads, spending the four nights in the stables of friends and relatives of the sisters. At each stop, they were fed and resupplied apart from their hosts in order to minimize contact. Before beginning the third day, they changed horses in Castrovillari, and they arrived in Arena on the evening of the fifth day with sore bottoms from the long ride. The marchese was not present, but he had made all the arrangements for Rosario and Guglielmo to be fed and given a room at his castle. He was staying with his wife and a small group of close friends at his hunting lodge in the countryside about ten kilometers from the town. He had left word for the two visitors to be escorted there the next day.

No one met them when they arrived at the hunting lodge the following morning. The driver halted the coach in the circular path in front of the stately building and directed them into a room off the right side of the main entry. They sat in chairs stationed behind a small table, which faced an opening in the wall, covered by a curtain coated in wax. From behind the curtain, a man's voice welcomed them. It was the Marchese de Concublet. He apologized and asked that they not take offence at the impolite manner of greeting, explaining that it was intended to protect his wife, his guests, and himself from the *peste*.

He then introduced his two guests who were behind the curtain with him. Rosario immediately recognized the name of one of them, Signore Lionardo DiCapua, the same name written on the outside of the letter from Sister Fiametta. The other was a Signore Tommaso Cornelio. The three men were interested in hearing about the condition of the city. Which quarters were the worst? Had they seen dead bodies accumulating in the streets? Had any of the sisters come down with the fever?

Rosario answered each question as best he could. When he mentioned the death of one of the nuns at San Gregorio, which prompted their departure to Arena, there was a long pause during which the three men spoke quietly among themselves. Signore DiCapua then asked detailed questions about the dead sister's symptoms—if she had fever, the length of her illness before she died, any contact she had with the others, and any treatment she may have received. Rosario described the initial fainting spell at Sunday Compline, the development of the swellings over the next few days, and her feverish death the following Thursday. Guglielmo added that she had been taken to the infirmary and isolated there until she died. Mother Superior called a doctor who visited her on two occasions wearing the coated robe and mask.

"Do you know if the doctor treated her in any way?" DiCapua asked.

"The sisters said that he bled her both times," Guglielmo replied.

Again, the men talked quietly behind the curtain. The marchese then thanked Rosario and Guglielmo and said that he would contact them if he heard anything from the convent. A week later, the two young guests showed no symptoms, and the marchese again summoned them to the lodge. This time he met them at the front door, alone and without the protective curtain.

He was an impressive, middle-aged man, over six feet tall, with a handsome face. His voice was of baritone pitch and his bright blue eyes seemed to disappear into narrow slits whenever his smile turned to a deep belly laugh, which it frequently did. His head was covered by a powdered white wig with curled sides and a bobbed tail. The doublet he wore, like his breeches, was of red silk trimmed in a braid of gold interwoven with navy blue. It covered a white waistcoat closed with gold braided buttons and bordered at the belt line with a fringe, also in gold. His elegant clothes belied the fact that he was an energetic, authoritative man, often temperamental and easily angered—a man more suited to the inconveniences of the countryside than to the comforts of his palace in Naples. He preferred a fast horse to a slow carriage, hunting and fishing to a formal ball, the company of thinkers to the inanity of sycophants, and a bracing ride in the countryside to the ceremonies of court life. His wife, Ippolita Carafa, was the older sister of the Mother Superior and the sister-in-law of Ippolita Cantelmo Stuart (an Italian noble who had married into the British nobility). Although the Carafa-Concublet union had been arranged, he was considerate of his wife, who had learned to tolerate his societal reluctance and his masculine ways. His quick temper aside, he was a gentleman and patient with his wife, even though she was unable to bear him children. In time, she had grown to love him.

The marchese invited the two visitors to sit in his parlor. He told them that he had received word from Naples that the *peste* had officially been declared and identified. Every day, people were dying in extraordinary numbers. Rosario asked if the fever had struck the *Capuana Seggio* and the marchese responded that all quarters were suffering. "I am afraid that the news from

San Gregorio is equally dire. Apparently after the first sister died, the pestilence spread within the convent." Rosario and the marchese looked over at Guglielmo who bowed his head. "As you know, Sister Nicola suffered from the lingering effects of ague for many years. She succumbed to a fever soon after your arrival in Arena. As for Mother Superior and Sister Fiametta, I have been told that, as of a few days ago, they were both still alive, although the younger looked ill."

Guglielmo began sobbing. In a soft voice, he asked if anyone could survive the pestilence once stricken. The marchese rose from his chair and put a hand on the boy's shoulder. "It is possible, I suppose. However," he paused to kneel before the boy, "it does not seem likely."

Rosario reached inside his doublet and pulled out the letter from Sister Fiametta. "This is for the Signore DiCapua," he said. "Sister Fiametta asked that I give it to him, should anything happen to her. After what you just said, it seems that now is the time." The marchese thanked Rosario and invited him and Guglielmo to stay for lunch. Signori Cornelio and DiCapua would be joining them. Rosario could deliver the letter directly, he said, although he added that Rosario should probably wait until after they had finished their meal to present it.

The mood at the table that afternoon was somber, with little conversation among the diners. Guglielmo was in such distress that he could not eat. Afterwards, the marchese, along with the two signori, walked the young men to their coach. It was a warm June day, and the air in the countryside was particularly clear. Concublet suggested that it would be a refreshing trip to the castle. An opportunity for them, he hoped, to ease their sadness by rejoicing in the blessings that the good Lord had ordained.

The young Neapolitans politely thanked the marchese, thence Rosario presented the letter to Lionardo, who stared at the writing on the envelope but did not open it. The driver led the carriage around the circular path and down the tree-lined lane that led to town. When the carriage was out of sight, Lionardo excused himself and walked to the stables. He asked the servant to prepare his horse while he went to his room to change into his riding clothes. He left the lodge and rode into the woods alone, not returning until dusk.

Chapter 23

Lionardo Returns

Naples—1656

Early the next morning Lionardo set off for Naples despite the repeated protests of his friends. He understood that it was risky and likely futile, but he knew that he had to go. He took along a waxed coat, mask and eye protection. He promised his friends that he would carefully avoid contact with others and remain in isolation for as many days as they thought necessary upon his return. The marchese sent two trusted servants with him.

As they approached Naples on the fifth day of his journey, Lionardo witnessed the increasing devastation wrought by the epidemic. He had not heard any news from the Irpino and, since it was out of his way, he would wait to stop there on his return trip to Arena. He was intent on getting to the convent.

It was overcast and humid when they arrived at *Porta Capuana*. A gale from the sea brought gusts of wind that pinned back the ears of Lionardo's horse. The jittery animal balked at passing through the gate. Lionardo dismounted and walked her through the portal into the wide square in front of the *Palazzo del Vicaria*. They would rendezvous at the marchese's castle when it was time to depart.

Near the base of the mammoth stone buttresses, Lionardo saw four double ox carts, each with two wheels as tall as a man laden with corpses. They were halted in a queue waiting behind a fifth cart that was being emptied of its limp cargo. Since the cemeteries were full, prisoners had been released to transport the bodies to the large piazzas throughout the city where other prisoners were digging mass graves and burying the endless supply of dead. From across the square, Lionardo could see that some of the corpses were wrapped in sheets, while most were stripped naked. Nearby there were men throwing a pile of clothing into a smoldering bonfire. An inescapable acrid black smoke mixed with the pungent smell of rotting flesh permeated the expansive piazza. In the distance, he could hear the mournful wailing of an old woman. Lionardo covered his face with a handkerchief, remounted, and rode deeper into the *Seggio of the Capuana.*

The streets were empty. Occasionally a body lay abandoned next to a building, its awkward posture yet another vivid testimonial to the torn fabric of tradition. Lionardo saw a priest dressed in a long black cape with a baretta covering his head, hurrying from a doorway in the direction of the *Duomo.* He carried a bag marked with a crucifix in one hand and held a white rag over his mouth and nose with the other. Lionardo dismounted and approached the priest.

"Good Father," he said, "I have been away from the city for some time. What can you tell me about this pestilence?"

"I can tell you that you should immediately return from whence you came. This is a scourge from God for our iniquities." The priest kept his distance from the stranger. "Everywhere, people are dying in a most disgusting way with large, pustulant tokens, burning fevers and a loss of mind. I cannot possibly be there to offer Extreme Unction, but to a few. I am exhausted and yet I cannot sleep." As he spoke, the priest fidgeted ceaselessly. He began to walk away then turned back to address his subject in a loud voice, nearly to a scream.

"The last days are upon us, I tell you. God's judgement is

rendered to Naples. If you are wise, you will be gone from this city. Again, I tell you, my son, return from whence you came, and may God protect you." He turned and hurriedly walked up the hill.

Lionardo remounted his horse and continued along the main *Strada della Vicaria* until he arrived at the Church of San Lorenzo. There, he led his horse down the narrow, empty side street that held the Convent of San Gregorio. It took some time before a soft voice hidden behind the gate answered the bell. Lionardo introduced himself and asked if he could speak to the Mother Superior. The sister said that she was very busy. Lionardo begged her to announce his arrival. After another denial, she finally agreed to pass his message.

In a few minutes, the voice of the Mother Superior sounded from behind the gate. "Signore DiCapua, why did you risk coming here? It is too dangerous to be in the city. You should have stayed with the marchese."

"You know why I came, dear Sister. May I speak with her?"

"You cannot," came the answer followed by a pause. "She is with our Lord."

Lionardo leaned his head against the gate. The tears came reluctantly at first, before he dropped to his knees and began rocking back and forth, repeating but one word. "No! No! No!"

Mother Superior tried to comfort him. "Her end came quickly and peacefully yesterday evening," she said. "She was her usual brave self until unconsciousness set in. The doctor was called as soon as she began to show the fever, but she refused to let him perform the *salasso*. She asked that I send a letter to you in Arena to let you know of this refusal. She knew you would appreciate that."

Lionardo smiled through his tears. He asked if he could see her body and was told that she had already been buried inside the convent garden. After a few tearful moments, he gathered himself and asked, "And you, Sister? How are you feeling? Is there anything I can do to help you or the other sisters?"

She said that she was saddened by the many losses within her convent. More than half of the sisters had succumbed. "Why God has spared me, the oldest, is a mystery," she said. She thanked Lionardo for his offer and assured him that they had everything they needed. She excused herself to return to her duties and asked him to give her love to her sister and the marchese. Her parting advice, after offering her blessing, was to take leave of the city as soon as possible.

Lionardo thanked her, wished her God's protection, and mounted his horse. He met the servants at the palace, and they galloped from Naples. For Lionardo, time seemed suspended in the bittersweet memories of the brief period that he and Celestina had been together and all that might have been. He had long since given up on sharing his life with her. Now that she was deceased, that small share of happiness that came with knowing that she was at least there in Naples, alive behind the walls of the cloister, was likewise gone.

It was early evening by the time they stopped in Nola. Lionardo wanted to avoid staying in a public house, so they rode to the country estate of a medical school classmate. Over dinner, taken outside at a long table, with the three guests sitting at a distance from the host, they discussed the extent of the pestilence. Lionardo related his observations in Naples and asked what the situation was like around Nola and further east, around Avellino and into the Irpino. His friend, Doctor Sandri, told him that many people passed through Nola on their way to the towns and villages in the countryside. The movement began in earnest ten days earlier when the *peste* had been officially declared in Naples. A few locals had died under suspicious circumstances within Nola, but only a few.

Furthermore, Doctor Sandri said that he had heard through

professional contacts in Naples, that no matter what cures the doctors made for the afflicted—applying hot concoctions in the region of the heart, prescribing a glass of goat's rue water in the morning and an electuary of mulberry throughout the day, incising and draining the buboes, giving purgatives and enemas, or worse, letting the blood—no matter what was offered to the patients, they usually died. Men and women, whether they be rich or poor, young or old—all succumbed, such that death was the common currency.

Regarding Avellino and the Irpino, there were, as of his knowledge, scattered reports of suspicious deaths in the south-eastern part of the kingdom. "As for me," the doctor added, "I am planning to remain here at my *palazzo* away from town. If asked to assist family or friends with the disease, I will wear the wax-covered coat, mask, and goggles for protection, although I can offer the stricken nothing that will help them. We shall prognosticate death rather than recovery, for I believe that this disease is pestiferous and inimical to our own vital spirits."

Lionardo agreed with his friend, adding that this great pestilence had confirmed in him the belief that most medicine remained uncertain, even as to the commonly held belief that the contagion spread through its venomous miasma. He knew enough to realize that he knew very little, he said, and in that admission, no shame had come over him.

Early the next morning Lionardo and his fellow riders departed for the safety of the marchese's palace in Calabria.

Chapter 24

The Plague in Bagnoli Irpino

Bagnoli Irpino—1656

Two victims that fled Naples in late June of 1656, a father and his son, made their way to Bagnoli Irpino, Lionardo DiCapua's ancestral village. Most likely, they were Bagnolesi who had moved to Naples, although there is no confirmation of that fact nor of their actual names. About a week after they arrived in the town, the father died, followed soon by the son.

The village priest, who had heard of the pestilence in Naples, recognized the cause of death and refused to bury the outsiders. Things remained calm until the twenty-third of July, when a local woman died from the dreaded contagion. Recognizing the imminent threat before them, the people quickly turned over control of the city council to the party of educated bourgeoisie that Lionardo and his friends had formed during the earlier revolution. They quickly issued emergency measures.

Everyone was encouraged to clean his or her immediate environment. Being aware of the terrible situation in Naples, the council voted to establish a *lazaretto* and additional sites for burying the dead. They designated an abandoned building on a large piece of land, north of town, as a pesthouse and a cemetery. On the southern flank, away from the city, they chose another burial area. The decision to have plots on opposite ends of the town meant that the dead could be evacuated without passing through the center. It was said that, out of consideration for their family and friends, some of the terminally ill dragged themselves to a gravesite in the makeshift cemeteries outside of town. There, a priest would administer communion with a long stick and a lawyer would write the last will and testament from a safe distance. Once dead, the person could be rolled into their grave with minimal amount of contact. In the more remote countryside outside of town, people often wandered about until they collapsed and died without burial, their corpses littering the woods. Most of these people were permanent residents, shepherds, or woodcutters. Some were probably escapees from the cities who, like the two men who came to Bagnoli in June, carried the disease with them.

By late fall, as the deaths started to mount in Bagnoli Irpino, no natural explanation or effective means of limiting the spread could be found, so the priests encouraged the people to seek relief through the supernatural. The clergy called the people to gather for sermons and processions of prayer through the town; whereas the council, accepting the miasma theory of causation, was aware of the connection between assemblies and the spread of the disease and tried to keep the people separate. But the council lacked proof that their efforts had been successful, as the random and ceaseless progression of the pestilence still ravaged the community. Relatives and friends succumbed without the usual assistance of family or the clergy to ease their passing. Victims included some of the councilmen. The surviving officers, who shared the religious convictions of the rest of the community, ultimately were powerless to stop the gatherings. As a result, the number of deaths increased soon after the processions began. In November 1656, the month with the highest mortality, 358 people—more than a tenth of the population—died. In total, 1089 people died, about one-third of the population.

Chapter 25

Gloom and Despondency

Naples—1656–1657

The end of the outbreak in Naples was officially declared in December of 1656, with deaths continuing for several more months in scattered pockets throughout the kingdom. When it was finally over, there was no dispassionate, systematic discussion of the event; no Defoe to tell the story.

Instead, religious devotion thrived. One would think that such an awful occurrence might have engendered a great deal of doubt toward a merciful God who allowed such an unmerciful affair. But if there were doubts, they were swept away by the acceptance of the blessing of life given to the survivors. Hence, people flocked to the churches, where the religious authorities assured the faithful of the religious cause of the disease. It had come due to God's anger, they said. And it ended, they were certain, through the intercession of the Virgin Mary. A torrential rainstorm was seen as the signal that she had interceded to soothe God's wrath. Who interceded with Mary became the subject of much conflict among the various religious orders— Jesuits, Dominicans, Fransiscans, Teatini-each claiming that their favored saint was the intercessor.

The true toll of the Neapolitan epidemic of 1656 is impossible to quantify. However, most estimates lie in the range of 240,000–300,000 people killed from a total population of between 400,000–500,000. Mortality figures are inexact since many people left the city and may have died elsewhere.

As for Lionardo DiCapua, no one, including Amenta, mentions his whereabouts or his activities during the great plague. No one suspected that he would escape to the Calabrian countryside, outside of Arena, with some of his closest friends, all of whom survived by minimizing human contact and abandoning the city. They were following the practice that was first recorded in Italian literature by Giovanni Boccaccio in his classic book *Decameron.*

Written around the time of the Black Death between 1349 and 1352, Boccaccio's one-hundred tales were organized in sections of ten fables in each of ten days. The ten main characters leave a plague-ridden Florence and stay in the countryside. To pass the time, they entertain each other with stories. Boccaccio's father, himself a victim of the curse, was the Minister of Supply for the city, hence the chief purveyor of food and other necessities decreed by the government. Most likely, he communicated his detailed observations to his son, who was living in another part of Italy at the time. Based on what his father related to him, the young Boccaccio opens his book with a vivid description of the epidemic as it ravages Florence:

I say, then, that the sum of thirteen hundred and forty-eight years had elapsed since the fruitful Incarnation of the Son of God, when the noble city of Florence, which for its great beauty excels all others in Italy, was visited by the deadly pestilence....It did not take the form it had assumed in the East....On the contrary, its earliest symptom, in men and women alike, was the appearance of certain swellings in the groin or the armpit, some of which were egg-shaped whilst others were the size of the common apple....Against these maladies, it seemed that all the advice of physicians and all the powers of medicine were profitless and unavailing.

From there, his stories take on a light-hearted, somewhat profane, sometimes erotic tone. It's as if, through his *lieta brigata,* (his "happy band" of characters), the young Boccaccio responded to the inexplicable disaster that surrounded him by mocking the pervasiveness of death and the utter foolishness of doing anything other than enjoying oneself in its omnipresence. Such was a common reaction noted by other writers, like Thucidydes and Procopius, who mentioned the lawlessness and debauchery that accompanied the plagues that they had witnessed.

But, when the Black Death receded, the shock of the devastation set in. Like other survivors, Boccaccio ultimately could not come to grips with it. His mistress, Fiametta, had died, and his own inevitable mortality and fear of divine retribution haunted him. After meeting with his mentor, Francesco Petrarca, he underwent an ascetic conversion and began writing more serious literature. Some claim that he then renounced his great literary effort and tried to burn all the extant copies. Whether this anecdote was true or not, his spirited pen, in fact, turned to pessimistic diatribes against women and those like him who had fallen from grace into misery.

After witnessing the deaths of many family members and his beloved Laura, Petrarca also fell into a dark depression after the plague had passed. His poetry became more austere and religious. To Petrarca, as to most survivors, there seemed to be no redeeming purpose to the disaster. In its wake, gloom and despondency were pervasive.

* * *

As it turned out, 1656, the year of the Neapolitan plague, would be the halfway point in Lionardo DiCapua's life. He had lived thirty-nine years, during which he had prepared himself for greater accomplishments in the ultimate half—not knowing, of course, how much longer he would live. As we shall see—unlike Boccaccio and Petrarca, who responded to the disaster of the Black Death with an ascetic despondency, turning inward in search of a supernatural explanation—DiCapua held on to his progressive ideas and resumed his attempts at reforming the practice of physick, despite the emotional exhaustion he felt from the devastation of the pestilence and his own personal loss.

Part Two

Chapter 1

After the Pestilence

Naples—1657

It is difficult to summarize the effects the great pestilence of 1656 had on the Kingdom of Naples and its people, which may explain why no one has written an in-depth account of the horrendous epidemic. There are reports from official documents and mortality data that lack objectivity, but a Neapolitan Defoe has not surfaced to write the complete story—fictional or real. Even among such noteworthy literati of Naples as D'Andrea, Cornelio, Conclubet, and DiCapua, no one ever attempted a complete analysis of the catastrophic event.

There were over two-and-a-half-million people scattered in the terrain outside the capital city of Naples at the time the plague struck. According to the official figures from Bagnoli Irpino and other small villages, from which the residents rarely departed and thus where a death would usually be more easily noted, about one-third of the residents in the hinterlands (roughly 800,000 people) died. In Naples, the largest city in Europe at the time, 240,000–300,000 people died from a population of around 450,000. Thus, one can assume that there were above one-million victims total in the kingdom; although any accounting of the mortality, especially within Naples, is impossibly inaccurate since many people moved in and out of the city through its port, or inland in all directions. Nonetheless, despite the uncertainty, it is no exaggeration to say that the number of deaths was truly astounding, particularly in a period below the length of one year.

The plague described by Defoe's vivid prose killed about 65,000 people in London, a number that pales in comparison to the Neapolitan outbreak. Some have posited that the overwhelming mortality of the Italian pestilence left the survivors so awed by its power as to leave them afraid to discuss it objectively. Such an explanation is merely a guess measured by the extraordinary disruption wrought by the epidemic. However, one could argue thar the terrible effects might be offered as an added stimulus for telling the story.

The epidemic in Naples was officially declared ended in December of 1656, although cases of the disease continued to appear into the early part of the following year. Survivors who had fled the city slowly began to return and, as is the way with human tragedies, people sifted through the wreckage of their lives to find some purpose and move onward, even if the impetus was nothing more than the necessity of doing so.

Now imagine the first tentative steps taken by those who survived. Not knowing the cause or the inexplicable reason that they had escaped the illness's grip, the living again came forth from their hiding to renew the kind of interactions necessary for the creation of a common society. It seemed to them that the worst had passed, yet they had seen such lulls in the activity of the disease, only to witness its destructive reappearance within a few weeks.

With each passing day, however, the certainty of its conclusion grew, as did the reality of what they now faced. Their larders were empty, many of the fields had been left fallow, the markets were closed, and a high proportion of the deaths had been among the *contadini* who supplied the necessary labor to produce the food. Hence, riding with the pestilence came the second scourge—famine—which accounted for how many more deaths? Likewise, the filth that surrounded the survivors bred further disease among a people already weakened by the wrath of plague and hunger.[1]

Certainly, much of the devastation was due to the *peste*, but not all of it, for it is worth remembering that within a relatively brief span of twenty-five years, the Kingdom of Naples also suffered through a massive volcanic eruption and a political revolution. The cumulative effects of such outrage created a dark impression on the survivors, who were left to wonder when the next catastrophe might occur or how many more victims it might claim. Stories of the earth splitting and swallowing people whole, as well as other fantastically horrible deaths, abounded.

Unable to find protection through prayer or superstitious preventatives, Neapolitans turned to the past for answers, a tendency that was reflected in the art of the time. Old Testament and primitive themes with a dark side, as well as New Testament scenes surrounding the crucifixion and the suffering of the saints, became common with Neapolitan artists. People were searching for the root causes of all the recent chaos by reflecting on the sad events of the distant past.

Consequently, many of the best artists of the time—Luca Giordano and Salvatore Rosa, among others—adapted the light and dark (or *chiaroscuro*) technique of Caravaggio with an emphasis on the dark (or *scuro)* side. This sentiment would have profound implications for a city culturally isolated from the rest of Europe. Thus did the capitol lose its sixteenth century title of *"Napoli Gentile"*—a setting where the inhabitants and visitors enjoyed a comfortably pleasant stay—and took on the character of a somber and inwardly brooding place. However, at the same time of this gloomy reflection and isolation, the kingdom, ironically, became ripe for a cultural renewal by forward thinking individuals who would place Naples in the vanguard of a new enlightenment.

* * *

Lionardo and many of his friends returned to the city sometime during 1657. Surveying his own life, he must have been struck with profound sadness. His Celestina was gone. One of the main guiding forces in his life, Maestro Severino, had died during the plague. Uncle Horace and his wife had also passed on. Lionardo had no medical practice, the Investiganti had been disbanded, and he had not performed any experiments for nearly two years. Given those realities, he must have struggled to avoid resigning his life to the melancholy that had overtaken Petrarch and Boccaccio after the Black Death. Lionardo had faced tragedy from a young age and had always managed to move onward. Now he needed to do so again. The impetus would come from a most basic biologic calling, a whisper within all of us.

From the pulpits, the priests urged their flocks of the necessity to increase and multiply. Capable survivors were expected to literally come together and procreate. The Church and civil authorities were willing to look the other way on mating practices considered adulterous in normal times. Amenta tells us that in Lionardo's case, "Having already reached a certain age, for whatever the reason, he insisted on marrying Annamaria Orilia born from a most honorable family."

There is no mention of the biological necessity of the time or any sense of how much of this union reflected that reality rather than being the result of a loving relationship. Since Lionardo's first love, the object of his sonnets, does not even exist in Amenta's biography, he never mentioned how much Signora Orilia knew of her.[2]

What can be said is that Signora Orilia was nearly two decades younger than Lionardo and polite and kind to all who came into their home. She and her husband heeded the necessity of the times; thus, by the end of 1658, had they already produced a son, Cesare, named after his paternal grandfather. Over the ensuing years, they would have six other children, some of whom died in childhood, adding sadness to the life of a man who had already experienced much grief. Thus, for the immediate period after the pestilence, Lionardo experienced the customary blessings and adversities of raising a new family, while convening on occasion with his old friends to discuss natural philosophy.

Since most physicians who had stayed in the city became victims of the epidemic, there was a great need for medical practitioners. Lionardo established a medical practice in Naples and simultaneously returned to teaching his controversial ideas on chemistry to interested medical students at the request of Tommaso Cornelio, who likewise returned to his position at the university. Cornelio communicated with members of the Academy of Science in Paris and, more so, the Royal Society in London, who believed that chemistry should be recognized as a formal discipline worth teaching in the universities.

The coalescence of the Neapolitans' ideas with the larger scientific community across Europe gave credence to the new teachings in Naples. Through Cornelio and DiCapua's advocacy and persistence at the medical school, Galenist methods were finally being scrutinized, placing both men increasingly at odds with the traditionalists. The medical and ecclesiastical authorities believed that any disagreement with the established teachings of Aristotle and Galen weakened their prestige and ultimately threatened their financial standing. Doctor Carlo Pignataro, the Chief Medical Officer in the kingdom at the time, became particularly lathered over these threats.

It wasn't just the teachings of the two innovators that galled the traditionalists, but more so the emphasis that Lionardo placed on the uncertainty of medicine. Here, he struck a chord for which the Galenists had a visceral understanding, yet (like his famous Galenist teacher, Luigi DiGrazia) they feared the changes to their system of practice and the effects any change might have on their prestige and their income. Consequently, through pressure applied by Pignataro and his well-connected office, an injunction was issued in 1662 against the teaching of chemistry at the University of Naples. At the same time, Pignataro arranged for the suppression of Sebastiano Bartoli's book *Exercitationes paradoxicae* (Paradoxical Practices), which was critical of the Galenists and their methods. Cornelio, Bartoli, DiCapua and other progressives were the victims temporarily silenced by this reactionary backlash.

Lionardo's intellectual pursuits, however, were not limited to topics medical. Successfully marginalized on one front, he focused his efforts on another. As a beacon of knowledge with an expansive set of interests, as well as once having been a writer of prose and poetry, Lionardo soon became the center of a literary movement in Naples that, in later years, would reverberate with other members of the Swedish Queen Christina's *Arcadia* in Rome. This *"Capuaism"* aimed to repair what people like Lionardo saw as a degradation of the Italian language into an excessively baroque form, most famously exemplified by the Neapolitan poet Giambattista Marino.

Marino created a style that was the rage throughout Europe. *Marinismo* was sumptuously filled with elaborate alliteration, complicated word play, digressions, and rich figures of speech that, in its sensuous superficiality, surpassed even the architecture and art of the time in all its rococo extravagance. He proclaimed it best when he described his writings: "Full of magnificent clarity and sustained fluidity, clothed in many majestic and delightful metaphors, ornamented with a light and capricious imagination, and abundant with its own light."

Indeed, Giambattista Marino's words reflected his own operatic and often scandalous life. His most famous poem,

"*Adone,*" retells the Greek myths of love between various gods and goddesses with blatant sexual passion in all its varied presentations, which assured its place on the Index of Forbidden Books, resulting in pan-European success. Some have suggested that Marino's poetry was a reaction to the Spanish obsession with religion. Others, that it was the natural consequence of the religious forces that generated the baroque, leaving one to choose between the primacy of the hen or the egg.

Lionardo DiCapua strongly believed in the importance of developing a clear and proper Italian language. He argued for the use of the purer, more direct style originally created by the greatest of Italian writers—Dante, Petrarch, and Boccaccio—when the vernacular had been coalescing into a distinct tongue separate from Latin. This longstanding literary tradition, enhanced through Tuscan literary academies, naturally led to the acceptance of the Florentine "dialect" as the official Italian language.

However, a good portion of the prose in Lionardo's time continued to be written in the local dialect of the region. Thus, in Naples the Neapolitan dialect was commonly employed, and the same was true in Venice, Milan, and the other great cities. In truth, these "dialects" were unique languages. Even though the Tuscan dialect had become the accepted standard, most of DiCapua's friends continued to use their familiar Neapolitan vernacular. Indeed, his friends often made good-natured jokes about Lionardo's adopted style, calling it "*grosso come acqua di maccheroni*" (thick like the water left after cooking macaroni). And when Francesco D'Andrea had seen the first draft of Lionardo's famous *Parere,* he wrote to Francesco Redi telling him that he had advised DiCapua to use the more conventional Neapolitan dialect.

DiCapua's effort to return literature to an older form might, at first, seem antithetical to his goal of freeing natural philosophy and medicine from their staid historic practices. But it seemed obvious to those who knew him well that he was motivated to cease the endless parsing of esoteric philosophical ideas by the traditionalists in their own obscure language. Instead, he called for a straightforward vernacular that promoted understanding of the subject. In doing so, he was echoing the atomist teachings of Epicurus who felt that information should always be presented clearly with a minimal amount of exuberance. Hence his literary purpose remained consistent with his overall philosophy.

During the years of the suppression of new ideas, Lionardo and the other innovators bided their time, fending off the barrage of accusations made by the traditionalists while monitoring their every assertion.

The opportunity to take the offensive returned in October of 1663, when an epidemic of fever broke out in the city. The Galenists were strongly persuaded that the retting and scutching of flax and hemp fibers from their woody stems, which was performed by *contadini* at nearby Lake Agnano, was the cause of the epidemic. They demanded that the procedures be stopped. The innovators countered that such an assumption was based on hearsay and lacked objective support. Furthermore, they argued that the economic effects of ending the work could be substantial at a time when the area was still recovering from the devastation of the recent plague.

Sensing the opportunity and realizing the need to formally present their ideas, DiCapua and Cornelio approached their well-connected old friend, the Marchese of Arena, Andrea De Concublet, with the idea of establishing the *Accademia degli Investiganti*-occasionally referred to by its Latin equivalent as the *Academia Indagatrix*-which would be modeled after the methods used during the earlier, informal gathering before the plague.

Concublet, in turn, encouraged the idea and offered his

palace in Naples as the meeting site and his own scientific instruments—which he had purchased on his travels for use in performing experiments—be used by the participants. He also agreed to take part in the presentations, which meant that his prestige would provide physical protection from the reactionary religious and civil authorities—hardly a minor consideration in those precarious times. The founders dedicated the new group to experimental natural philosophy and adopted the motto of Lucretius: *"Vestigis lustrat"* (It shows the way through the darkness.).

About the same time in 1663, as a demonstration of the seriousness with which the members of the new Investiganti would pursue their arguments with the traditionalists, Tommaso Cornelio published his masterwork *Progymnasmata physica* in Venice. He had been working on it for some time with the original intent of publishing in 1661.

Known for his aggressiveness on the pitch, Tommaso was otherwise a shy man who preferred to remain in the background, away from center stage. Keenly aware of that tendency, the group that gathered around him encouraged him to give the work more of a political tone, which would clearly define a break from the old culture to a more enlightened way.

Thus, the final product was a frontal assault on the Galenists presented in the form of a dialogue between three protagonists. Their statements presented forceful arguments favoring the modern against the antiquated Galenic medicine, the Scholastics, and the organization of medical officials under the control of Pignataro. In addition, Cornelio presented a defense of atomist philosophy, a discussion on the mechanistic philosophy of Descartes, and a new metaphysical theory of the acquisition of knowledge. The writing was done in the classic Tuscan idiom, avoiding the flowery excesses of the baroque. Lionardo DiCapua shared his admiration for Cornelio's gifted insights and the importance of their friendship in his preface to the book.

The initial release of Cornelio's book came in a year of great controversy between the progressives and traditionalists and added to the acrimonious environment. Over the next few decades, it was republished five more times in other cities across Europe, reflecting its importance at this crucial moment in the history of science and medicine. If there was a negative effect of the book, it was that Cornelio's arguments were presented in such a coherent and cogent manner that Pignataro and his associates came to realize the necessity of uniting together to meet the forceful challenges of the Investiganti with a group of their own.

And so, another academy was formed.

NOTES

1. I write these words more than sixty years since the epidemic, and I can tell you that the ruinous effects are still upon the region.
2. It was not a topic that one could comfortably pursue, nor was Lionardo willing to discuss it when this biographer broached the subject.

   I could speak at length about a daughter, Giovanna, who was named after her paternal grandmother, but I will forgo the opportunity at this time. Another son, who is still alive as I write, was named in honor of Uncle Horace.

Chapter 2

The Discordanti and the Investiganti

Naples—1663

During the seventeenth century, numerous private academies sprang up in Naples and across Europe. Universities had been nearly paralyzed by an arthritic formality that advanced classical teachings yet presented little opportunity for innovative research. Likewise, bookstores offered publications that were generally safe with religious and political authorities, especially during the first half of the century. Hence, serious scholars realized the need to ban together as formal academies where they could share manuscripts from their own private libraries and discuss literature, the arts, or—in the case of the *Investiganti*—natural phenomena without the bias of faith or politics.

At their meetings in Concublet's palace, which took place at least every twenty days, one of the Researchers presented a dissertation, which was followed by open discussion. In addition, *Investiganti* would perform experiments like those done at the famous *Accademia del Cimento* (Experimenters) in Florence, founded by Evangelista Torricelli and Giovanni Alfonso Borelli. The ultimate purpose of the gatherings was to follow the Renaissance-inspired ideal of applying the discovered knowledge to the solution of practical problems.

Following that ideal, Torricelli built the first mercury barometer, and his *Cimento* (testers) built thermometers and hygrometers, which the Grand Duke of Tuscany sent, along with instructions, to various scientists on the continent. In return, they were asked to record their data and relay their findings to Florence for comparison and analysis. This was the first attempt to understand the patterns of weather that so greatly affects many aspects of life on our planet. The *Investiganti* applied the model of the *Cimento,* and at their first meeting, DiCapua presented a discussion on the phenomena of sensory appreciation, a subject that was frequently discussed by the ancient atomists. He contrasted the natures of fluids and solids, hot and cold, sweet and bitter, and colors with white light. The notes from that presentation have been lost, but Lionardo would incorporate the ideas and its criticism in later writings. Amenta tells us that the lecture was well received. It set the tone for high scholarship and open debate that would mark the *Investiganti* as one of the most important scientific academies of the time—particularly on medical topics.

Besides DiCapua, Marchese Concublet, Cornelio, and D'Andrea, several others joined the group, including the lawyer-historian Giuseppe Valletta; natural philosophers-physicians Sebastiano Bartoli and Lucantonio Porzio; poet Carlo Buragna; chemist Giuseppe Donzelli, the bishop of Campania; and other progressive clerics and nobleman. One of the most brilliant scientists in all of Europe, Giovanni Alfonso Borelli, who had at times participated in the original informal gatherings in Cornelio's home, joined the meetings of the *Investiganti.*

Physicist-mathematician-astronomer-physician Borelli was gifted with the passion of an irascible Neapolitan, along with a brilliant and far-reaching mind. He was a founding member of the *Cimento* and brought many of their ideas and experiments to the Researchers and other scientific academies throughout Italy. His work on the motion of planets and the mathematics involved in their attraction was the stuff that, later, Edmond

Halley built upon to the great advantage of us all today.

In medicine, Borelli became the founder of "Iatrophysics," which applied the mechanistic principles of physics to the functions of the human body—the movement of the limbs, the circulation of the blood, the motion of the lungs, the beating of the heart.

While a professor of mathematics at the University of Pisa, Borelli had met Marcello Malpighi, the young professor of the newly appointed section on theoretical medicine. The anecdotal story of their meeting may have been fabricated, but it speaks to their common intellectual instincts. It is said that during his first lecture, Malpighi stressed his open approach to medicine, which caused such animosity in the audience that, one by one, they got up and left the room. When he finished, the only person remaining was Borelli.

Malpighi was twenty years younger than Borelli and possessed a more agreeable personality. The two men became colleagues in experiments as well as good friends. Each helped the other attain new heights in their fields. Malpighi helped focus Borelli's wandering interests on the importance of biology. Borelli taught his younger friend the physics of Galileo. He also encouraged him to leave theoretical medicine for the blossoming world of experimentation.

Following that suggestion, Malpighi began using his microscope to study the comparative anatomy of humans with the lower animals and insects. The complete list of his discoveries justifies his titles as the Father of Histology and Father of Embryology. Some of his findings include the cortical cells of the brain and their connection with nerve fibers, identification of the organ of touch, the pigmented layer (the Malpighian layer) within the skin, and the complete development of the chick embryo. His greatest discovery led to the completion of Harvey's theory about the circulation of blood.

Marcello Malpighi observed sections of a frog's lung under his microscope and became the first to identify the bridging capillaries. These "Malpighian Tubules" were the missing minute connections between the arterial and venous systems that Harvey had postulated but never found. Galen—and even Vesalius—had incorrectly proposed unseen passages between the chambers of the heart to explain how the blood went from one side to the other. Malpighi's capillaries had finally and indisputably completed the circulatory loop. His innovative work earned him the respect of his contemporaries and was published among the first Philosophical Transactions of the Royal Society in England.

At Cornelio's invitation, Marcello traveled to Naples and presented to the *Investiganti*. As he later wrote, "I met with the learned Cornelio and Lionardo and others of that school and talked and consulted with them as long as I was able, to the great recreation of my mind."

Later, he was appointed a member of the Royal Society of London, where Giuseppe Valletta of Naples had previously established a connection with the Italian academies. Valletta was a friend of Richard Waller (then secretary of the Royal Society), such that close communications on their findings were maintained by the two academies. Over the years, several members of the Royal Society visited the *Investiganti* in Naples, including Sir Thomas Finch, Thomas Banes, Francis Willoughby, and his naturalist instructor, John Ray.[1]

Probably the most immediate benefit to the *Investiganti* was the realization that their effort at cultural and scientific renewal was in harmony with the innovative changes happening in the more ample, more diversified, and certainly less Catholic north. This was a small group of Neapolitan men who displayed a great deal of courage in challenging the status quo of a conservative kingdom. Any support that they received validated their effort and bolstered their confidence, which then emboldened them to continue pressing their case with the traditionalists.

On the other hand, the British benefited from a passage of the new ideas through an historically important culture that could blend them with the ideals of the Italian Renaissance as well as the Baroque. The Royal Society of London received its official charter from King Charles II in July of 1662. Like the *Investiganti*, the Society had been reconstituted from an earlier, informal gathering of men headed by Robert Boyle and Christopher Wren. The original group formed in 1645 as a private academy without direct connections to the government. This independence would prove beneficial—and probably lifesaving—for many of the members since the Puritans, under Oliver Cromwell's leadership, beheaded Charles I in 1649 and attacked Royalist sympathizers thereafter.

As with the *Investiganti,* whose initial gathering was dissolved due to the plague, the turmoil following Cromwell's death in 1658 caused the informal Society to disband until the newly restored king conferred its official charter as the Royal Society of London for Improving Natural Knowledge. Unlike the French *Academie des Sciences*, which received its Royal charter from Louis XIV in 1666 providing each member with an annual salary, the Royal Society of London maintained its political and religious neutrality. By so doing, it became arguably the most prestigious scientific academy among the many that were then in existence throughout Europe.[2]

The goal of applying natural philosophy for the betterment of man's life on earth was finally being realized. It should be clear, however, that this revolution of thought had very few active participants. Most people held strong, superstitious beliefs. Thus, even in the most progressive countries, the protagonists had to tread carefully. Notwithstanding the general tenor of the era, the innovators throughout the continent communicated their ideas to each other, creating a vast web of intellectual progress that, at least for the time being, superseded the borders of the nation states. Most of the countries of Western Europe participated in this Republic of Letters, including France, Holland, Germany, Switzerland, Italy, England, Scotland, Sweden and Denmark.

The one glaring omission from that list is Spain, whose absence is even more noticeable considering that it was the strongest empire of its time. How did this happen? How was it that, for more than a century, no great scientists were produced from a country, which was—at least in its political power—the envy of all the others, a vast empire upon which the sun never set? The answer can be traced back to 1560, when Philip II packed up his retinue and moved his half of the recently divided Hapsburg Empire to Spain.

Philip was a man who was influenced by the superstitions and prejudices of the Catholic Church. As such, he held a strong persuasion to prevent the spread of Protestant heresy. Early in his reign, he became convinced that the way to do this was to limit the introduction of foreign ideas. All books had to be reviewed by the newly established Spanish Index. Book publishers and vendors were subject to licensing. Those caught attempting to circumvent the restrictions could have their possessions—or worse, their lives—taken. Spanish students were ordered home from most universities. Orthodox universities in Rome and Naples were among the few exceptions. Added to Philip's fundamentalist religious tendencies was the continuing deterioration of the Spanish economy. Despite the extraordinary wealth of the Spanish aristocracy, it failed to acknowledge the need, nor did it feel any compunction to use their riches for the betterment of the vast majority below them. Instead, they became caught up in ostentatious displays of opulence, which they lavished upon the Church and themselves. The great universities, like most of the citizens, became impoverished. The Inquisition kept all unorthodox writings out of the country. The magnificent period of Spanish art and literature had passed. Spain effectively became isolated from the new currents of European thought. The implication to any future empire was clear.

In the practice of medicine, Spanish physicians remained strongly supportive of traditional, Galenic medicine. Given the entrenched authoritarian tendencies of their Spanish masters, the Galenist doctors of physick within the Kingdom of Naples felt no need to accept the new ideas. Thus, despite the flowering of academic activity among the *Investiganti* and their connections with other European academies, the stranglehold of reactionary authority would again attempt to choke the intellectual life out of southern Italy as well.

Spain would not begin to recover some degree of respectability until after the death of Philip IV in 1665, when his son Don Juan José began to encourage the development of medicine and other sciences. This support laid the groundwork for the loosening of scholarly restrictions that occurred throughout the empire (including the Kingdom of Naples) during the latter part of the seventeenth century. Through the agency of the Neapolitan viceroys, this led directly to Lionardo DiCapua's most brilliant writings and the implementation of his suggested reforms of the medical school.

After the release of Cornelio's book, an angry Carlo Pignataro expanded the polemics against the Researchers. In 1666, he established the *Accademia dei Discordanti*, a self-revealing name that reflected the true intent of their agenda without using a euphemistic title. Luca Tozzi, the leading Galenist practitioner of the time, was appointed to head the academy.

In those days, to obtain a license to practice medicine within the kingdom, one had to pass an examination that was based on the traditional teachings of Galen, Hippocrates and Aristotle.

Pignataro and Tozzi believed that attacks against the ancient teachings eventually would undermine the elevated standing of physicians. The appeal of this argument was strong among those whose lucrative practices often depended on prestige to survive. And their prestige invariably depended either on luck or the amazing ability of the human body to heal itself because patients either recovered or worsened, despite the efforts of the doctors. In their hearts, many realized the ultimate irrelevance of their treatments (even if they would not openly admit it), which, as already mentioned, was the reason for Lionardo's emphasis on the uncertainty of medicine.

Humans tend to take comfort in the status quo and thus are often resistant to change. For the sake of continuous function, we develop patterns and stick with them, taking comfort in their familiarity. Something or someone that upsets that dynamic is often met with suspicion and anger. Why change what seems to be working, especially if one benefits from the established system?

To the *Discordanti,* challenging teachings that had been followed for millennia was inconceivable. They argued that the new ideas were theoretical points for discussion within the Researchers' esoteric academy and not the kind of teachings around which one could build a practical system for treating patients. Their argument was well taken. If the system is to be torn apart, what might replace it? The practical benefits of the new method of building upon observation and experimentation—if valid at all, they argued—would take years of growth and pruning before bearing fruit.

To which the *Investiganti* would answer that the renewal must begin somewhere, and why not have its basis in experimentally derived truth rather than blind tradition? The intent of the *Discordanti* (so perfectly named) became the cancellation of the visceral harmonics achieved by the Researchers and the maintenance of the primacy of the Galenists and, by extension, the scholastic philosophy pronounced by Aristotle and perfected by Thomas Aquinas. The lines had been sharply drawn, such that educated men of the kingdom joined the fight either for or against the innovative ideas of the protagonist *Investiganti*. The arguments that evolved took on a more vindictive tone when the debates spilled into public journals. Such open hostility might seem inappropriate to some; however, in truth, the defamation of opponents in print was a common and accepted way to deal with adversaries in Naples at the time. To appreciate the degree of animosity between the rivals, consider the following scatological diatribes. The *Discordanti* asserted that, "The ideas proposed by the Researchers prove that they were hidden in a dark room when they performed their so-called 'experiments,' unable to see what was happening. Each member was required to stick his pointer finger up his arse and repeat over and over the selected idea that the experimenter wanted him to take away from the meeting."

"The noisy *Discordanti*"—came the reply from the Researchers—"are so constipated with the ancient teachings that, even if they wanted to, there would be no room for the insertion of even the smallest finger up their impacted arses."

Over the next two years, the viceroy became increasingly concerned as the exchanges continued to escalate, taking on ever more violent and threatening tones. The hot-tempered Concublet (no lilting flower himself) took note of the threats against his scholarly friends, whom he felt a duty to protect. The opportunity—or, as he saw it, the necessity—to strike back soon presented itself when the *Discordanti* published a flagrant denunciation: "It would be best for our fair kingdom and for the sinners themselves if the palace in which they meet were torched to the ground sending those atheists-atomists to their home in hell, where they are already accustomed to the sting of the burning flame."

Concublet viewed this statement as something more than just a threat to his friends. He was a temperamental man of action, who viewed the threat as a personal affront to himself, his family, and his heritage. Such aggression, he believed, required a vigorous response that he was determined to deliver. Hence, he set a trap for his foe, having his men secretly observe Pignataro's routine throughout the day to determine the time when he would be most vulnerable.

What they discovered was that, weather permitting, Pignataro usually took a walk after his evening meal, oftentimes alone. His course never varied and included a segment along the old walls. And it was there—at the dark corner where the walls form a sharp angle near the *Porta Reale* gate—that one fair evening in June 1668, two of Concublet's men attacked and assaulted Pignataro about his head and torso with fists and sticks. He was found lying on the ground, unconscious and bleeding from his face and scalp. There was no attempt at robbery.

Word of the insult spread quickly. Rumors as to the person behind the assault focused on Concublet, though they could not be confirmed. The viceroy responded by issuing a proclamation closing the two academies. Pignataro recovered, yet he and his supporters (who were convinced as to the source of the outrage) were not about to turn the other cheek, nor would they call a truce. Regardless of his noble status, they had come to a strong decision that one day they would have their revenge on Signore Andrea Concublet, Marchese of Arena.

NOTES

1. Based on my own personal experience, it appears to me that this unification of the southern Italian culture to that of England has been fruitful for both regions.
2. In retrospect, it is remarkable how fruitful and exciting were the last fifty years or so of the seventeenth century—the epoch of a revolution in science and medicine. One fact alone bears witness: half the structures in the human body are named after seventeenth-century men.

Chapter 3

Dissolution, Depression and Amazing Cures

Naples—1669–1675

After the viceroy disbanded the academies in 1668, a small group of the *Investiganti* continued to meet informally. Also, a group of a dozen or so young scholars began to gather with Lionardo DiCapua in his home in Naples. He proposed that this new group follow the model of the Researchers by discussing and freely criticizing their observations on various natural occurrences. Many of the leading Neapolitan thinkers of the next generation, including the nephew of Tommaso Cornelio, were among those who met on a regular basis.

As for the mild-mannered Tommaso Cornelio, the beating of Pignataro and the subsequent closing of the academies had persuaded him to leave Naples. Despite Lionardo's attempts to keep his friend involved in the academic life of the city, Tommaso decided to seek the quiet of the countryside. Likewise, in due course and for various reasons, most of the old innovators felt the need to retreat from the fight.[1]

During the early part of Cornelio's travels, he interrupted his correspondence with his friends in Naples and the Royal Society in London. Thence, in 1672, he again began transmitting to the Royal Society on his observations of the phenomenon of *Tarantism*, which is seen in small towns throughout the south of Italy. Tarantism is a disease believed by some to afflict those who have been bitten by a tarantula. The victim falls into a manic state of movement that lasts sometimes for days before the poison is said to be released and a state of exhaustion (or death) ensues. The frenetic Italian dance called the "Tarantella" has its origins in this induced state of mania. Tommaso was apparently not persuaded by the popular folklore. Instead, his letters emphasized his belief that the disease was a manifestation of the mental state of the victim.

To his circle in Naples who tried to entice him to return to the city, he wrote of his desire to stay removed from the hostile Neapolitan atmosphere where one was always exposed to the *"morso dei sicofanti"* (the bite of the sycophants). He also kept in touch with his friend Marcello Malpighi who, in 1674, arranged a position for Tommaso to teach practical medicine at the medical school in Padua. Here again, for some inexplicable reason, the project never materialized. In 1676, he returned to live in a quiet area outside of Naples where he remained in solitude with the intention, as he wrote to Malpighi the following year, of no longer practicing medicine.

A few years before Cornelio's departure to the south, another leading light of the *Investiganti,* Francesco D'Andrea, succumbed to a pronounced melancholy and sought relief and invigoration elsewhere. In 1667, he wrote to his good friend Francesco Redi, admitting his plight. He told the Tuscan scientist that he managed his problem by getting rid of his fine furniture and spending time outside of his home. The method apparently helped ease his distress—at least for a while. Two years later after the death of his father, Francesco's anxiety and apprehension worsened. He took to traveling throughout Italy, meeting with friends and other contacts. During this time, he diverted his mind by concentrating on mathematics and scientific studies and avoiding legal issues. He would remain away from Naples until April 1675.

Over the years, another original member of the *Investiganti*, the eminent polymath Giovanni Alfonso Borelli, had remained in contact with his Neapolitan friends. He had been working in Pisa and Florence, where he was often looked upon as a rough Neapolitan, lacking in Tuscan polish. When he first began his tenure at Pisa, his students had been known to greet their professor with catcalls, claiming that he lacked eloquence and that he was long-winded and dull. In time, however, the precision of his experiments and the wisdom transmitted through his pen became so obvious as to negate his rough exterior. The insults of the students turned to admiration, yet the irascible Borelli remembered those earlier days.

Borelli had also been angered with a decision by the members of the *Cimento* to publish their works as a group of *"Saggi"* instead of as individuals; he was just about to release his major work on the motion of the moons of Jupiter. Hence, he decided to leave Tuscany in 1666, which coincided with the end of the *Cimento*.

He stopped in Naples in 1667 while on his way to Messina, Sicily. While in Naples, he met and performed experiments with Conclubet, DiCapua, and the small group of remaining *Investiganti*. During this visit and in earlier times, many of Borelli's theories passed through the review of the Researchers. Out of respect for this wise Neapolitan, Andrea Concublet offered to provide the funding for part of what would become his greatest work, incorporating many of the ideas that he had presented to the *Investiganti*. After he had moved on to Sicily, Borelli wrote the dedication of *De motionibus naturalis* to Concublet. In it, he praised both the marchese and Lionardo for their wisdom and kindness.

After the viceroy's order to break up the academy in 1668, while many of the other founding members of the *Investiganti* departed the city or were otherwise incapacitated, Lionardo remained in Naples, spreading the innovative ideas with Concublet. At the same time, he remained a loving father, watching over his surviving children, providing for their necessities, and directing their education. Likewise, he continued practicing medicine in a way that reflected his belief in the uncertainty of the traditionalist approach. He would not use any medicine unless it was certain to be "innocent," as he would say. By avoiding those treatments that he considered reckless, he would thus obtain cures without endangering the patient. A few anecdotes would best describe his tendencies.

The first came from Amenta, near the end of *La Vita*. Lionardo was called to the home of a renowned lawyer, Signore Onofino Parrilli, who had lately developed a severe catarrh infection. (Amenta was present during the following exchange.) Parrilli, who could hardly speak due to his infection, managed to relate his symptoms: "I have fallen into a state of congestion, dear doctor. My nose is full, my throat is sore, my lungs burn with the cough. A fever comes over me at times and, as you can hear, my voice has departed."

"Allow me, Signore Parrilli, to examine you." Lionardo placed his ear against Parrilli's chest while feeling his pulse at the wrist. Thence he pronounced his advice: "Signore Parrilli, you truly suffer from catarrh. I would suggest that you stay in your home, away from others, so that you are not required to converse, allowing your voice to rest along with your body. Take some hot tea several times throughout the day and, if the fever comes, cover your brow with a cool cloth. Do you have oil of eucalyptus in your home?" Parrilli shook his head to the negative. Lionardo searched in his medical bag and found a jar of eucalyptus balm. "This, my good man, should be rubbed onto your chest and neck. Thence should you cover the area with a woolen scarf, which you should leave in place until you repeat the oiling at least three times per day."

Parrilli responded with difficulty, "My dear Lionardo, surely you can see my discomfort. I feel horrible. I must have a remedy that will actuate an immediate cure, for I am a busy man with much work planned for the week to come."

"I understand, Signore Parrilli, and I pity your plight," Lionardo answered. "Yet, there is nothing more that you need and nothing more I can give you. Your body will heal itself. I promise."

"My dear doctor," the patient replied, "I do not think you understand the degree to which I suffer. I feel as though the good Lord will take me from this world if I do not soon come to my previously healthy state. You must write for a cure. I beg you."

So, Lionardo put pen on paper writing these words, "I will not give you something that will harm you."

He handed the prescription to Parrilli who read it and responded in his raucous voice, "What do you mean, 'something that will harm you'?"

"I do not know anything that will help you other than what I have already suggested." Hence did Signore Parrilli follow the regimen, and within three days he recuperated.

Amenta continues in the same section to briefly describe other cures that he had observed. One was performed on a Signore Giovanibattista Pistoia, the brother of a famous Neapolitan judge. Lionardo, as we have seen, for personal and professional reasons, was opposed to the letting of blood, so he prescribed only the water of thistle *cardosanto* and cool cloths to the forehead, which cured the malignant fever of the young man and quickly restored his health.[2]

Thus, despite the general melancholy that came to the other innovators, Lionardo DiCapua maintained his placid temperament and avoided the maudlin anxiety that overwhelmed his friends. He was, by disposition, never too elevated, nor likewise too low. In this manner, he continued to help others in need of his medical knowledge. Much of his fortitude was undoubtedly due to his personality, yet it is also true that he had arrived at a more positive condition because of his family life. He was happy in his home, surrounded by his caring wife and gifted, loving children. Suffice it to say that this was especially the case with his eldest son, Cesare, and his beautiful and intelligent daughter, Giovanna, for whom Lionardo and those of us who were blessed to have known her held a special place in our hearts.

NOTES

1. I must admit that Tommaso Cornelio always remained an enigma to me. He was undoubtedly a genius and a man of immense intellectual capabilities, possessing excellent taste in art and music, a sweet personality, and a kindly heart. Yet, despite a powerful physical presence, he was not inclined to push his agenda, preferring to remain in the wings rather than on the stage. Like Lionardo, he was a humble man who shunned the limelight.

   By no means would I ever presume to cast aspersions upon that great man, but I must allow that it seemed to me that Tommaso bore secrets that he wished to keep private. It could have been some insecurity rooted in the past, perhaps a touch of melancholy, or possibly something in his personal life. Whatever the cause, from his days as a student, he would often recede into a quiet place to seek the solitude he obviously desired. And so it was again in 1670. Tommaso left Naples and traveled to the small villages of Puglia.

2. I could add several of my own observations as well. However, I will defer to Niccolo Amenta as he concludes this section of *La Vita* with a summary statement most fitting for our Lionardo: "I will stop for the

sake of brevity, counting all the stupendous cures he made either with few medicines or with good regimens, which were very well accepted."

Chapter 4

The Murder of the Marchese Concublet

Lionardo's dear friend, the Marchese Andrea Concublet, was never convicted in the beating of Carlo Pignataro. Since the assailants surprised the victim at dusk in a dark section of the old walls, they were never identified and the whole matter remained unsolved—although suspicions persisted.

Andrea continued to meet privately with the members of the *Investiganti* after the viceroy had closed the academies and after Borelli had departed to Sicily. In 1673, Concublet left the city to travel across Italy, where he gathered more instruments with which to perform scientific experiments. He brought these back to Naples and his efforts sparked new life among the remaining innovators who were anxious to renew their gatherings. This smaller group occasionally reconvened at his palace, where experiments were performed using such extraordinary new instruments as the thermometer and the barometer. The marchese himself made the initial presentations as excitedly as a child in possession of a new toy.

Despite the invigorating energy that Concublet brought from his travels, he and the other innovators remained under the scrutiny of the reactionary forces. As early as 1671, the Congregation of the Inquisition had written to the Archbishop of Naples advising him to keep a close watch on those who might be propagating the ideas of Descartes. They noted that the diffusion of these concepts should be crushed, and the promoters should be reported to the Inquisition. This, then, was the opening round in Naples of the notion that Cartesian thought (and for that matter, the philosophy of the atomists, of Galileo, Gassendi, Hobbes and Locke) was, at its core, heretical. And more was yet to follow.

How many times throughout history has a subtle hint given license to those willing to turn to the dark side of our nature? Hatred runs deep, jealousies are long harbored, and scores must be settled. A nod, a side-glance, the use of a cue word or a phrase, the hidden message contained within the official notification. The voice of righteous retribution, unwritten, between the lines, speaks to those attuned to its calling. And who knows in what dark corner of some hidden room those who wait for their opening and lust for violence might meet to hatch a brutal plan?

The Marchese Concublet never received any direct threats, at least none that were made public (although, knowing him, he would not have cared a pin if he had). Well into his seventh decade, he remained a strong and vibrant man. He did not suffer from any debilitating health problems, he still enjoyed his rides in the country, he spent months traveling across Italy, and his intellectual abilities continued as keen as ever. By all objective measures he appeared to be a man in his fourth or fifth decade of life, not the seventh. Yet, as vigorous a man as he was, his physical prowess was no match for the clique sent to destroy him.

On the evening of the eighteenth of April, 1675, four assassins hired by Giacomo Milano, marchese of San Giorgio, ambushed Andrea as he rode in his carriage to visit a friend. The actual site of the attack was on the *Portici Strada* at the cross of the *Laguo*. The driver was forced to stop and was himself assaulted. Andrea was dragged from the carriage and beaten badly, despite giving his assailants a few knocks of their own. Six days later, to the intense sorrow of all those who loved him, he died from his multiple wounds.

Be assured that several nobles, relatives, and friends much affected by the loss of the beloved Concublet prepared a vendetta against the marchese of San Giorgio. (Neapolitans were infamous for such a response.) But he escaped their wrath by seeking immunity in a nearby convent, a common practice in those days. When the case went before a judge, San Giorgio claimed that the brawl was actuated because of an unmet duel, which was never proven, leading to his conviction and incarceration.

Years later, in 1681, Concublet's young cousin Giovan Girolamo Acquaviva, the Duke of Atri in the Abruzzo, was arrested for refusing to offer his word of honor to foreswear revenge against San Giorgio. Acquaviva was a man of great natural aptitude and devoted to scholarship. He loved his older cousin dearly. It was to the young Duke that all Concublet's papers, including those from the proceedings of the *Investiganti*, had been given. Subsequently, in 1707, after a long and valiant siege, he lost his town to the overwhelming military might of an Austrian prince. This was at a time when the threadbare Spanish Empire was coming apart, leaving all its vast holdings (including the Kingdom of Naples) vulnerable at the hands of its enemies. Acquaviva was banished from his domain and ended his mortal days destitute in Rome in 1709. Concublet's papers, along with the rest of Acquaviva's patrimony, were dispersed or lost during the final two years of his life.[1]

Some who read this account might say that the Marchese Concublet deserved his tragic end since he had, likewise, resorted to the use of violence.[2] Yet, humanity values retribution far more than forgiveness, and, as noted earlier, comes to the actuation of battles—great and small—as if by a natural persuasion.

With the murder of Concublet, the innovators had lost their main source of protection and a constant well spring of inspiration. Lionardo DiCapua was particularly affected by the loss. Andrea was the connection back to those younger days when a naïve Lionardo was so touched by his first love. Now, his remorse once again dredged up the memories of that period, both joyful and sad.

The spirit of youth is a volatile substance that burns intensely, fusing bonds that remain strong throughout our time on earth. Life thus becomes an accumulation of gains and losses that leave the living profoundly enriched and simultaneously saddened. Lionardo profited immensely from his close friendship with Andrea Concublet. In the end, he could find no solace in this calamity, and he realized, in Andrea's passing, the approaching end to his own life.

NOTES

1. What remained ended up at his former palace in Atri where I found just a few of them. Most of the proceedings, however, were never published and unfortunately remain lost.

2. I cannot argue against this assertion for, in truth, violence begets violence. Not being a religious man, I rarely quote the Scriptures except to say that one of Christ's most revolutionary precepts was his insistence that we refute the Old Testament aphorism of an eye for an eye and, instead, turn the other cheek.

Chapter 5

An Accumulation of Sadness

Naples—1675–1677

The murder of the Marchese Concublet was a profound shock to the innovative thinkers within the kingdom. Coupled with the earlier warning issued by the Inquisition to monitor those who expressed an interest in the new philosophies, a foreboding sense of gloom descended upon the progressive forces like a cold, dense fog that chills to the core and obscures the path ahead.

The depression that gripped Francesco D'Andrea darkened as he struggled to find meaning beyond a great accumulation of wealth. A year after Concublet's murder, in 1676, Tommaso Cornelio returned from his travels to a quiet residence outside the city. Thence he continued his search for solitude, shunning his previously active, intellectual involvement save for private communications with his old Florentine friends, as well as with Marcello Malpighi and DiCapua. Out of respect for Tommaso's desire for solitude, Lionardo rarely saw his good friend in person. Others from the Academy were likewise immobilized.

Although much affected by the loss of Concublet, only DiCapua seemed able to maintain any semblance of his former life. Having felt the pain of separation at a young age, Lionardo possessed a visceral understanding of the fleeting nature of human existence. The successes and disappointments that he faced with regularity as an adult were apparently always tempered by the realization of that childhood experience. Furthermore, his persistent efforts in caring for his patients, the continuing invigoration he imbibed from the group of young intellectuals that gathered around him, and especially the embracing love and support of his family helped him to resist the maudlin calls that echoed with each accumulated loss. All this was true until 1677, when he and his family suffered a tragedy that in a rather singular manner abandoned Lionardo to a deep depression as it did for everyone who knew and loved Giovanna DiCapua.

* * *

In July of 1677, during a spell of close, inclement weather, nineteen-year-old Giovanna developed a sudden illness. Her symptoms began with anorexia and a cramping pain in the abdomen accompanied by constipation. She thought that her problems were the result of her menstrual flow, which had begun four days earlier. With the cessation of her flow, however, the pain worsened.

Left without an appetite, she took to her bed, finding some relief lying in a fetal position with knees flexed. Occasionally she would, with some apprehension and increased pain, rise from her bed to ambulate to the water closet, bent at the waist in hope of relieving the plenitude in her bowels. Unable to pass anything, she would return to her bed and resume the fetal position.

Her mother became concerned and sought the advice of her husband. In the past, mother and daughter had been too embarrassed to discuss problems related to their sex with Lionardo yet, as the symptoms progressed beyond the termination of Giovanna's menses, both women realized that he was the one who held their certain hope of a cure. Lionardo listened to Giovanna's complaints, took her pulse, felt her brow for fever, palpated her swollen abdomen and observed her bent ambulation. After his examination, he realized that this was not a simple case of impacted bowels, yet he endeavored to avoid frightening his daughter and his wife.

"Giovanna," he advised, "lay on your back in a comfortable position and I will have Mother try to help you." He asked Annamaria to heat some oil and rub their daughter's belly softly following the path of her colon up the right and across to her left side, then down. "This will help her pass gas and hopefully stool."

The pain Giovanna experienced was initially centered at the umbilicus. The rubbing with oil eased, yet did not eliminate, it. When she had finished her first treatment, Annamaria found her husband at his desk reading from a medical text. She explained that the rubbing seemed to help, although there was no production. She asked if she should continue.

"Yes, perhaps for another thirty minutes," he said in a somber tone. "Is she resting?"

"She is tired and trying to sleep, yet the fullness is uncomfortable and prevents her from attaining a deep rest."

Over the ensuing hours the cramping gradually migrated to the right lower section of the abdomen near to the groin and there intensified. The slightest touch caused discomfort, such that Annamaria was unable to continue the rubbing. Along with the pain came a higher fever and more nausea. Lionardo was now convinced that his daughter suffered from Typhlitis, and another younger physician who examined the young woman the next day confirmed his diagnosis.

Surprisingly, on the morning of the third day of her illness, Giovanna's pain suddenly eased, and her fever defervesced. She sat upright, and her color returned. Everyone around her felt relief as she seemed to be healing. By mid-afternoon, however, the pain had returned with a vengeance now throughout her entire belly. Her skin, at first hot and drenched with a warm sweat, became pale and clammy. Delirium gripped her mind and, with it, came a rambling speech of incoherent phrases. Before long, she lapsed into an immobile, comatose state.

Her parents, siblings and friends tried to comfort her and provide solace to each other as the spirit slowly ebbed from this beautiful young woman just recently so full of life. The burden of his failure competed with the deep sorrow within Lionardo. The uncertainty of medicine now haunted him in the most abysmal way, for he knew he was helpless in reversing the course of the disease. To pronounce such a disposition on a patient was always difficult for him. To pronounce it upon his own flesh and blood was the worst agony he had ever suffered.

By the following morning, Giovanna was completely unresponsive, breathing in short quick bursts separated by increasingly longer periods of apnea. The priest was called to administer extreme unction. Just before noon, she took her last breath, then passed peacefully away.

* * *

Suffice it to say that the depth of one's sorrow, no matter how profound, seemed shallow in comparison with the grief of the parents. Annamaria was inconsolable, and Lionardo could find no rest. They passed through the days of mourning, of friendly visitations and scripted traditions surrounding the burial in a mechanical manner, too numb to do otherwise.

For several weeks afterwards, Annamaria spent most of her time in her bedroom in her nightclothes. She ate little, slept fitfully, and cried constantly. In the yard was a great oak tree from which ghostly birds sang to her. She would sit in a rocking chair and rub one hand above the other as if stroking her daughter's hand while she whispered indecipherable words. When the weather turned that winter, Lionardo would often find her staring out the window in the middle of the night haunted by the same remorseful thought: "Do you think she is cold, our sweet girl? She was always so cold in wintertime."

For his part Lionardo came to a deeply melancholic state as if in a social and spiritual hibernation. He took a sabbatical from his medical practice and spent hours immobile in his study, abandoning his intellectual pursuits, obsessed with the need to apologize for his failure to save his precious daughter. He thought of all the times he would return home to her waiting smile, how she would take his coat and usher him into a seat, remove his shoes, and bring him some refreshment. He tried to picture her now, with that bright glow on her face, the welcoming embrace from the family behind her. But all he could see was that agonized look as she lay there, alone in her pain. How he wished he could have removed that agony and taken it upon himself.

Giovanna was a young woman of infinite promise, up and alive one day, gone to her dark grave within a week, beyond the embrace of family and friends, and deaf to the pealing Neapolitan bells that marked the time of those desolate days.

Chapter 6

Reconciliation and Revival

Naples—1678-1681

Some wounds to the soul never heal, their painful scars woven
with remorse. Time, it has been said, is the great mender. And
it took time before some sense of purpose returned to those who
loved Giovanna DiCapua.

It was their oldest child, Cesare, who eventually persuaded
his parents to rejoin the rest of the family. During their period
of grief, Cesare had kept the family together and dealt with
the practical details of running the home. Once Annamaria,
Lionardo, their other children and close family friends began
emerging from the irreconcilable loss, Cesare decided to accompany an acquaintance, a well-traveled gentleman, on a holiday
in England. Lionardo and his wife were hopeful that the sojourn
would ease the strain that had been placed on their son and allow
him to release the sadness that he had contained by necessity.
The two young men sailed from the Bay of Naples in the spring
of 1678, with no set date for a return.

That summer, Lionardo resumed his medical practice,
although he stopped taking new patients and minimized his
consultations. He also reconvened the meetings with younger
literati who had replaced many of the original *Investiganti*.
Disillusioned by the burdensome power of tradition, there was
perhaps too great a tendency on the part of the older members

to recount the glories of the past. But with this infusion of youthful vigor, an uplifting sense of purpose slowly returned to the DiCapua home.

In such ways did time pass until the autumn of 1678 when a momentous event occurred, one that would resurrect the spirit of the innovators and provide an opportunity for the reassertion of their ideals and, simultaneously, the renewing of the animosity between them and the forces of authority.

* * *

One of the certainties of history is that meritorious ideas are rarely restrained; the truth will eventually come out. In this regard, despite the success of the *Discordanti* in suppressing the teaching of chemistry (*notomia vitale* in distinction from human anatomy, or *notomia semplice*) in the medical school, the importance of chemistry in explaining the intricate processes of life—and its potential for creating healing medicines—continued to advance in Naples and throughout Italy; the country had been behind other European countries where chemistry had been taught in universities since the first half of the century.

Lionardo had remained a champion of chemistry among the younger physicians of the kingdom, and his ideas (originally tested with the use of the Jesuits' bark to treat Diana's ague) continued to gain acceptance. Even some of the Galenists, recognizing the repeated failures of their methods, began to experiment with chemical cures. The rumors developed much faster than the science, so that much of this experimentation was based on hearsay, and the inevitable ill effects upon patients sometimes proved fatal.

Such was the case when a Galenist physician, a dilettante in the science of *notomia vitale*, produced a supposed chemical cure for a noted Neapolitan resident, Ottavio Caracciolo di Forino, a man of noble lineage and a close friend of the viceroy.

Caracciolo died soon after receiving a medicine that was based on the element antimony. Why this concoction was being used by a doctor of physick was a question left unanswered. But the death of a well-known noble caused an immediate stir in higher circles. An investigation was ordered. Answers were demanded from the physician and any other involved parties. One would think that the Discordants would keep a low profile since one of their own had made the concoction. Instead, they seized the opportunity they had long desired to discredit *notomia vitale*. They approached the Collateral Council in support of the official inquiry, asking that chemistry studies be banned, and all medicines regulated.

The Viceroy Marchese de los Velez wisely asked for a response from several noted progressives, among them Lionardo. Answering the petition became the focal point around which DiCapua rallied his brilliant mind, and the effort he would put forth over the ensuing months provided a distracting modicum of relief for his tattered spirit. His *Parere* (opinion) was a compilation of the ideas about medicine and natural philosophy that he had learned through his own studies and through the meetings and experiments of the *Investiganti,* plus his years of practical experience with patients. It was initially presented simply as a response to the viceroy. Amenta tells us that Lionardo had no intention of publishing the manuscript. Nonetheless, when his friends read it, they insisted that it be published for the common good. Due either to his natural reticence or perhaps a desire to shelter his family and himself at a delicate time in their recovery from their great loss, DiCapua at first declined. His friends, however, continued to highlight the good that would come with the publication of the manuscript. Eventually, he agreed.

And so, in 1681, Antonio Bulifon published the manuscript for the first time in Naples with the title *Parere del Signor Lionardo DiCapua; Divisato in otto ragionamenti: ne quali partitamente narrondosi l'origine e'l progresso della Medicina; chiaramente l'incertezza della medicina si fa manifesta (The Opinion of Signore Lionardo DiCapua; divided into eight reasonings: in which is expressed in detail the origin and progress of Medicine; clearly the uncertainty of medicine becomes apparent).* The first chapter was "made English" in 1684 by a gentleman named John Lancaster, who addressed it to the well-known British scientist, "The Honourable Robert Boyle, Esq." for his perusal. Although he did not say so directly, Lancaster must have realized the commonality between DiCapua and Boyle, as both men maintained the necessity of uniting anatomy and chemistry in medical practice. Boyle was not formally trained as a physician; yet, like DiCapua, he held great hope for cures resulting from the study of chemistry and recognized the importance of mathematics as a foundation for any scientific endeavor.

Carlo Buragna, a friend of DiCapua and a member of the *Investiganti*, wrote the introductory letter to the reader. He mentions the occasion that prompted Lionardo's response and elaborates Amenta's point that its ultimate publication was deemed necessary for those appreciative of its learned style, as well as for all those who were wary of the practices of physick. Buragna concludes:

> Moreover, who does not perceive how advantageous this treatise may be to such young men, who study Physick, since by the reading of this alone, they may arrive at a more exact knowledge of its Nature, than by turning over the great Volumes of the most reputed and solemn Masters thereof, and may in an hour understand what in the Method of Curing is to be taken by him, who, laying aside cozening Tricks and Cheats, intends, as his profession obliges him, to honor himself by the help he brings to such Patients as come under his hands.

Of the eight essays, the first six dwell on the frailty of medical practice, while the seventh and eighth present the viceroy with practical steps for improving the art and dealing with the immediate issue at hand—the study of *notomia vitale* and the regulation of chemicals as medicines.

After Buragna's introduction comes the first and, by far, the longest *Ragionamento primo*, which, as mentioned above, was translated by John Lancaster into English. It begins by praising the viceroy's valiant purpose of protecting his subjects from the domestic mischief of unscrupulous physicians. Lionardo equates the effort with the political protection provided against foreign enemies during wartime, an analogy repeated throughout the book. DiCapua then sets the stage for his main theme, oft repeated throughout the text: "The wisest and most intelligent Physicians have oftentimes fallen in giving permanent and certain Laws to Medicine, an Art, of its own nature—in the highest degree—uncertain, dubious, and inconstant."

What follows is a history of medicine beginning in Egypt where, he tells us, the study and practice of the art of healing truly began. Lionardo demonstrates the influence of the Hermetic tradition that sees a golden age of primitive immediacy when essential knowledge was imbibed. He quotes the famous historian Herodotus on the degree of specialization that evolved among the Egyptian physicians, each organ having its own specialist. This led to a strict adherence to the master's principles, such that, if the physician followed the acknowledged laws of the sacred book and the cure failed, no charge was laid against them. But, if he went contrary to the written rules, he became subject to a judgement of death. Here, Lionardo notes, was the beginning of an overly dogmatic approach to the art, in which experience and reason became subverted to a rigid system of generalizations.

Throughout the first essay—indeed, the entire manuscript—Lionardo inserts multiple quotes from famous writers who had lived during those days, which adds a verisimilitude to his narrative and gives an indication of the breadth of his research and knowledge. He heaps praise upon the Greeks for exceeding other nations in the arts and sciences, but he also chastises them for prohibiting the study of physick by women and servants, whom he finds capable of practicing the art. Lionardo uses passages from the famed Hippocrates to explain the Athenian system of justice for failed medical cures: "There is no penalty set upon the Practitioners of Physick in these cities, but that of infamy."

Despite the efforts of Hippocrates and his successors to give some uniformity to the art, multiple sects with their own rigid ideas evolved. In the later days of the Roman Empire, Galen united many of the ancient ideas by selectively interpreting the writings of his predecessors to suit his theory of the four humors. The practical application of the theory oftentimes failed, hence was a plebiscite passed among the Romans that was intended to punish physicians for their failures. He quotes a Latin poem that summarizes the general feeling of the time:

If to each Crime its punishment be due,
What pain, Physicians, is enough for you?
Who with your Drugs Diseases frequently
Do cause, and the Sick before their time to die,
This Opinion, which the whole World sways,
Indulg'd to you, by others' harms to raise
Yourselves, and by their deaths, to merit Praise.

Moving beyond the Romans, DiCapua harbors no great respect for the famed Arabian Physicians, who often contradicted the teachings of Galen, yet offered no rational method of their own. Thus medicine, like philosophy, continued to fall prey to the many prejudices of its opposing schools. But that began to change when Theophrastus Paracelsus started propounding medicinal chemicals, delivering the first forceful volley against the Galenists. Then came the anatomical work of Andreas Vesalius and William Harvey, among others, further discrediting the traditionalists, who reacted by denying the truth evident before their curtained eyes.

Lionardo reserves special praise for his friend Marcello Malpighi and the German chemist John Baptiste von Helmont. Von Helmont, he says, exceeded Paracelsus in his perfection of chemical cures; and of Malpighi, he tells us that, together with Harvey, their discovery of the closed circulation of the blood far exceeds all the inventions of antiquity put together.

Finally, there is one other philosopher of whom Lionardo DiCapua wrote admiringly at the end of his first Ragionamento. She was Oliva Sabuco de Nantes Barrera, a Spanish woman, born in 1562. Well before Descartes, she described the brain as the site where the soul interacted with the body. By extension to the field of medicine, she concluded that this close connection between the soul and body could be useful in the treatment and prevention of disease. At the time that she wrote her ideas, philosophy and medicine remained (as they still do) overwhelmingly male-dominated professions. In a reference applicable to Descartes, DiCapua attributes Sabuco with promoting concepts that others later claimed as their own. To Lionardo's credit, he lauded her for promoting the assertion that would become the fundamental principle to guide his practice: that the art of physick is inherently uncertain.

DiCapua concludes his first essay by reminding the viceroy that the recent irrefutable advances among the moderns are rarely attacked in the presence of knowledgeable scholars. Yet, there are still many Galenists who deny the anatomical truths:

> They covertly mutter and murmur, impudently presuming to say, That so many different things cannot anyway

be in the bodies of Animals; that if they had been there, their Galen was not so simple or foolish, but that he long before these Modern Inventors appeared in the world, would distinctly have discerned and described them: forasmuch as being most accurate and ingenious, and having given Physick its last and most perfect Complement, it is not credible, that he should in this alone have so grossly erred."

He ends the first essay by requesting that the Viceroy de los Velez avoid applying the restraints. His rationale is straightforward: Medicine is an uncertain art that requires freedom to advance. Open inquiry and intellectual freedom are the methods to attain that progress. Thus, physicians who apply their experience and their senses to a free inquiry are not bound to any dogmatic sect and are enemies to none.

In the second essay, Lionardo continues to praise the ideal of open inquiry and exalts the humanistic spirit of the Renaissance. He reminds the viceroy that, throughout Europe, Galen's practices are being openly questioned by philosophers who are far cleverer than the ancients.

Epistemology is the subject DiCapua explores in the third Ragionamento. The human mind, as the Atomists contend, is intertwined with the body. The mind perceives the external world through the fibers of the nerves that spread throughout the body, sending their messages to the brain. The senses are the windows through which the first perception of things arrive at the mind and, since they may occasionally fool us, the result can be division, argument, and uncertainty among philosophers, including those who practice medicine.

Lionardo begins the fourth essay by refusing to mourn the loss of ancient medical texts, since the ones that survived had proven to be of little worth. To emphasize his point, he analyzes the twenty-three aphorisms of Hippocrates and concludes that the acknowledged master was a good and wise man, yet he could not elaborate a correct diagnosis or a proper treatment. He criticizes Aristotle for his lack of knowledge of comparative anatomy and notes that, for all their brilliance, the Greeks drowned in their own endless speculation—the same with the modern practitioners of physick. Their addiction to interminable philosophizing over some trivial detail keeps them from a true search for knowledge.

Beginning with his parents' experiences in his childhood, DiCapua had been a harsh critic of the Galenist practice of the Salasso, or bloodletting, and in the fifth Ragionamento, he explains its prevalence and attacks its foolishness with the passion infused by his own experience. By using the Salasso, he notes, one does not dissipate the illness but strengthens it, for in the blood is the "noble substance" that can thwart the disease. If the blood itself is indeed noxious, letting the blood, he says, is like a foolish vintner who thinks he can cure a bad batch of wine by removing a small part of it.

Through a selective interpretation of the writings of earlier practitioners, Lionardo says that Galen fabricated support for his theory of the four humors and his system of balancing them by prescribing treatments that raised or lowered the opposite essence. Like Aristotle, Galen relied on a system of deductive logic, which kept him from further experimental investigation. Over the ensuing centuries, Galen's followers built a tightly limited system around his teachings, resulting in the use of noxious therapies, like the Salasso and harsh purgatives and emetics. These treatments were protected by a pretentious dogmatism that justified the barbarous therapies. He then uses a political metaphor to make his point: "As in the well ordained Republic, to sudden Changes dangerous Disorders follow; such is the case for Bodies as well."

The choice for the physician is between servitude to the ancient system of Aristotle and Galen or to a method based on freedom of inquiry. Lionardo asserts that it was time to break that dogmatic reliance.

DiCapua begins the sixth Ragionamento by praising the Renaissance for bringing back to life the Greek and Roman languages that were the mother of every science, as well as poetry, architecture, music, and painting. He tells the viceroy of the many changes occurring in medicine, yet persists in his assessment of the uncertainty of the art. Then, in an amazing demonstration of his skeptical nature and intellectual honesty, he tempers any overly enthusiastic acceptance of even the new theories by questioning the teachings of some of the men he had earlier praised, including Paracelsus, Campanella, von Helmont and Sylvius.

Lionardo moderates his admiration for Paracelsus, who insisted that remedies must resemble the illnesses they treat. This rigid principle is the mirror image of Galen's advocacy of opposites, and DiCapua finds both theories wanting. The renowned Dominican Father Tommaso Campanella, despite his free philosophizing, propounded several medical concepts, which, according to Lionardo, showed how much easier it is to point out the errors of others than to find the truth himself. He praises Campanella for his "acute understanding and free philosophizing." Then he quickly tempers his appreciation by criticizing "the damage caused by attention to astrology and other vain swindles, from a childish love of riddles, and from a foolish belief that such things, or fabulous entities only imagined by him, had something to do with the things of nature."

Lionardo laments the fact that the chemist John Baptiste von Helmont did not study anatomy and never revealed the contents of his renowned medicines. DiCapua also conditions the theories of another otherwise respected chemist, Fabricius Sylvius, who made sweeping generalizations from simple observations. Lionardo uses a lyrical metaphor to explain:

> However, just as a brave but inexpert Pilot might have at his Disposal all the sheets, ropes, sails, and compasses a well-stocked ship might have, and wretchedly die shipwrecked because he knows little as to the use of this Equipment when navigating in new and as of yet unknown Seas, so Sylvius, equipped with good Philosophy, as he claims, and with considerable Knowledge of Medicine nonetheless miserably failed because he did not know how to use Them, and like the inexperienced Pilot, barely having opened the high sails of his Art, disastrously drowned.

Finally, at the end of the sixth essay, Lionardo explains to the viceroy that despite all the disagreements between the various sects, no wise Prince or well-ordered government ever sanctioned physicians for their sincere views. And he suggests to the Viceroy Marchese de los Velez, "Whenever any Prince or Magistrate ever tried to intervene in Medicine and restrict even the smallest area of It by particular Regulations, such Statutes have always plainly produced doubtful Effects."

Having made the case for the historical, technical, and philosophical difficulties that have led to the uncertainty of medicine in the first six essays, DiCapua offers his proposed reforms in the final two.

The seventh Ragionamento contains Lionardo's most reasoned support for the study of chemistry. The ancients, he tells us, never were able to perceive the true properties of the primal elements. The therapies of the wisest among them were based on their long experience. Through centuries of trial and error, practitioners had arrived at the understanding that certain herbs cured certain illnesses. Explaining the mechanism of the cure was another matter. Lionardo quotes Cicero on herbal treatments: "We may wonder at the variety of herbs that have been observed by physicians . . . and though reason has never explained their force and nature, yet through their usefulness they have won approval for the medical art and for their discoverer. . . . I see their power and that is enough. Why they have it, I do not know."

Which brings DiCapua to his main assertion. Not only should there be teachers of chemistry to perform the necessary experiments, but also a garden of simples should be developed at the medical school and accompanied by an expert herbalist who can teach the physicians how to identify the various herbs, their constituent properties, their effects, and their wise usage. To understand the formative principles of natural materials, each must be broken down in a way that preserves all its essential components. Ultimately the investigator will arrive at the smallest particles, from which he will gain an understanding of the true operation of the chemical by knowing the nature and properties of its parts.

In addition to requesting chemical and herbal studies, Lionardo adds anatomy, logic, mathematics, and the Greek language as required learning of all medical students. He believes that they must have a natural inclination to the work, plus a mind sharp enough to accomplish the rigorous task, and that they likewise maintain the highest ethical standards and strive to be a lover of truth, justice, and honesty. The physician should maintain contact with literati, as well as with older women and men, gypsies, vagabonds, and peasants who understand folk healing. He also suggests that the physician follow a practice that was common among many ancient physicians, yet one that he himself never pursued; namely, to travel about the earth to learn the infinite variety of nature. Then he again counters with a note of uncertainty from his Sceptic-Atomist beliefs: "And even though the physician will struggle to learn all the aforementioned skills, he must not consider himself to have reached the highest level of understanding."

Lionardo concludes his suggested curriculum by arguing for an open education of physicians, allowing them to come to hear from all sides, since none of the partisans, including himself, possess all the answers. He calls for tolerance from those who insist that only the teachings of Hippocrates and Galen should be presented, and reminds those sectarians that Galen himself had chosen the best ideas from all the available sects.

DiCapua ends this most practical section of his manuscript by recommending that the viceroy add no further regulations or additional licensing requirements. Complete liberty and intellectual tolerance should be granted to all students of medicine.

In the eighth and final Ragionamento of the original 1681 *Parere*, Lionardo praises the Academy of the *Investiganti* for their support of free-philosophizing and open investigation into the wonders of nature. By doing so, he tells us that they have arrived at an understanding of the many errors of the Aristotelians. As an example of one of those mistakes that plays an important part in our story, he contradicts Aristotle, saying: "I have seen that the Rainbow does not appear only as a half Circle, but also as a full Circle when the Sun is high and a person observes it from a very high Mountain."

He extends his criticism of the ancients to also include his beloved Atomists by questioning the renowned Atomist, Epicurus, who argued that the atoms were the smallest parts of nature, indivisible in their makeup:

I do not see how his Followers can ever defend what he says about Atoms, which he sees as indivisible; for however unbelievably small they may be, nonetheless they can certainly be divided by one or more Pyramid formed and sharp Atoms even smaller than them . . . since an Atom that attempts to crack and divide another one certainly can penetrate it after repetitious strikes.

Aside from this one technical disagreement with Atomist philosophy, however, DiCapua accepts most of their teachings. He was able to incorporate Atomism with his Catholic faith by insisting that creation was inspired by an Eternal Maker and could hardly have been left to chance.

As noted earlier, Lionardo's critique of the uncertainty of medicine also extends to modern theories as well. What is there about humans that can possibly elucidate our complicated nature? He answers his own question with an explanation of the "anima," or the soul. The soul, he says, is our most noble part, united to the body and dependent on the senses. The anima regulates all human functions, and the physician must understand the *"passion d'anima,"* which often causes disease, since maladies can be healed through the passions. As examples, he notes the effectiveness of placebo medications and the healing power of music. Hence, to heal the whole person, the physician must engage the soul. To separate the cure of the body from the soul is a foolish—and sometimes harmful—abstention.

Lionardo concludes his original *Parere* by emphasizing the importance of practical, clinical experience and observation. He exhorts those who wish to become physicians: "Students of Medicine who study Philosophy, Chemistry, and Medications also must spend an amount of Time studying and working on illnesses in the Hospital."

One of the most striking aspects of this book is DiCapua's great, natural aptitude for fair and balanced appraisal. Long before he wrote his *Parere*, he had resigned all attempts at offering a dogmatic approach to the study of medicine. His eight Ragionamenti reinforced that method. The only certainty that he posits is that medicine is an uncertain art. But, having endeavored by constant personal effort to improve his own station and seek the truth in all matters, Lionardo did not despair at the uncertainty. Instead, he accepted it as backdrop to the state of the art. The best hope for improving the art was to teach young physicians practices that adopted uncertainty and a healthy skepticism as guiding principles.

* * *

Within the *Parere*, DiCapua elaborates an historical framework, which is continuously shifting between progress, interruption, regression, and recovery. The progress of medicine has been variable since any worthwhile improvements eventually fall prey to intellectual prejudices. Centuries might pass before the resulting stagnation once again cycles upward to a new advance. This conceptual spiral of history was expanded upon by Giambattista Vico in his book, entitled *Principles of New Science*. He had been a protégé of DiCapua, part of the group of young literati that gathered around the venerable scholar in his final years. Vico admired Lionardo and was greatly influenced by him.

Vico asserted that societies can be divided into three repetitive stages, the first being the primitive Age of the Gods, when superstitious men were controlled by the religions of priest-kings. The second was the Age of Heroes. This was the time of strong temporal rulers upon whom society relied for protection. The third stage was the Age of Peoples, an advanced state when human reason created enlightened laws that defined rights and privileges. This last phase of the cycle produced too much luxury that always led to decadence. Society would then regress, although never back to its earlier state. Vico used the terms *corsi* and *recorsi* to explain the phenomenon of this continual spiral, alluded to by DiCapua in his *Parere*.

The immediate reaction to the presentation of the *Parere* to the viceroy centered on the more practical medical controversies, which had prompted the viceroy to seek the advice of the opposing sides. But the eventual publication of Lionardo's book became a significant event in the cultural and academic life of the Kingdom of Naples and would soon be recognized throughout the rest of Europe. In Naples, not surprisingly, this contest of ideas among the literati, physicians, political and ecclesiastical authorities split along established lines. The progressives leaned on DiCapua to publish what they considered a most enlightened and beautifully crafted work. On the other side, the Discordants and the ecclesiastical authorities found innumerable opportunities to decry Lionardo's thoughts and suggestions. Indeed, during the last decade of the century—both before and after Lionardo's final days—the *Parere* became a prominent exhibit in the theological accusations of atheism elaborated against Lionardo and other *Investiganti* by the vocal Jesuit DeBenedictis.

In La Vita, Amenta offers a lyrical assessment of Lionardo's critics, who deserve the same kind of response that would be given to a person who,

> walking through a magnificent royal palace, would not stop to admire the expansive and bright entrance, the spacious and comfortable stairway, the well-ordered and comfortable rooms, the beautiful and airy balconies, the rare and noble paintings, the superb and admirable tapestries, the rich and fluffy feather beds, the many and very precious furnishings: but would instead concentrate on the toilets saying: "Oh, what a terrible smell I find here."

The ideas promoted by DiCapua in his *Parere* advanced the reputation of Neapolitan scholars throughout the 1680s. And for Lionardo, this period would provide the fulfillment of his life's work.

Chapter 7

Fulfillment and Acclaim

Naples—1680s

The Viceroy de los Velez was impressed with the insightful arguments presented by DiCapua, and he accepted the most important of Lionardo's suggestions. No further licensing requirements were placed on physicians. The teaching of *notomia vitale* was permitted in the medical school and chemical cures were allowed without the added burden of restricted regulations. Furthermore, the viceroy permitted the propagation of a garden of simples within the courtyard of the *Ospedale Incurabili*. An herbalist would teach the use of the various herbs and work with his students to determine the origin of their effectiveness.[1]

Lionardo and his supporters were pleased by this outcome, while his detractors were greatly disappointed. At the conclusion of the viceroyalty of de los Velez, the traditionalist faction hoped for a reversal of their fortunes with the expected arrival of his replacement, Marchese del Carpio in 1683. However, after taking control of the kingdom, the marchese continued down the reformist path of his predecessor.

Within Naples, despite the efforts of the ecclesiastical authorities, there was minimal control over the publication and importation of books, including those of heretics and libertines of all stripes. Sensing the tenor of the times, the civil authorities resisted the latest demands for a crackdown, allowing editors and booksellers to publish and sell works considered immoral and dangerous by the Index. The religious authorities were notoriously inefficient at reviewing questionable titles, and the lack of cooperation by the civil authorities further hampered their incapacity. The natural outcome of the confusion was the formation of great collections of books and manuscripts that could be used in support of the expanding intellectual climate. In particular, the library developed by the progressive Giuseppe Valletta consisted of more than ten thousand titles written in several languages on subjects including philosophy, theology, the classics, politics, history, legal studies, and poetry. Valletta also subscribed to all the major journals from across Europe, as well as the *Italian Giornale de'Letterati*, which carried reviews of Neapolitan books.

Valletta opened his library to his old compatriots, like Cornelio, DiCapua, and D'Andrea, and to the younger group of scholars who grew up learning from them. In addition, Valletta, like Michelangelo Ricci in Rome, became a hub for the network of literati with whom he transmitted and received manuscripts and books. In 1681, Valletta gave a copy of DiCapua's *Parere* to Antonio Magliabecchi who was the head librarian for the grand duke of Tuscany. This introduction began a fertile relationship for both librarians whose aim was to enrich their collections with a wide variety of works. Other Neapolitans, including DiCapua, D'Andrea, and Lionardo's first publisher Antonio Bulifon also communicated with Magliabecchi, thus further extending this evolving web of personal contacts that reaffirmed the new thinking.

Giuseppe Valletta became the most important connecting point among the Neapolitans of the time, uniting Naples with the Republic of Letters across the continent. He was a constant source of inspiration for his fellow scholars who, even in the best of times, needed to keep one eye over their shoulder for fear of reprisal. And for this, he truly deserves the praise and gratitude from those who benefited from his efforts.

Foreign travelers and scholars soon became commonplace in Naples during the decade of the 1680s, with Valletta receiving them in his library. Among the visitors were two of the leading lights in philosophy from the continent: the Catholic Jean Mabillion of France and the Scottish Protestant Gilbert Burnet. Burnet praised the intellectual climate in Naples: "There are societies of men at Naples of freer thought than can be found in any other place in Italy. The Greek learning begins to flourish there, and the new philosophy is much studied." (That praise would later be used by the religious authorities as proof of the innovators' sinister connections, coming as it did from a Protestant.)

And so, in a relatively short period of time, the cultural renewal that began with the publication of the *Parere* and was reinforced by the tireless efforts of Valletta eclipsed the provincialism that had been a hallmark of the kingdom. Andrea Concublet was gone and the mercurial Giovanni Alfonso Borrelli had also passed away in 1679. Yet the sense of belonging to an international community of learned men had built upon their legacy and became the harbinger of a Neapolitan enlightenment.

One of the younger members of the original *Investiganti*, Lucantonio Porzio had taken his anatomic skills to Rome after the academy had been disbanded. There, he connected with the Roman academic circles and opened the channels between the two Italian cities, which helped advance the scholarly efforts in both.

Porzio was a native of Naples, born in 1639, a few years before Galileo's death. Although he never knew the great Galileo, Porzio (at least according to Vico) was the last philosopher of the Galilean School. Around 1670, he became professor of anatomy at the *Accademia del Sapienza* in Rome. There, he befriended Michelangelo Ricci, the mathematician who was the Roman connecting point for the Galilean *Accademia del Cimento* of Florence.

Through his ties with the Catholic hierarchy, Ricci often intervened to prevent the Church authorities from censoring the newly evolving scientific theories. He somehow managed to maintain his precarious position, never to fall from the good graces of the Church. As proof, in 1681, Ricci was nominated Cardinal, a Prince of the Catholic Church. Ricci also befriended the controversial Queen Christina of Sweden who had abdicated her throne and established residence in Rome. The Queen had also invited Lucantonio Porzio to join her intellectual circle.

About the same time that Lionardo began working on his *Parere*, Porzio began writing his book – *"Erisistratus sive de sanguinus missione" (Concerning the Releasing of the Blood)*. The book scorned the use of bloodletting at a time when it remained as well accepted in Rome as it was in Naples for, in both cities, Galenist physicians were still in the majority. Not long after Porzio's *Erisistratus* was published in 1682, his Eminence, Cardinal Ricci died following multiple treatments of bloodletting by his Galenist physicians. The nature of his illness remains obscure, as does the reason why he would not have consulted with his friend Porzio who undoubtedly would have treated the Cardinal in a more reasonable manner.

Suffice it to say that the death by the *salasso* of such a famous personage as Ricci exposed the controversy over bloodletting at a time when Galenist medicine was being challenged on multiple fronts. DiCapua and Porzio had just published their books, placing them in the vanguard of the debate over the *salasso* and other Galenist theories in southern Italy. Of course, for many years before the publication of his *Parere*, Lionardo had been a harsh critic of bloodletting. Porzio was aware of Lionardo's criticism and expanded upon the subject in his *Erisistratus.*

Porzio's admiration for DiCapua probably brought Lionardo's *Parere* to the attention of the erudite Queen Christina. After reading it, Christina requested an audience with the author. Here was the opportunity of a lifetime for a scholar to meet the great lady of arts and sciences, an honor that very few were granted. It would represent the pinnacle of recognition and, along with the acclaim, came the protection of her patronage. Yet, the venerable Lionardo remained a reluctant traveler who, by habit, shunned the fame of his efforts. Porzio was long aware of his friend's tendencies.

About this time, Lionardo's oldest child, Cesáre, had returned from his voyage on the continent. He had always been a quick study, and the experience gained through his travels had generated within him the desire to advance the progressive ideas that he had imbibed since his youth. Although he resembled his father in stature and somewhat in appearance, he did not harbor Lionardo's disinclination to travel. Thus, he proposed accompanying his father to meet with the queen in Rome, and Porzio, who had returned to Naples for a visit, offered to deliver father and son to Christina's palazzo. But Lionardo could not be convinced. Instead, he suggested that his son represent him before Christina and, upon returning, deliver a report of his audience to a gathering of interested Neapolitans in Valletta's library.

The elder DiCapua asked Porzio if he would meet with him and his son for them to learn all that they could from the man who knew her quite well, for Porzio was a charter member of the *Accademia dell Esperienza,* founded by the Queen in 1677. Porzio agreed to meet them for dinner at a restaurant on a side street near the *Incurabili,* famous among the students and professors for its traditional Neapolitan seafood. Afterwards, the three men spent the evening conversing over a bottle of wine in the crowded dining room.

Like many other Neapolitans, Lucantonio Porzio's hands seemed possessed of their own vital element, capable of making the point without necessarily using words. He began the discussion by presenting a short history of Christina who was the daughter of the "Lion of the North," Gustavus Adolphus— the same warrior-king Gustavus who had been killed fighting the Catholic forces, led by Wallenstein, at Leipzig during the Thirty Years' War. The complicated politics of the war aside, he noted that that battle was the decisive turning point in a war that ultimately saved Protestantism. "One can imagine Gustavus rolling over in his grave," Porzio mused. "His heir abdicated the throne he had given his life to protect; thence did she abandon his beloved Sweden for a life as a Catholic in Rome—God forbid, the lair of the Papist beast!"

"After Gustavus had been killed," he continued, drumming his index fingers into the table, "his body was returned to Sweden where his funeral lasted, we are told, for nearly two years. Not surprisingly, the young Christina developed an aversion to the somber, Lutheran ceremonies and their unending hell-fire sermons. Unfortunately, her mother, Maria Eleanor was a melancholic woman who provided little solace. She cried incessantly and could scarcely let her daughter, her only child, out of her sight, even at night when she made the child sleep with her in a bed, which, according to the story I have heard, lay beneath a hovering gold box that held Gustavus's heart."

Regarding Christina's upbringing, Porzio explained that Gustavus was aware of his wife's shortcomings; thus, before proceeding to the battlefield, he left explicit instructions for his daughter to receive the rigorous formal education of a boy prince, which suited the young Christina. She possessed a great natural aptitude for her studies and, likewise, enjoyed her out-door training in which she learned to exercise, ride, hunt, and shoot. She was comfortable with taking long horse rides dressed in the rough clothes of a hunter, which, along with her riding style and dark masculine features, allowed her to pass for a man, creating fodder for endless gossip about Christina's excessive virile qualities.

"Christina blossomed under the strict training prescribed by her father," Porzio continued. "You may judge for yourself, but in my opinion, she is a most enlightened regent. And if you think I am exaggerating, my friends, consider her qualities." He raised his right hand and used his fingers to enumerate the points. "She speaks eight languages fluently," he began. "While still in the wilds of her isolated Sweden, she sponsored and participated in grandly produced ballets at her court. Third, she remains a shrewd strategist in dealing with political intrigues. Fourth, since her relocation, she has made it a habit of gathering artists around her salon in the Palazzo Riario." His little finger concluded the points with his open hand facing his small audience. "And she surrounds herself with literate people." He turned to Lionardo and added, "That is why you have been summoned."

Lionardo thanked him with a courteous nod. "I have heard others confirm her brilliance," he said, "and her ability to match wits with the most cunning of princes."

"But why did she abdicate?" Cesare asked. "Do you think she had a true conversion to the Roman Church?"

It was a question that remained open to interpretation, just like other parts of the enigmatic Queen's past. Lucantonio's initial response was non-verbal, yet succinct. He tilted his head, wrinkled his brow, and smiled, while simultaneously raising his shoulders and extending his hands, palms upward, in a gesture which demonstrated his own vacillation over the question. "Here is my thinking on the matter," Porzio said. "Recall what I told you about Christina's experiences as a child after the death of her father. She did not take to the somber ceremonies. Furthermore, her religious education was carefully controlled in the strictest Lutheran tradition, although an amiable and tolerant bishop directed her scholastic training. His ideas, I believe, may have turned her thoughts to more comforting possibilities. And as her more open thinking evolved, a great conflict developed with the religious authorities, something that those of us from Naples have ourselves experienced." Porzio paused, and the three men nodded with expressions that demonstrated a common understanding.

"The dire Protestants forced her kind maestro, Bishop Mathiae, to make a public apology for a book he had written calling for a unification of all the Protestant sects. Soon thereafter, Christina's good friend and confidant Chanut, the French ambassador, was told by the Swedish Diet that he could not have the Catholic mass performed in his home. Both declarations were very upsetting to her Majesty, for they clearly demonstrated that the intellectual air of her kingdom was as stifling as the icy climate.

"Whether she had made her plans by then is uncertain; however, she must have understood that if she abdicated her throne, she would jeopardize her chances for continued financial support from the Swedish Diet," Porzio explained. "And since money would be needed to maintain her accustomed lifestyle, she had to make appropriate arrangements, as she had no intention of living otherwise."

Lionardo quietly asked, "My dear Lucantonio, are you suggesting that somehow Her Majesty's conversion was calculated to provide a permanent sinecure?"

"What I am saying, or perhaps what I *should* say, is this." Porzio paused to look around the restaurant, thence lowered his voice to a whisper to further emphasize his point. "What others close to her have told me is that Christina may be a brilliant scholar, yet her head is not floating in the ether. She is of a pragmatic persuasion. She knew that her conversion would become an even more compelling reason for the Swedes to abandon her. Yet, she was also aware that it would increase her prestige in the Catholic world, especially in Spain. Such prestige could lead to permanent financial assistance, which is what she needed to secure."

"So, the conversion was merely a sham?" Cesare whispered. "Is that what you are telling us?"

Lucantonio hesitated, broke eye contact with Cesare, sat upright, and stared momentarily beyond Lionardo into the noisy hall. Thence, he leaned close and looked into Cesare's eyes. His hands came to a prayer position and bounced whenever he needed added emphasis. "To a certain extent, yes; it probably was. Although, in truth, I cannot say with any degree of accuracy the importance such an event deserves."

Lionardo was wise enough to realize that the true motives of a person (especially one of royal personage) were often obscured by rumor and conjecture. He took a short sip of wine, replaced his glass on the table, stood upright, and began a gentle pacing. "Allow me to stretch my hips." He cleared his throat and rubbed his right elbow as he walked, adding, as an aside, "It is no fun getting old. And since I am the only one among us with gray hair and a vengeful attack of gout, pardon my peculiarities. I hope that God spares the both of you this misery."

He returned to his seat and continued. "Anyway, in summary, your sources suggest that Christina was unhappy as Queen of Sweden. That she never planned on having an heir." He leaned inward and lowered his voice. "That she decided to abdicate her throne. That she decided to convert to the Roman Church to secure a stable source of income after her abdication." He leaned back in his chair. "Is that correct?"

"Yes, perfectly," answered Porzio.

"Have your sources offered any proof for their theories?"

Porzio possessed the dark features of a Neapolitan and came

to about the same medium stature as his two friends. He leaned back in his chair and clasped his large hands (made rough by years of anatomical dissection) and then lifted them behind his head to help extend his back. After a few audible cracks, he broke the position and took a long drink of wine before leaning close to his friends again, their heads forming a symmetrical circle of varying colors. "I cannot recall the name of the French writer who visited Her Majesty at the *Palazzo Farnese*. By the way, the pope had provided the *palazzo* for her once she arrived in Rome with great pomp in late 1655. Anyway, this Frenchman complimented Christina on her conversion, and thence did she candidly announce her feelings to him, saying something like, 'My religion is the religion of the philosophers, which I prefer to all others.' And she went on. 'This religion is indeterminate, has uncertain limits, yet was it well defined by Lucretius in his *De Rerum Natura*. And it is the only one of which I approve.' I wonder what our Holy Father would say if he heard that statement?"

"And since taking residence in Rome?" Cesare asked.

Porzio took another sip from his glass, returned it to the table and made a rosette of the fingers of his right hand, which he then bounced continuously in front of his chest. "Yes, and since that time, Christina has become an increasing problem for each of the four popes who have occupied Peter's throne since her arrival in Rome. From her early days in Sweden, she has despised the false piety of religion and her independent nature will not be tamed, regardless of her situation. The rumor mill abounds with stories of her female lover, her masculine style, her nonchalant manners, and her love affair with Cardinal Azzolino."

"I have heard the rumors of Azzolino," Lionardo said. "But there is also a female lover?"

Porzio shook his head and torso from side to side in a gesture of uncertainty. "The female was supposedly a lady at court years earlier in Sweden. Since arriving in Rome, Cardinal Azzolino has become her closest friend and confidant. He has prudently managed her financial affairs, and it is commonly held that he is the male love of her life. He has risked much to help her."

"She has an Italian to manage her finances and share her bed." Cesare smiled. "That tells me that she is a wise woman who makes good choices." Lionardo glanced at his son with an expression that hinted at displeasure.

Lucantonio sat up straight. "Cesare, as your father knows, Her Majesty provided the finances to publish Borelli's *De Motu animalum* after his death. Likewise, her *Accademia Reale* has attracted great artists, musicians, scholars, and thinkers from many disciplines. Her ability to discover genius is exceptional. Her *palazzo* is filled with classical sculptures, tapestries, and famous paintings, and the concerts she presents are famous throughout the city." He turned to Lionardo. "Time spent with her is very rewarding. You really should go to Rome to meet her, my dear friend."

Lionardo nodded and remained silent.

Porzio looked at Cesare who sighed, thence rapped his knuckles against his head, tilted towards his father. *"Testa dura"* he said, with a smile.

Lionardo raised his glass in a salute. "To the hard heads of this world."

"Salut!" they chimed, touching glasses.

"My friend," Lucantonio persisted, "you should consider yourself lucky that she decided to move to Rome. Otherwise, you might have been summoned to Upsala Castle to meet her."

"And then it would have been an easy decision for me to stay away."

Lucantonio assumed a more serious demeanor. He stared at his hands now folded together on the table. "In some respects, I must tell you that Christina remains a contradiction to me.

Consider this. Her support of legitimate scientists does not preclude her from a passionate belief in alchemy. She keeps a court alchemist as part of her household, and, I have been told that she has found a fellow believer in Azzolino."

Lionardo smiled. "We may be evolving from magic to science, but superstition will never die."

Porzio and the younger DiCapua again prodded Lionardo to make the trip to Rome with them. But he remained steadfast in his refusal. Lionardo instead insisted that Cesare go alone and relay to the queen his father's sincerest apologies, for he was not feeling well enough to make the journey. "Tell her, also, that I admire her greatly and that I remain at her service. And say that perhaps someday I will have the honor of meeting her in person."

* * *

A few weeks later, Cesare traveled to Rome. At the time of his meeting with Christina, she was nearing her sixtieth year. She had come to a relatively happy and secure position in the Eternal City. The sedentary life she now led had added to her physical presence. Never a beautiful woman, she was admired by many artists for her patronage and was repaid by some with portraits that covered her deficiencies—as best they could. She was relaxed and informal during their conversation, as if she had known the young DiCapua all his life.

Cesare DiCapua was an able representative for his father. He was just above twenty-five years, well read and well spoken. Having seen much during his recent travels, Cesare was not awed by the richness of the queen's surroundings, yet did he show the proper admiration for her cultured taste evident in the art and sculptures she had collected. After a tour of her palace, they spent a pleasant morning discussing a variety of subjects before settling on the matter at hand: Lionardo's *Parere*.

Cesare was proud of his father's recent accomplishment. He realized its importance, not only for what it proclaimed, but also for the good that it had done for his father in the writing. With proper decorum, he explained to Christina his belief that his father's *Lezioni delle Mofete (The Lessons of the Hot Springs),* which was essentially ignored outside of Naples, was also beautifully written. He told her that his father had recently begun an update.

She was interested in the subject, she assured him, having experienced the pleasure of hot springs on many a ride in her younger days in Sweden. And for a moment, as Cesare would later recount, the dowdy queen lost herself in a reverie from those carefree days of her youth.

Christina was most impressed with the *Parere* and looked forward with anticipation to reading Lionardo's earlier work. She held a particular appreciation for his purity of style, and she praised him for presenting his thoughts in a logical manner without all the gaudy pretentiousness so typical of the Baroque. The queen noted that at the end of the Eighth *Ragionamento,* Lionardo had promised to write his opinion on the use and the effects of chemical medicines in treating disease. The subject greatly needed to be enlightened, she announced to the son. Hence did she hope that his father would soon take up the effort. Cesare assured her that Lionardo would be most honored to pursue her suggestion.

Upon his return to Naples, the young DiCapua passed on the details of his audience and Christina's expectations to Lionardo. They then met with a gathering of young and old Researchers in Valletta's library, as Lionardo had requested. It was a lively meeting that generated a great deal of excitement among everyone who attended. During the presentation, Lionardo remained in the background (as usual for him) allowing his son to hold center stage.

NOTES

1. DiCapua's garden of simples remains at the *Incurabili*,
    crowned today by the branches of a great camphor tree.

Chapter 8

A Circle of Colors: the Controversy

Lionardo DiCapua agreed to the Queen's request, promising to add to the *Parere* by writing his opinion on chemical medicines, which would be released at an unspecified time. In the meantime, he completed the updated version of the *Lezioni delle Mofete* in the year of our Lord 1683, twenty years after its original publication.

The *Mofete* contained an opening dedication to Queen Christina written by Cesare DiCapua, who sent the Queen a copy as he had promised. Typical of the writings from those days, Cesare effusively praised the Queen for having invited the great minds of her time—Descartes, Borelli, Gassendi, Porzio and others—to participate at her court. He presented the book for her to read and explained that his father was already working on completing the *Parere*.

The newly published *Mofete* was written in Lionardo's neo-Petrarchan Tuscan style that had come to be known in the Naples area as "Capuaism." The book contained three lessons, which delved into the origin, chemical composition, causes, historical references, and location of the hot springs. In addition, he offered his opinions regarding the physiologic effects on the cardio-respiratory system and the therapeutic potential of the hot waters. The descriptions of the sites—many of which were around his native Bagnoli Irpino—were precise in their presentation, yet poetically written so that one could imagine the natural beauty of the area without the over-exaggerated, baroque word play that would have been an unnecessary distraction.

Amenta, being more inclined to poetry, felt that this was Lionardo's finest and most lyrical effort: "And in spite of the Fact that the *Parere* is now considered his great book, nonetheless, it seems to me that in the *Mofete* Lionardo surpassed himself—not only in regard to the originality, the presentation and to the eloquence and beauty of the language, but also in regard to the erudition and to the Philosophizing."

The noted biologist and close friend of Francesco D'Andrea, Francesco Redi also praised the work in a letter to DiCapua just before Christmas of 1683. He described Lionardo in the effusive language of the time as most educated and most gallant. He continued: "I am never more contented than when I read your incomparable Book because I found that the Lessons brighten the world and free it from the ties in which it has been strangled for so long by the cheating or ignorant or mean-spirited beliefs of so many authors."

The acclaim that came to the venerable scholar increased his desire to discover and write more of the truths concerning natural philosophy. To help him accomplish that goal, he sought the insights of Tommaso Cornelio, his oldest and dearest friend. The success generated by the *Parere* and the *Mofete* increased DiCapua's status and afforded him some protection from the harassment of his detractors.

Cornelio, on the other hand, was the one known to have brought the new thinking to Naples through the many books he had gathered on his northern travels. Consequently, he became the scapegoat for the authorities whenever they wished to attack the innovators. They considered him the maestro in disguise. It was he, they asserted, who directed this new movement, which was attempting to replace Aristotelian philosophy with the teachings of the atheistic atomists.

Tommaso typically offered little response to the familiar charges. Instead, he took quiet pleasure in the re-publication of his masterwork *Progymnasmata physica* in the cities of Leipzig, Jena, and Venice in 1683—the same year that Lionardo had re-published the *Mofete*. Cornelio maintained his self-imposed isolation outside of Naples, in his modest home with his dog Bellona, a small mutt, skittish of humans that had been wandering about the streets near his house for months. Being the gentle soul that he was, Tommaso attempted to entice her into a trap with scraps of meat. Bellona was wise to his tricks, yet so famished that one day, as he told the story, she allowed herself to be caught. It was the beginning of a new adventure for both her and her master. Tomasso secured Bellona's confidence by fattening her with table scraps and caring for an inflammation in the skin of her hindquarter. Thence he began taking her on daily walks through the streets that had been her home. Once secure with her loving master, she showed no inclination to escape, providing good company for him. He talked to her—even sang to her. And she returned the attention by keeping the local population of rodents in constant fear of extinction. Named after the Roman goddess of war, the sister to Mars, Bellona became very protective of Tommaso. Anyone who happened to come near the house was warned with vengeful barks. Tommaso's friends exchanged tales of harassment by the surly dog, and they learned to approach the house carefully.

Tommaso sent a copy of the newly edited version of the *Progymnasmata physica* to DiCapua to proofread prior to printing. After reading it, Lionardo decided to return his copy directly to Cornelio. Lionardo sent word in advance to his friend so that he might contain his infamous dog. When he arrived at Cornelio's home, he was greeted with loud barks from the other side of the entry. He waited outside while Tommaso struggled to seal Bellona in another room. Eventually, Cornelio opened his door, welcoming his guest with a warm embrace. DiCapua thanked him and joked that, even though he had not directly experienced Bellona's bite, it was said to be worse than the *"morso dei sicofanti"* from which Tommaso had escaped by isolating himself in the country.

Lionardo had not seen his friend for several months and the decline in Tommaso's health during that interval was painfully evident. But they avoided discussing the obvious and spent the day in familiar conversation over their recent literary efforts and the temper of the times. The viceroy's acceptance of Lionardo's suggestions had been a fortuitous occasion. Yet they also realized the fragility of their gains since, despite the positive effect that DiCapua's *Parere* had on the viceroy, it likewise generated a renewal of the animosity between the Innovators and the Discordants. Domenico D'Aulisio, Lionardo's nephew, had recently become quite lathered over a section in the *Parere* that dealt with the illusion of a circular rainbow. Lionardo had written in his Eighth *Ragionamento* that, contrary to Aristotle's teachings, under the right conditions, it was possible to see the *arco baleno* as a complete circle:

Now why would we believe that the rainbow cannot appear larger than a half-circle when contrary to the belief of Aristotle, Pico della Mirandola, Campanella, Gassendi, Blancano, and many others observed that it was bigger than a half-circle? I have observed that it appears not only bigger than a half-circle, but also sometimes as a complete circle when the sun is high and one looks at the rainbow from a very high mountain.

After hearing Lionardo's assertion about the shape of the rainbow, his young proteges communicated the idea to their friends and, in this way, it passed among the literati in the kingdom, including D'Aulisio. He had been critical of the *Investiganti* for some time, particularly his uncle Lionardo.[1]

Whatever the cause of his aggressive personality, Domenico used it to good effect. I have no hesitation in saying that he was well suited for his position as an instructor in legal studies. He loved to hear himself speak and was not fond of listening to others. Added to his assertive style were his skills in the art of debate and his abilities as a capable public speaker with a command of minutiae. Hence, he could be a formidable foe.[2]

After hearing of Lionardo's hypothesis concerning the rainbow, and without attempting their own experiment to disprove the theory, D'Aulisio and his followers began to call those who believed DiCapua's suggestion "madmen." Lionardo's circle argued forcefully in favor of their teacher and both sides began writing satirical papers against their opposite. The barbs spilled over into the public journals and soon became so insulting that the viceroy had to intervene with the threat of incarceration against the authors of the lampoons. Each side came to such a strong persuasion that there was fear among the authorities that weapons might again be brandished.

Neapolitans have always been too willing to cast insults and dishonest satire with the unspoken desire that they might lead to a more physical exchange. Amenta laments this bad habit, suggesting instead that criticism should be leveled "only by those who have found the hair in the egg and the spots in the sun."

D'Aulisio's most famous insult was the publication of his epigram in Latin:

Capua facundo perfusus pectora vino
  Montis conscendit culmina summa celer
Tempuserat medio quo Sol disceditab axe,
  Pendebat dubiis horridus imber aquis.
Iris mille trahens adverso sole colores,

Orbem completum pingere non poterat.
Invida terra vetat, qui partem occultat Horizon,
    Dipintique areus cornua summa rapit.
Capua sed lippus de celso vertice montis
    Clamat: Io cyclum discolor iris Habet.
Credite, nam video,clamat. Nos risimus omnes
    Mordaci quidem sic sole perficuit.
Mira refers, in cyclum si tibi vertitur orbis
    Non sic res geminas ebria turba videt.

Translated into English, it reads:

Capua, his breast suffused with eloquent wine,
    Climbed the highest peak of the mountain quickly
The time when the sun departs from the middle of the
celestial axis,
    A storm bristling with changeable waters was overhead.
Iris drawing one-thousand colors opposite the sun,
    Was unable to paint a complete circle.
Envious earth forbids, and the Horizon hides a part,
    And Areus seizes the tops of the horns of the painted
image.
But Capua, bleary-eyed, shouts from the lofty peak of
the mountain:
    Lo! Multicolored Iris has a full circle!
Believe me, for I see it, he shouts. Not all of us smiled.
    To be sure, he brought this about because of the pierc-
ing sun.
You report wondrous things if the rainbow in your view
turns in a circle,
    But even a drunken crowd does not in this manner
see things doubled.

DiCapua and his friends responded with their own satirical poem titled in Italian "*La coda del Cacamusone epigramma-tico.*"[3] Unfortunately the text has been lost; although, as the title suggests, one can be assured that it was pithy and full of sarcasm.

Experienced advisors to the viceroy had suggested that he closely monitor the diatribes leveled against each side by its opposite to prevent the kind of physical violence that had occurred during the previous decade. With the publication of D'Aulisio's poem and the response from the Capuaists, the viceroy realized that the issue of whether the *arco baleno* appears as a full circle needed to be resolved. Hence, he called for representatives from each side in the debate to take an excursion up a mountain during the spring when the weather would be conducive to the appearance of a rainbow.

Local guides would be employed to help ease the difficulties of the voyage. The details of choosing the site and the guides would be left to the participants to negotiate. For his part, the viceroy would appoint a reliable amanuensis, who would record the findings and present them to a gathering of both groups to deal with other contentious issues over the use of chemical medicines.

Lionardo told Tommaso that he had agreed to make the journey up the mountain. Some of his younger protégés had offered to accompany him. No definite date had been set, but the excursion must occur within the next few weeks since the spring weather would be fortuitous, and the follow-up meeting had been scheduled for early May 1683.

"Do you think that they will admit the truth when they see the circle?" Tommaso asked, as they sat in front of his warm kitchen fireplace.

Cornelio twisted the corners of his lips downward while shaking his head.

Tommaso gave the answer to his own question. "This will

be like the time—when was it? Above forty years ago? You know, when Pascal sent his brother-in law up the *Puy de Dome* to prove his and Torricelli's thesis about the barometer. The bastards still would not accept what was obvious.

"Traditionalists everywhere will never give in," he continued. "They will never despair, for despair comes only to honest men whose proposals exceed what is possible to prove. They have been corrupted by their prejudices and, as such, they always believe they are right. They will never admit to failure. Why waste your time and energy?"

Lionardo stood closer to the fire to warm his hands. "Someone must go since the viceroy has called for proof," he replied. "Frankly, I don't care what the diehard fools say. I am going because I want to see it for myself. Based on what I have already observed, I have no doubt that it will happen if the conditions are correct. It is just that I have never actually *seen* a complete circular rainbow. Many years ago, while in the hills near Vesuvius, I saw a near-circular rainbow with an unseen section that dipped below the horizon. I have seen a double rainbow, and I have seen the circle that sometimes forms around the sun on a foggy day. But I have never seen a complete circular rainbow on the horizon. Have you?"

"No. I haven't."

Lionardo continued, "The viceroy insisted that there must be an equal number of representatives, with at least two from each side—preferably more. D'Aulisio was not anxious to make the climb, but he was shamed into going. However, no one else has offered to go with him. So, I suspect that only two in each group will make the journey."

"Is it possible for an old man to join you? I would like to see it as well."

Lionardo returned to his seat, uncertain of how to answer. He welcomed the opportunity to share the victory with his good friend, yet he knew that Tommaso was ill. "Nothing would make me happier," Lionardo said. "You know that. But let us face the reality that you are not in possession of the strength you once had. I'm not sure I can make the trip myself. If I were not required to go, believe me, I would not. I promise to give you a full accounting."

"My friend," Tommaso said, "you and I have a long history of facing difficulties together, have we not? So let us face the reality that our days are numbered. You most likely will pass after me, but we both know that there will not be another opportunity such as this."

Tommaso stared into the fire. "Time has gotten tangled for me as of late. I mean, sometimes the past seems so distant that all I can recall are tableaus. No sound. No words. Just hazy, blurred visions. And at other times, in the middle of a thought, I will clearly recall an event or a person from when we were schoolboys in Naples, and it seems as if it just happened or that the person was just then talking to me."

He paused to look at Lionardo, then said, "It is then that I feel as though I am once again young and strong and quick of mind." Tommaso reached for Lionardo's shoulder. "My dear friend, we have shared some wonderful experiences, and we must share this one in memory of our Don Ruggero. He and I would be honored to accompany you if you would have us go along."

Lionardo's voice failed, leaving him merely to nod in acquiescence and add haltingly that he would be the one honored.

Tommaso promised that he would not be a burden but would hold up his end of the bargain. He would wait to hear the date of departure. In the meantime, he would prepare himself for the journey by increasing the time of his daily walks and searching for someone with enough fortitude to feed and walk Bellona during his absence.

NOTES

1. I mentioned earlier that I knew D'Aulisio. He was my junior by some eight years; a very bright man, well educated, capable of speaking several languages and a professor of civil law at the University of Naples. During his younger days at the University, he had spent his time studying ancient religious and legal texts. However, he was not a serious student of natural philosophy, and perhaps the jealousy he felt for his uncle stemmed from the fact that Lionardo had abandoned the study of law and gained notoriety in his pursuit of medicine and the sciences.

    Many people admired D'Aulisio, none of whom were friends of mine. The biggest problem I had with him was his enormous and to me unjustified pride. If he chose a side on a particular issue, he refused to admit that it might need modification. He was a contrary man who would often choose to be an antagonist for no apparent reason other than to prove his contrariness and his skill at debate, which admittedly was considerable. He would take a stand sometimes against the traditionalists, sometimes against the moderns, a sign to me of an avaricious and prideful nature.

    Please, do not misunderstand me, for I admire those who can evaluate an issue without the presumption of a predetermined mindset, as the *Investiganti* had fostered. But the problem that I had with him was that he pronounced his opinion, not by the inherent veracity of the argument nor by a progressive development of a coherent philosophy, but according to whoever was the protagonist. Hence, with D'Aulisio, nearly every debate turned personal.

2. Overall, I was left with the impression that he was more interested in creating a melodrama than in experiencing the fullness of life. Indeed, because he was such an insufferable egotist, he became the laughingstock of the innovators and, even as his star rose, the butt of many a joke.

3. It would diminish the effect to remove the scatological references, hence I beg your pardon as I translate it into English as "The Poem of the Witty One with a Great Shitty Face."

Chapter 9

A Circle of Colors: the Odyssey

Campania-1683

On a Monday morning, the twelfth of April in the year of our Lord 1683, the group commissioned by the viceroy began their climb up the foothills above Bagnoli Irpino. Their destination was a ridge on the west-facing, windward side of Mount Cervialto, where generous, spring tempests unleash their seaborne tempests on one of the higher points in the Apennines. The site was chosen as it was a familiar campsite to D'Aulisio and DiCapua, both of whom had hiked the Irpino mountains.

In the company were D'Aulisio, the Neapolitan physician and former head of the Discordants, Luca Tozzi; plus Cornelio and DiCapua of the Researchers; along with the recorder, a Domenican priest named Don Pietro Starigido; and two brothers from Bagnoli who served as porters, guides, cooks, and assistants. The representatives hoped to observe a rainbow within a day or two of their arrival, although five days of provisions were sent in case the weather was uncooperative. If necessary, one of the guides could hike down the mountain to acquire more provisions. In any case, unless there was some need to quit the excursion sooner, the most the company was to remain on the mountain was seven days.

The group had spent the previous night in the village. After a hearty breakfast, they departed in three carriages, taking the road that wound its way uphill above the village. In time, it opened into the expansive plateau that contained Lake Laceno in its southwest corner near the base of the mountain. From there, the carriages continued up a steep, narrow road, which caused the horses to strain under the weight of their loads. They wound their way through a stark forest with an underbrush carpeted by a thick layer of brown leaves, which had been collecting for years beneath a canopy of tall, white-barked birch trees. The road ended nearly halfway up the peak. There, they stepped out of their coaches, loaded their packs, and began the climb. The weather was clear, crisp and sunny without a cloud in the sky.

Other than the guides, the company was not accustomed to the rigors of the climb, keeping the conversation to a minimum. The group remained close together, with Lionardo following Cornelio at the back of the pack. The pace was slow. They stopped every quarter-hour for rest and refreshments. After three hours, a cool breeze aided the final part of their ascent and carried a batch of billowy clouds to the ridge along with the hikers. The younger guides erected the tents and prepared a meal, while the others rested their aching feet and tired backs.

Tomasso was exhausted by the rigorous climb. His head ached and his breathing was labored, even at rest.

The corpulent Don Pietro was likewise drained. It took no longer than the first few minutes of the climb before he had realized his mistake in accepting the viceroy's request. The Father Superior had approached the monk with news of the appointment as if it was an honor for his faithful service. He could hardly have refused, although now he wished he had.

* * *

After dinner, the group remained around the campfire under a canopy of stars. The combination of fatigue, food and the mesmerizing flames kept the conversation to a minimum, and a stilted formality defined the brief interchanges that did occur. Indeed, the animosity that had gathered over the years between the two sides had spilled over into personal dislike. Such an atmosphere was hardly conducive to the kind of friendly discussion that might typically occur on an outing in the wilds. Thus, the entire company retired early, with hopes that a change in the weather might bring a quick resolution to the question at hand.

Although exhausted from the arduous climb, Tommaso had a fitful night. Every time he drifted toward sleep, a frightful feeling of suffocation would awaken him with the need to increase the pace of his breathing. Aware of his friend's difficulties, Lionardo bolstered Tommaso's head with a makeshift pillow, which provided relief of the oppressive sensation and allowed him to doze, if only for a few hours.

In a nearby tent, Don Pietro fell asleep as soon as he put his head down. He kept up a chorus of stertorous snores throughout the night, while D'Aulisio and Tozzi, (who shared his shelter) tried in vain to block the hoarse noise from their ears.

By the next morning, suffice it to say that, with the added stress of insomnia, the mood around the campfire was even more strained than the previous night.

* * *

The campsite was set up in an opening that was surrounded by tall evergreen trees, which shaded the morning sun and kept a bracing chill in the springtime air. The patch of sky directly above was broken with a few wispy clouds that held little promise of rain. Don Pietro announced the improbability of a storm as the group sat around the fire eating a breakfast of toasted bread and warm tea prepared by the guides. Afterwards, the men dispersed into the woods to relieve themselves.

When he finished, Tommaso walked into a nearby clearing dotted with wild cornflowers as blue as the morning sky. He stood for a while on the edge of the meadow observing the quiet beauty, thence took a seat on a fallen log. Don Pietro entered the clearing and sat down next to him. The monk had descending jowls that drew his lips into a thick pucker and exposed the upper front teeth. Wide gaps separated the dry teeth, which funneled exhaled air in bursts of soft whistles.

In Naples, Don Pietro had acquired a reputation not only as a faithful recorder of the reports from the archbishop, but also for his distinctive flourishes when copying manuscripts. Such artistic eruptions required a steady hand and an eye for color—skills that were no longer in great demand since the advent of the printing press. The monk was proud of the fact that his talents were at least recognized by his older brethren who had labored to near blindness in earlier times. They had recently recommended him to head a group charged with choosing an artist to paint a triptych featuring St. Dominic, the founder of the order on one side panel; St. Gennaro, the patron saint of Naples on the other; and the Holy Family in the center. The work would hang above the altar in a chapel donated to the Dominicans by a wealthy banker. The donor had instructed the group to award the assignment to a fellow Neapolitan.

This request had presented a problem for Don Pietro because it seemed to him that there was an unusual dearth of quality painters in Naples at the time. The renowned Luca Giordano was busy appeasing the whims of far greater patrons. He had recently completed a series of frescoes for the Medici in Florence, and it was known throughout the kingdom that the King wished to bring the artist from Naples to his court in Madrid. Two of his most famous contemporaries—the impetuous Salvatore Rosa and "The Little Spaniard," Ribera—had already passed away. Francesco Solimena was gaining a reputation throughout the city, but he was young and untested. Don Pietro related this predicament to the banker, who then agreed to allow the commission to go to an artist from outside Naples if necessary. But the insulated monk had not traveled elsewhere in Italy and most of the painters from the continent were unknown to him. Consequently, Don Pietro took advantage of the few opportunities presented to him to question those who had journeyed throughout Europe.

Although he knew of Tommaso Cornelio's controversial reputation, the monk knew that he was also a cultured man who had traveled north to gather the writings of the leading scientists and philosophers. Don Pietro could care less about science, and, for him, philosophy was impossible to separate from theology. However, he was interested in hearing any suggestions for an artist whose works Tommaso had seen—perhaps a painter unappreciated in southern Italy—who could paint the triptych and, at the same time, enhance the monk's reputation as a connoisseur.

Don Pietro began the conversation, "I see that you are, like me, taken by the beauty that surrounds us."

"I enjoy the way the flowers match the color of the sky, Father."

"Yes, the beauty of nature reflects our Lord's goodness. From the simple flower," he pointed to a tall bud, thence pulled himself to his feet with a sweeping wave toward the sky, "to the grandeur of the firmament. Come," he added, "let us walk."

Tommaso followed the monk on a stroll through the field.

"Signore Cornelio, I was told that many years ago you traveled north. Tell me, while you were traveling, did you have the chance to see any sacred art?"

"Yes, I did. I've always felt a connection between the characteristics of a locality and its art. I think that art reflects the overall spirit of the region. Everywhere I traveled, I tried to meet artists who were friends of my contacts. I saw their works and those of the old masters. I also asked those who had traveled on the continent for their impressions of the art in the countries they had visited."

A few more clouds began to gather from the west as they entered the far end of the meadow that was covered with shoots of wild oregano. Each step unleashed a spray that filled the buoyant air with a pungent scent. The monk, excited by the possibilities, pressed Cornelio. "Signore, please elaborate. Which works did you find most pleasing?" The question took on musical tones as the whistle became most pronounced with the repetition of the 'S' sound.

Tommaso carefully picked his way around an outcropping of fractured rock and found a flat ledge on which he sat to consider his response. Even in this, his penultimate time upon the earth, the paintings remained indelibly clear. "As for the northern countries," he said, "what I discovered was that, although some of the greatest mathematicians, scientists and philosophers lived in England, their art was lacking. But in Flanders and Holland, several renowned artists dwelled; one of them, Rembrandt, I consider a master. I appreciated the landscapes of van Ruisdal and the vistas of Jan van der Hayden that focused on the beauty of the natural world in a manner that appealed to me and my friends. In France, I found the panoramas by Nicolas Poussin of the Italian Campania and the provincial hill towns most appealing."

He paused to take in the landscape of lush Apennine peaks surrounding them. "In Rome," he continued, "with all its great art, I was most impressed with the sculptures of the incomparable Bernini; the canvases of that churlish Milanese, Michelangelo Marisi, known as Caravaggio; and the paintings of Peter Paul Rubens, who had studied in Italy. These were artists with whom I felt an immediate connection."

The clouds continued to gather, shielding the sunshine. The bird chatter disappeared with the sun and that peculiar calm felt before a storm suddenly descended on the mountain. Tommaso rose from his stone seat and walked around the outcropping to face the monk who had found a comfortable spot facing the opposite direction.

He addressed the monk directly: "My favorite works were Bernini's delicate *Apollo and Daphne* and Caravaggio's chiaroscuro masterpiece, *St. Matthew and the Angel.* And, although I never saw it myself, others have told me that Rubens' *Elevation of the Cross* is a work of pure genius."

Don Pietro could not hide his disappointment. He shook his head as he rose to take a few steps into the meadow. "Bernini has recently met his Maker," he said, "and Caravaggio probably saw Him only briefly before being banished to the place where murderers and miscreants are deposited. And as for Rubens, his fame has spread throughout Europe, but, as you probably know, he has also passed on. I was hoping you would give me the name of a living artist."

"Perhaps I might," Tommaso answered. "But, before I do, allow me to ask if you share my admiration for the artists I mentioned?"

"For Bernini, of course I do," Don Pietro responded. "Bernini was a genius whose abundant talent, in my opinion, was derived from his lifelong devotion to Our Lord and His sacraments. As for Rubens, I have never seen any of his works. As you said, he spent time studying in Italy, where he fell under the diabolical influence of Caravaggio, whose works I have seen."

The whistling sounds rose in frequency before he paused to consider what words he might use to emphasize his intense dislike for the Milanese artist. "Caravaggio never learned the delicate art of fresco, and his emphasis on the vulgar is a constant distraction from the inviolable purpose of holy art. When an artist subscribes to the imperfections of human nature, he ultimately leads us to contemplate our own flaws instead of lifting us closer to the divine, which should be the main purpose of all art. Caravaggio reminds us always of our human failings. I am sorry, Signore Cornelio, but ugly peasants with distorted features and ragged clothes do not appeal to me. Caravaggio was a crude man."

Tommaso accepted the priest's critique with the understanding that there was no way to settle an argument over matters of taste. Just the same, he was accustomed to discussing disputes, and he remained anxious to engage an opposite opinion. "As for Gian Lorenzo Bernini," he said, "he truly was a born genius. And he was also a fervent Catholic. Still, it is important to remember that some of his best work occurred at a young age, before he had begun his intense devotion to the sacraments. And as for Caravaggio," he concluded, "I believe that the realism displayed in his art was his attempt to follow the directives of the Council of Trent. He never painted nude bodies. His characters, while at times disfigured or dirty or barefoot, as you mentioned, were never distorted to the point of excess. My guess is that he was responding to the Church's demands that simple people be able to relate to religious art. He may have been a sinner; yet, in his paintings, one cannot help but observe an intense appreciation for the sacredness of the subject."

Tommaso paused, anticipating a response. Instead, he heard silence.

Don Pietro was unaccustomed to the kind of open interchange that enlivened Cornelio and the other Researchers. The monk had taken a vow of obedience and he had scrupulously observed it throughout his time at the monastery. Whatever came down to him from his superiors, he accepted it. He might disagree, yet he never openly voiced an argument. As a man of the cloth and a respected authority within his religious community, he expected the same from a layman, regardless of his age or level of education. Averting his eyes from Cornelio, he stood up and began walking through the meadow toward the camp. Tommaso followed, hoping that the monk might still respond.

The sky was now thick with gray clouds. Out of the west, a cool wind broke the earlier stillness, rustling through the nearby pines in sighs with each gust. The two men walked through the field, the monk in the lead, ignoring the old man. Just before Don Pietro entered the wood surrounding the campsite, Tommaso called to him. "Stop, please, good Father. Allow me at least to offer an example of my theory for your consideration."

The monk paused momentarily with his back to Cornelio, then started walking again.

Tommaso offered another appeal. "Please, Father. You asked for my opinion and what I am offering you is only an opinion. I may not be in possession of the most sophisticated taste, but I know what I like." He continued addressing the monk in a voice rising in volume. "You hold to a different ideal, as do many others. Even if I do not accept it, I respect your opinion. Should you not offer me the same consideration as well?"

Don Pietro stopped just before the wood. He turned to Cornelio and looked into his eyes. "Signore Cornelio, I thought you were a cultured man. I was hoping to gain some insight that would help me choose a painter whose style would reflect the sincere devotion of a generous donor. He is a man of some wealth who wishes to commission a work that would glorify Our Lord, our Blessed Dominic, and the patron of our beloved city." The pitch of his whistle rose. "I did not expect to receive a diatribe about the merits or the sources of inspiration of a handful of dead artists."

The monk paused, braced his posture, folded his hands across his ample belly and continued. "And consider this: If you think you can convince me of your ideas, Signore, you are mistaken."

"Good Father." Cornelio smiled. "Convincing you was never

my intention. I wish to present another viewpoint for the sake of discussion. So please, allow me to offer an example of Caravaggio's work that I believe encapsulates our varying positions."

"Signore Cornelio, a storm approaches. I will listen, but please be brief."

Tommaso walked to the same fallen log he had found when first entering the field. He sat down close to where Don Pietro stood, leaned forward with elbows on knees and dropped his forehead into both hands, as if to concentrate his thoughts. He was accustomed to open debate; rigorous mental exercise that kept his mind agile, despite his failing health. He hated the arrogance of the monk, whose privilege came merely from his cloth habit.

After years of arguing with the traditionalists, Tomasso knew where this discussion was headed. At one time he might have shown his anger, but now he remained calm and proceeded with his position. He looked up at the monk. An occasional drop of rain struck his face. "Good Father, as you and the weather require me, I will be brief. Please allow me to take a moment to apologize for failing to help you in your search. Our great city has always produced excellent painters, and undoubtedly you will locate a Neapolitan who will meet your needs. Domenico Gargiulo. Andrea Malinconico. I believe they merit your consideration. Also, Francesco Altobello. I do not think it necessary to look elsewhere."

As he spoke, the pace of the raindrops increased. He cleared them from his face with a kerchief and then continued. "Have you been to the *Santa Casa* in Loreto?"

The monk looked away and nodded yes.

"Then I am sure that you have seen Caravaggio's *Madonna di Loreto*. The pilgrims in that painting have bare feet covered in dirt. Their fingers are gnarled. Their clothes, soiled. One of them wears a torn hat. I can appreciate how, to some observers, these defects can be a distraction. To me, they are the perfect counterpoint to the gracefulness of Our Lady as she stands above them, holding the baby Jesus in the doorway, welcoming those poor, fallen souls into Her house. No matter how wise or how holy we think we have become, we are, in truth, like those peasants—imperfect in our soul if not in our body. We can approach the *Santa Casa*, but it is only through the intercession of Our Lady that we can hope to enter."

Tommaso paused to wipe his eyes. Thence he looked off into the surrounding hills and continued. "Neither of us knows what tormented Caravaggio. How hard it was to live his life. He was, after all, just a man; as imperfect as the rest of us. Yet he possessed a great gift that set him apart, that allowed him to rise above his failings and attain something very special: works of art that carry the rest of us closer to our God. That painting at Loreto is evidence to me that Caravaggio knew that he was a sinner, that he longed for the indulgence that came with a visit to the shrine. He was a devoted pilgrim whose tribute, whose act of contrition, was offered as an admission of his failings."

Don Pietro remained standing above the old man. The noise now emanating from his rapid breathing was nearly as loud as the wind that was gaining strength with the gathering storm. "I have listened as you requested, Signore, and my final response will be direct." The monk unfolded his hands from his waist, pinched his thumbs and index fingers together, and moved them in bouncing circles to emphasize his words. "Caravaggio was a murderer, a whore monger and, himself, a whore," he said. "I have been told that a few years before he died and was sent to his just reward, he painted an altarpiece of the Madonna presenting the Rosary to our founder, Blessed Dominic. That painting was rejected by our order for the same reason that I despise his Madonna at Loreto. You see, the blasphemous man used the lecherous Count Colonna as a model for our holy founder and, worse still, the model for Our Lady at Loreto was the filthy courtesan known as Lena."

He paused and turned away, apparently finished, then turned back to complete his thought. "He made a habit of using prostitutes as models for Our Blessed Virgin Mary because he knew of their pleasures and, God forbid, he was also a deviant who sold his soul to the devil for the sake of carnal pleasure with other men."

The monk's face was flushed, his eyes widened, and the whistling sounds ran together like a hectic flute solo as he concluded his response. "Therefore, it is more than his verisimilitude that I despise; it is the beast himself that I find disgusting. His paintings do not reflect the guidance of the Council of Trent. They are the product of an evil man and, therefore, despite their subjects, they are also evil." He turned to the campsite then back to Cornelio. "By the way, I have been told that after the Madonna was rejected by the Dominicans, it was purchased by a group of artists from Antwerp. Do you know who arranged the purchase?"

"No, I do not father."

"Peter Paul Rubens."

The monk turned and quickly walked away before Tommaso even realized that he was gone. Alone with his thoughts, the old man seemed unfazed by the gathering wind, and he promptly formulated a counter argument, which began with Jesus' admonition to the crowd of stone throwers. He had more to offer, but there was no one to hear him. The last word, as usual, was claimed by the priest.

Chapter 10

Titus And Giuseppus

There was a sense of excitement in the camp when Tommaso returned from his walk. At D'Aulisio's suggestion, the guides had erected a cover over a nearby clearing that looked across a broad valley from east to west. With the arrival of the rain, the members of the expedition adjourned to this observation area.

Lionardo offered his friend a hat and a heavier coat as protection from the storm. As the two friends walked slowly to the ridge, DiCapua mentioned the peevish manner exhibited by Don Pietro after his morning exercise and, having seen him follow Cornelio into the wood, he wondered if Tommaso was the cause.

"He does not appreciate my taste in art," was all that Cornelio would offer.

The group remained on the ridge until it was time for lunch. By then, the sky was completely gray, and the rain had resolved into a fine intermittent mist without a break in the clouds. Sunshine, the other necessary ingredient for the rainbow, was an unlikely possibility.

Disappointment registered on the faces of the two Discordants, which matched the monk's persistent irritation. The fare offered by the cooks did little to change the mood. Following the meal, everyone returned to their tents for a siesta.

* * *

By late afternoon, Lionardo peered from the opening in his

tent. No one was about, save for the younger guide who was engaged in trying to keep the campfire burning. Lionardo looked skyward through the ring of trees and, from this vantage, the weather appeared the same as earlier. He retreated inside where Tommaso had propped himself into a sitting position and was reading from a book.

"I do not think we will be seeing any part of a rainbow today," Lionardo said. "Neither circle, arc, angle or even a sliver. The sky remains thick with clouds, which seem unlikely to part before sunset." He prepared a bolstered spot for himself and asked what his friend was reading.

"It's Malpighi's *De Pulmonibus*. He asked for some suggestions on the style as he is thinking of republishing it with updates from more recent dissections. And you?"

"Well, we seem to be stuck on the miniscule wonders of the world. I am reading Robert Hooke's *Micrographia*. Have you read it?"

"Valletta loaned me his copy." Tommaso responded. "Malpighi and Hooke have maintained communications through the Royal Society."

"As did Borelli," offered Lionardo. "Did you ever hear whether Hooke sided with either?"

Cornelio laid his book upon his lap. "No. I never heard."

"Nor I."

The episode they referred to was regarding the enmity that had torn apart the relationship between Malpighi and his early maestro, Borelli. They were brilliant men, far advanced in their fields of study, as well as close friends. That is, until their friendship was bested by their competitive pride. The genesis of the disagreement had to do with an essay published by a friend of Borelli's that was critical of Malpighi's theory on skin structures. Malpighi suspected that Borelli was behind the assertion, and he stopped all communications with his former close friend. Then came a series of heated public exchanges as to which of the men had first noted the spiral shape of the muscle fibers of the heart.

These two giants of Italian science, blinded by pride, turned their keen minds against one another in a tangle of nasty accusations. Cornelio, DiCapua, and most of the *Investiganti* remained on good terms with the contestants, although some chose one against the other, thus expanding the ring of animosity. After Borelli's death, the arguments continued within the two camps, an outcome too often seen among the most progressive and forward-thinking of innovators. Such is the baggage of a prideful spirit and, frequently, the price of the struggle for fame.

By contrast, one of the most admired aspects of the relationship between Tommaso and Lionardo was that they gave precedence to their friendship over the very human desire for individual glory and prestige. It may have been an innate trait within their personalities, or a lesson learned by experience, or something taught to them during their classes with Don Ruggero, or, perhaps, some combination of all these factors. Whatever the reason, they had long ago come to a visceral understanding of the admonition by the atomist philosopher Epicurus, who praised friendship as the most important source of happiness in life and encouraged his followers to maintain a permanent affection towards one another.

Hence, Tommaso could forgive Lionardo's reluctance to travel, and DiCapua could allow his friend to remain as secluded as he desired. They encouraged each other to write, and they spoke with the highest regard for each other in their writings.

In *La Vita*, Amenta compared their friendship to that of Titus and Giuseppus, the main characters in the eighth story of the tenth day in Boccaccio's *Decameron*. In the beginning of that tale, which takes place during the early reign of Caesar Augustus, a young noble Roman, Titus, comes to Athens to study philosophy. His father arranges for him to stay in the home of an old friend whose son, Giuseppus, is the same age as Titus and is also a philosophy student. Boccaccio says of them: "Being regularly in one another's company, the two young men discovered that they shared many interests in common, and this gave rise to a powerful sense of mutual friendship and brotherliness, which lasted for the rest of their lives." The two characters go their own ways after completing their studies. Following a series of difficulties, they eventually are re-united, and Boccaccio celebrates their friendship and kindness towards each other:

> Friendship, then, is a most sacred thing, not only worthy of singular reverence, but eternally to be praised as the deeply discerning mother of probity and munificence, the sister of gratitude and charity, and the foe of hatred and avarice, ever ready, without waiting to be asked, to do virtuously unto others that which it would wish to be done unto itself. But very seldom, in this day and age, do we find two persons in whom its hallowed effects may be seen, this being the fault of men's shameful and miserly greed, which, being solely concerned with seeking its own advantage, has banished friendship to perpetual exile beyond earth's farthest limits.

Amenta paraphrases Boccaccio when describing the relationship between Cornelio and DiCapua: "Because the great men, when together, found that their sentiments and habits were the same; and so a great brotherhood and friendship was born between them that only death was able to separate."

Chapter 11

The Circle Is Unbroken

Frustration was palpable among the members of the group the following day. The sky remained layered with clouds, and intermittent showers continued to fall, adding to the general misery. The men were cold and hungry. It was mid-afternoon before there was a break in the rain long enough for the guides to prepare a warm meal. As they sat around the fire, Tozzi and the monk announced that they would not stay on the mountain beyond the fifth day. They would hike with the guide back to the end of the trail, catch the coach that was due to deliver more supplies, and depart for Naples. Don Pietro encouraged the others to do the same. "Perhaps another group might return in the fall." He added, "I can assure you that I will certainly *not* be among them."

Being the one most critical of the circular rainbow theory, D'Aulisio was now in an uncomfortable position. He had never wanted to make the excursion in the first place. The physical hardships of the expedition reinforced that feeling. Still, if his elderly uncle decided to stay, he would be forced to do the same. Hence, he remained silent, awaiting his uncle's declaration.

Like the rest of the group, Lionardo was distressed by the discomfort of the journey, yet his biggest concern was with Cornelio's health. They had discussed the possibilities, and Tommaso had insisted that they stay if their opposites did. Lionardo turned to his nephew and announced his decision with a friendly jab. "It is useless for us to confirm what we already know about the circular shape of the rainbow without having the skeptics here to witness the event."

D'Aulisio was not amused. He gazed at the flames knowing that the viceroy would be upset if he did not remain on the mountain for the required time. He poked at the coals with a stick, as a code of silence descended over the gloomy gathering. The guides passed around bowls of warm red wine, which soothed the hikers and lifted their spirits. Don Pietro broke the silence by remarking as to the general health benefits of warm wine. He told the story of a nobleman in Naples who was said to have recovered from the plague by drinking wine heated to near boiling, for several days in a row. The monk said he was skeptical of the claim.

Feeling increasingly relaxed as he drank, Don Pietro rose to his feet, in a wobbly tilt, to declare that the venerable physicians were incorrect. The plague was not caused by hot gases from the earth but was due to the sins of humanity. "People are sinners, all of us by degree, with the worst among us depraved." He looked directly into Cornelio's eyes. "The good Lord can only take so much evil before He is forced to punish the perpetrators. There was and remains a plenitude of sinners within the kingdom. The pestilence came and will come again as His righteous response."

The alcohol had loosened the stout monk's lips, allowing him to pronounce his usual diatribe against the iniquity of the corrupt masses and the vanity of the literati. He looked around the otherwise quiet campfire and waited for a retort from the others, yet no one took the bait. "That fight is beneath you," Cornelio whispered to Lionardo.

After dinner, as the darkness descended, heavy rain again began to fall. The fire was soon extinguished by the wet projectiles in a barrage of puffs and hisses, causing everyone to return to their shelters. In the middle of the night, Tommaso was awakened by the need to relieve himself. Like a drunken sailor onboard rough seas, he found his legs with some difficulty and, as quietly as he could, stole away from the tent.

Once outside, he beheld a glorious night. The rain had stopped. The air was cold and crisp. The sky was littered with stars. A full moon lit his path into the nearby brush. Soon he heard footsteps and Lionardo's familiar voice calling to him. Lionardo found a convenient spot to relieve himself as well. "Are you alright?" he asked, yawning deeply.

"Other than taking forever to discharge my piss, I am fine. And you?" asked Tommaso.

"Oh, yes. It takes forever. And the wine made matters worse. The intake is pleasant, but the release, well . . . most assuredly, you understand."

"Truly! But there are also benefits to this difficulty we share. We would never have seen this beautiful night otherwise!"

"Beautiful, yes. But good Lord, it is cold."

They returned to their tent where Lionardo helped Tommaso reshape his bedding. Both men lay there in silence, robbed of sleep by the anticipation of what they sensed. Eventually, Tommaso announced their common sentiment. "Tomorrow, my friend. I feel it. Tomorrow will be the day."

* * *

The fourth morning arrived sunny and bright, accompanied by the clean fragrance that follows a heavy downpour. To the west, a few patchy, dark clouds hung above the foothills, casting long shadows across the symmetrical terraces and verdant fields of the Campania countryside. A pair of hawks circled above the camp, gliding together with steady wings on the magic of warm currents, squawking in praise of a beautiful day.

Tommaso and Lionardo were the first to join the guides around the campfire. They finished their warm tea and bread and set off for the viewing area along the ridge before the others awakened. The two *Investiganti* left word with the guides to have the others join them as soon as they had finished eating.

By midmorning, the entire company had assembled at the ridge in time to see the clouds coalesce in the west, then move across the distant valley in wet packets, before being replaced by the gathering of the next squall. And, best of all, the sun continued to shine as it rose in the east. Suddenly, a bolt of lightning discharged from the darkest cloud. Behind the flash, and filling in the shaded space, came a veil of rain moving across the lower fields like a wavy mirage about to overtake them. On either side of this wide curtain the sun shone brightly. The storm advanced directly toward them, consuming the sun-laden fields in its path while releasing those behind from its wet shadow. The crack of thunder that followed the flash was slow to arrive and its rumbling echoes continued to bounce off the surrounding hills and fade into the distance. In its wake, an incredible stillness came upon the ridge. Bird chatter ceased. The sweet-smelling air seemed charged with buoyancy, raising the gray strands on the back of Lionardo's neck. The young leaves of the surrounding oaks turned pale before the tempest.

Thence came the wind. At first, a small breeze rustled through the brush, followed soon by a steady gale. Streaks of lightning became more frequent, accompanied now by sudden booming claps of thunder. And still the sun continued to shine. A corner of the covering, which the guides had erected for protection, tore from its attachment, flailing wildly. Tommaso braced himself against a small tree for protection, as did all the others save for Lionardo, who remained in the open trying to shade his eyes from the wind, while straining to scrutinize the heart of the storm.

And then it happened. Tommaso was the first to see it through tear-filled eyes. He screamed to his friend above the howling wind as he pointed to the great circular bands of color that shone from the north of the approaching wall of rain. The others followed his finger into the distance. The circle glistened with the seven colors brighter at the sides than at the top or the bottom.

At first D'Aulisio, Tozzi and the monk claimed that they could not see anything due to the wind in their eyes. But the two brothers followed Cornelio's course and saw it immediately; they redirected the orientation of the other three, such that it was impossible to miss. D'Aulisio's face flattened. Don Pietro seemed mystified by the radiance of the hues, while Tozzi looked away, claiming debris in his eye.

Cornelio struggled against the wind to find Lionardo's right side. He placed his arm around his friend's back in a tight hug. The seven colors pulsed in a great luminous ring before them. Tommaso leaned his head close to Lionardo's ear. The wind blew. The rains cascaded down on them. "Reach out and grab it, my friend. The honor is yours." Lionardo lifted his arm across Tommaso's shoulder and held a wide smile. "Let's cherish this moment together." Lionardo responded. "Reach out with me, dear Tommaso, for the honor is ours."

Conclusion

After Tommaso Cornelio returned from the Irpino, he remained at his home for the rest of his life. He was visited on occasion by close friends, and he could be seen walking his Bellona until the late summer of 1684, when his health rapidly declined. Lionardo visited him often. The last time he did, on the twenty-eighth of November, Tommaso kept lapsing in and out of consciousness. During a lucid interval, he smiled at Lionardo and whispered, in failing voice, a final atomist wish: "There are places that I will never forget nor leave behind. Don Ruggero's office, Severino's anatomy theater, the chapel at the *Santa Casa*, Concublet's palace. I give the memory of them to you for safekeeping and I hope that someday, in some form, in some other place, we might share them, once again."

* * *

Cornelio's funeral was a bittersweet occasion for his friends, especially Lionardo. In a moving tribute, he praised Tommaso's loving ways, his intellectual valor, his courage, his brilliance, and most of all, his loyalty as a dear friend.

After the funeral, Cornelio's spirit struggled to find the lasting solitude he had sought throughout his life. Always considered by his enemies to be the evil instigator behind the atomist-atheist conspiracy, the Church would not allow him to be interred in holy ground—one priest calling for the body to be burned in a most un-Catholic manner. Thus, Cornelio's remains were placed in a temporary site, while his friends sought legal recourse to have him buried properly. It took over a year before Francesco D'Andrea, using all his skills in jurisprudence and his connections within the government, was able to convince the authorities to allow for burial in a consecrated cemetery.

Still, even after the internment, some officials of a most zealous persuasion would not let Tommaso rest in peace. They publicly called for his remains to be extracted from the hallowed ground and burned, with his ashes scattered in the winter winds.

With the passing of one of the Researchers' foundational leaders, the reactionaries sensed opportunity and went on the offensive. The atomist-atheist accusations that were raised around Cornelio's burial were the beginning of an aggressive backlash to the modicum of success generated by the cultural renewal that had begun with Lionardo's *Parere*. The fact that the traditionalists felt the need to prosecute the innovators was an indication of their concern over the degree to which the progressive ideas of the *Investiganti* had penetrated the cultural climate.

Leading the opposition were the ecclesiastical authorities, with a few Jesuits being the most tenacious in their opposition. They stood for the forces of scholastic authority, and in the latter half of the 1680s, they continued attacking the "atheists" with all their considerable agency. The innovators were denounced in print, from the pulpit, and even, rumor has it, in confessionals. The accusations accelerated with the arrests of three younger innovators in 1688, who were charged with various heresies; the worst, as far as the archbishop of Naples was concerned, was their supposed assertion that miracles never happened. This implied that the liquefaction of San Gennaro's blood was a hoax, a denial that touched to the heart of Neapolitan orthodoxy enough to bring in the Holy Office in Rome for an investigation.

Never one to lose sight of his commitments and goals, in 1689, DiCapua brought to his Neapolitan publisher, Giacomo Raillard, three new *Ragionamenti*, his *Incertezza de medicamenti (The Uncertainty of medicines)* which were requested by Queen Christina. He also republished his *Parere* with the additional three essays in a single volume. The new work dealt with the uncertainty surrounding the use of medications, the confusion among various doctors over the process of digestion, and the unknown interaction of medications within the body. This updated *Parere* would receive a third printing in 1695 by Raillard, and a fourth and final printing (which also included the text of the *Lessons of the Mofete*) was published in Cologne in 1714.

Just as he did in the original *Parere*, Lionardo asserted that there were, in those days, two foundational studies for physicians to understand the functioning of the body: anatomy and chemistry. He had always been a strong proponent of observation, but he admitted that it was impossible to accurately assess the effects of medications with the senses alone. The way to understanding pharmacology, he believed, was to study chemistry like Von Helmont and the other great chemists of the era. Their work, he said, was directed at demonstrating the most basic components of medicines—the chemicals—and their effects on the human body.

Medicine, he continued, was caught in the "web of a confused labyrinth." He found fault with physicians who mix the ingredients of various medicines without understanding the nature of each one and how they interact. "At best, the art is in its early stage," he said, "yet many physicians mix and prescribe medications with the same confidence with which the painter and sculptor use their tools."

DiCapua concludes the final *ragionamento* with a cryptic statement as to how the other categories of medicine were vast and impossible to summarize since *"l'ora tarda non permette"* (the late hour does not permit it). Most likely, he was reflecting on the fact that medicine was in the beginning stages of becoming a science. Deep study must be done to continue the effort, he was saying. And perhaps he sensed the approaching end to his own life, the limits to his once scholastic energies. He anticipated the future of medicine, but he knew that he wouldn't be there to fully participate.

During the proceedings against the three young innovators in 1688, the ecclesiastical authorities also took aim at the mentors of the accused—the surviving *Investiganti:* DiCapua, Porzio, Valletta, and D'Andrea. The papacy had claimed a feudal right over the kingdom since the twelfth century, and now some of the churchmen were determined to apply it by casting a wide web of insinuation and contempt. The prefect of the Neapolitan Jesuits, Giovanni Battista DeBenedictis, arose as the most vocal antagonist.

In my opinion, any dispassionate review of the fanaticism displayed by that man leaves one wondering what happened in his past since the saved sinner often becomes the most ardent zealot. DeBenedictis was bent on preserving the primacy of Aristotle such that he connected to the *Discordanti* soon after they had formed. He saw the leaders of the *Investiganti* as the main promoters of atomism and Cartesian rationalism within the kingdom. Hence, they were marked and monitored as dangerous nemeses to the orthodox tradition.

Over the year, DeBenedictis wrote a series of fanatical essays in defense of Aristotelian scholastic dogma. In 1694, using the pen name "Benedetto Aletino," he published an "Apologetic Letter" in which the author carries on dialogues with various individual Researchers. The other *Investiganti* were presented under pseudonyms, although they were easily identified. DiCapua was the only one openly named and accused of being an *"ignorante, superbo, vanglorioso ateista"* (ignorant, superb, vainglorious atheist).

It was left to Francesco D'Andrea and Giuseppe Valletta to answer the accusations of DeBenedictis cum Aletino. Both men replied with extended manuscripts. D'Andrea's *"Risposta a favore del sig. Lionardo di Capoa contro le lettere apologetiche del p. De Benedictis gesuita"* ("A Response in Favor of Signore Lionardo di Capoa Against the Apologetic Letter of the Jesuit Father De Benedictis") Is a detailed essay written in defense of his good friend and considered by some to be his best philosophical work. He argues that DeBenedictis unjustly offended a man who never censured a book, even if it were foolish; a man who tried to help everyone by his teaching and his medical practice.

Other defenders of Lionardo used the less formal and more aggressive style that was commonly employed in the public exchanges between Neapolitans at the time. One of them was the writer Constantino Grimaldi whose triplets flow right to the point:

> *Leggo un poco un dotto libro e bello*
> > *Contro l'orgoglio Aletino*
> > *Che ha lingua accesa al par del suo cervello,*
> > > *Scritto a quatt'occhi da Sor Constantino*
> > > *Ed e il secondo che ha fatto a difesa*
> > > *Nostra piu del DiCapua divino.*

Translated:

> I read a little wise and beautiful book
> > Against the prideful Aletino
> > Who has a tongue burning like his brain
> > > Written with care by Sr. Constantino
> > > This second one was made in our defense
> > > More than of the DiCapua divine.

The Inquisitorial proceedings ultimately failed to have the intended effect. Instead, they reawakened an old resentment on the part of the Neapolitan *Seggi* and other legal officials who pressured the viceroy, Count of San Stefano, to expel the inquisitor. The case was transferred to Rome, where it dissipated after several more years of internecine arguments.

The actions of DeBenedictis highlight an ironic feature of Lionardo DiCapua's scholarly life, bracketed as it was by the influence of members of the Society of Jesus. His earliest days as a student at the *Ratio Studiorum*, through the intercession and encouragement of Don Ruggero, provided him with the opportunity to advance in free-thinking. In his final days, members of the same order did their best to suppress his ideas by spreading lies and false accusations. The irony is not lost on those of us saddened by the regression that occurred within the Jesuit Order during those intervening years of the seventeenth century.

The Society of Jesus has always been considered the most scholarly of the Catholic orders, while also the strongest supporter of papal authority. It is unfortunate, if not tragic, that it refused to use its academic notoriety to unite the Catholic Church with the evolving principles of science, choosing instead to resist the inevitable tide of human progress—a tragedy for the Jesuit Order and a tragedy for the progress of mankind.

As for Lionardo's three additional *Ragionamenti-Incertezza dei medicamenti* that Queen Christina had requested that he write—it is possible that the great lady may not have seen them before her death. She died on April 19, 1689, in the presence of her companion Cardinal Azzolino at her palace in Rome. Recalling the endless ceremony that accompanied her father's death, she had left instructions that there should be a simple funeral and a simple grave in the Pantheon. Despite Azzolino's best efforts, however, her last wish was not granted. Instead, her body lay in state in her *palazzo* for four days. Afterwards, she was taken in a grand procession first to a smaller Roman church, where she again lay in state for a few more days, before proceeding to St. Peter's, where she was buried and remains as of this writing—the only female ever interred inside the basilica.

Three years after Christina's death, Giovanni Maria Crescimbeni founded (in her honor) the *Accademia Arcadia.* The elected members called themselves "shepherds" and took bucolic names. Their meetings were held in the fields and forests, and, in time, branches were established throughout Italy. It has now become the most important Italian Academy of this the eighteenth century.

Francesco D'Andrea (who lived until 1717, more than ninety-nine years) was elected a member of the Arcadia, taking the name "Larisco Iaseo." Lionardo DiCapua was also elected, taking the name "Alcesto Cilleneo." The poet and biographer of our Lionardo, Niccolo Amenta, became a member with the pastoral name of "Pisandro Antiniano."

After Tommaso Cornelio's death, DiCapua remained the admired and venerable representative of the innovators. Despite being crippled by painful gout, he stayed active to the end of his days, meeting with the younger progressives, where his leadership was as apparent as it had been within the original *Accademia degli Investiganti.* Amenta also says that Lionardo maintained his habit of reading at least ten hours a day while working on a biography of Andrea Cantelmo, a heroic military figure in the kingdom of the early seventeenth century. In 1693, he published the biography, which he had written in a straightforward manner that, as always, emphasized clarity over the flowery elegance of the baroque. Gianbattista Vico called the Cantelmo book "exemplary." It is an historical biography that demonstrates Lionardo's diverse ability to write a narrative quite different in style from his medical and scientific writings.

* * *

Lionardo's health continued to decline as the debilitating gout took a toll on his aging body until late afternoon, on the seventeenth of June 1695, when he passed from us in the company of his family and dearest friends. He was a few months shy of seventy-eight years. Following a modest funeral, his body was laid to rest in a side chapel in the church of San Pietro Maiella in Naples, a church built to honor the devout hermit-monk from the Abruzzo who formed the Celestine Order.

The Celestine monks honored the taciturn Lionardo DiCapua with a permanent place in one of the chapels within their church, along with a memorial that praises him as a most learned physician. After Lionardo's death, many of the great scholars of the kingdom (as well as men of the cloth, friends and family) filled a large room at the Dominican Monastery in Naples to present essays honoring his memory and mourning his loss. It was a most fitting tribute.

In my remembrance, I recall Lionardo DiCapua as a man born aside a constant spring that sprouted an unlikely tree. Through his wisdom and persistent effort, he became a fountain of truth that nourished the tree of wisdom for all of us who were lucky enough to have found ourselves in his shadow.

* * *

I will conclude this effort by asking you to recall my original intentions that I stated in the introduction to this biography. The first was to tell the story of a great and courageous man who lived during a time of unparalleled change, when the European continent was in the beginning stages of a revolution of thought. The nascent concepts and methods of natural philosophy—which we now know as science—were eclipsing the ancient ideas of magic and tradition. And in that transformation, the modern era was born. Lionardo may have been a "minor" character in that overall evolution; however, for those of us who were so profoundly influenced by him and revered him, he was an intellectual giant, a passionate warrior for truth. A warrior who used his mind and his quill pen to eclipse prejudice and superstition rather than to impose his beliefs by sword or inquisition. And because his efforts were directed at finding the truth by peaceful, academic means, his influence will last far longer than that of those who have resorted to violence.

The second purpose was to try to understand why Lionardo DiCapua was such a reluctant self-promoter. Was it true humility, or was there some ulterior cause? Having given this subject a great deal of thought, I would suggest that he was by his nature and familial predisposition inclined toward a taciturn personality. Furthermore, his studies of neo-Stoic and atomist philosophies enhanced that pre-disposition, such that he shunned public accolades and found fulfillment in life's simple pleasures.

At the same time, we must not forget that persecution was (and, in truth, remains) not an uncommon plight for those who question the status quo. Lionardo was aware of the difficulties suffered by men before him like Bruno, Campanella and Galileo. Early in his own career, he felt the stinging reprisal of an outraged Duke and Duchess. Later, he saw his devoted Maestro Severino and other friends—Cornelio, Bartoli and Borelli—abused by accusations and threats. Lionardo was a man of great talent and immense courage who had no choice but to follow his intellectual pursuits. Yet, he was also a loving family man and a devoted friend. Maybe his apparent equanimity was an attempt to protect his family and friends from the consequences of his endeavors to the extent that he could.

In the writing of this book, I have come to understand Lionardo DiCapua as a complicated man whose life contained contradictions. He possessed a gentle personality, yet he could be a relentless fighter for his friends and their shared ideals. He was a literato who became heavily involved with civil affairs at a time when scholars generally shunned such activities. In the *Mofete*, he wrote lyrically of the countryside around his small village, yet he used the Tuscan idiom in preference to the Neapolitan dialect. He was a modern man, yet he remained connected to his small Campania village, and he never left the environs of his adopted city.

I have learned that to get inside the head, so to speak, of a person like Lionardo and try to explain his actions or categorize him as a certain type of personality in possession of a particular set of characteristics is futile. It seems to me that, most likely, he was affected by a variety of impulses, some of which I have listed above. Now that you have nearly completed his story, perhaps you, Benevolent Reader, might suggest other possibilities.

The third reason for this undertaking was to set the record straight regarding the omissions in Amenta's *La Vita di Lionardo DiCapua*. Niccolo Amenta was an ardent admirer of DiCapua and was influenced by him. I have no doubt that he was well-intentioned in leaving out certain details of Lionardo's life. However, I felt it was my calling—for literary as well as personal reasons—to tell his complete story; for, in truth, I am the only one still alive who knew many of the intimate details. I saw it as my duty to tell this story that will hopefully provide the honor that Lionardo DiCapua truly deserves.

Epilogue

Courteous Reader

I will conclude this tale of the great Lionardo DiCapua by adding the fourth reason that I began this effort, having gained perspective from living in the English countryside, far removed in time and place from seventeenth century Naples. I said little about it at the outset, but, in all honesty, it remains the main purpose for writing this book.

The initial stimulus arose as an aside, a flippant remark mentioned in passing by Lionardo's son, Cesare, during the spring of 1678. Recall that after Giovanna DiCapua's death, Lionardo and Annamaria encouraged Cesare to take a holiday in England with an older gentleman who was a friend of the family. I was that person who accompanied Cesare, and I can remember the moment that Cesare made that remark quite clearly (even though I was inebriated at the time).

The doldrums had descended upon the sea causing a longer sailing than expected. The captain had decided to stop at the harbor in La Rochelle to take on extra supplies in case the winds continued to fail us on our northern excursion. While the boat was being loaded, Cesare and I took a stroll along the quay. We had an unspoken agreement to avoid talking about Giovanna's tragic death; I knew the burden of the loss weighed upon him, and he knew that I had been in love with her. Hence, we walked in the warm sunshine chatting idly until we found a tavern full of sailors and the kind of women who find their means in such a place. The noise was boisterous. I ordered two glasses of red wine. Perhaps sensing our plight—or maybe out of habit—the bartender sent a whole bottle and then a second.

Over the next few hours, the wine released our anxiety and

loosened our tongues such that Cesare was having a difficult time putting a sentence together and I had arrived at a maudlin state, sobbing uncontrollably. Cesare pulled his chair over next to mine and put his arm around my shoulder. "I know how you feel," he slurred. "But I will tell you what I told my parents. You must get on with your life, dear Guglielmo. That is what my sister would have wanted."

"You do not understand, Cesare," I replied, uninhibited by the alcohol. "She was my life. She was all that I had left."

Smiling through his gathering tears, he responded, "No! You still have the rest of us." And then he added the memorable line, the one that was the genesis of this effort: "You must know that even though he discouraged your affection for Giovanna, my father loves you . . . like his own son, and I have always felt a close connection to you as my big brother." Throughout the rest of our voyage and our travels—and, truly, the rest of my life—that remark, made and received under the haze of tight spirits, has stuck with me.

Meanwhile, sensing the need to remove myself for a longer period from Naples, I decided to stay in England as a guest of my mother's family after Cesare had taken ship for his return voyage to Italy. My adopted mother, Ippolita Cantelmo Stuart, was the sister-in-law of Ippolita Carafa through her marriage to the Marchese Concublet. Signora Carafa was also the sister of the Mother Superior at the Convent of San Gregorio.

Years before I had met her in Arena, Ippolita Cantelmo had married into the Stuart family in England. Having lost her only two children in their infancy, and her husband due to a fever, she left England and returned to Arena before the time of the great pestilence. We met there, in Arena. I'm not sure who may have interceded on my behalf, but, in any case, she adopted me and provided for all my needs, including my medical training in Naples. After her death, she left me with a large enough inheritance to make a well-set gentleman capable of a proper presentation before a branch of the same Stuart family into which I married and gained the title of the Fourth Earl of Bainbridge.

Just as Cesare had noted, I had always received the not-so-veiled impression from Lionardo that he was opposed to my marrying his daughter, oftentimes remarking as to her youth and immaturity. I took no offense at his wish, but justified it as a natural response, believing that if I had a daughter as beautiful and intelligent as Giovanna, I would have been likewise protective. Thus, out of respect, I never mentioned the obvious—that Lionardo's own wife was even younger to him than Giovanna was to me.

Interestingly, and by using the same feeble argument about the discrepancy in our ages (feeble because the practice was so common), my adopted mother also discouraged my infatuation with Lionardo's daughter. I soon connected this fact with other curious coincidences and statements by her, until I began to wonder as to who my father was—and my mother. For you see, I was raised in the Convent of San Gregorio without ever knowing my parents.

Mother Superior, Sister Fiammetta, Sister Nicola, and the other nuns cared for me, yet they never disclosed my lineage. When the great pestilence struck Naples, it was I who had departed the city with Rosario, the son of Sister Fiammetta's deceased servant, Sophia. The day we left the convent, Sister Fiammetta promised to answer my questions regarding my parentage when we met again. And as you know, we never did.

Rosario and I traveled together to Arena where we both found a new life: I as the adopted son of Ippolita Cantelmo Stuart, with all the associated blessings that fortune had placed before me; the capable Rosario, whose great natural aptitude had secured him a position within the financial network of the

Concublet family. As a young adult, I pursued my vocation as a physician, studying at the medical school in Naples under the guidance of Signori Cornelio and DiCapua. I was much influenced by their ideas and their methods, and I became a staunch supporter of the reforms they were advocating. Because of this, and through the agency of my adopted uncle, Andrea Concublet, I became a regular attendee at the meetings of the *Accademia degli Investiganti*. My particular interest was in the chemical debates that were and remain ongoing throughout Europe.

Due to the animosity of the Galenists and their supporters among the ecclesiastical authorities within the Kingdom of Naples, the Researchers were constantly struggling to advance their ideas under the threat of physical injury. I had become increasingly disturbed and impatient with this harassment, such that, following the beating of Carlo Pignataro and the closing of the academies by the viceroy, I decided to accompany the Marchese Concublet on his tour of Italy. After more than seven months on the Peninsula, we parted in Florence. I continued my travels north, through Paris and Amsterdam, eventually making my way to England. By the circumstance of the many academic and familial connections that I had been fortunate to gain, I was able to spend several months assisting the renowned scientist Robert Boyle in his laboratory at his sister's home in London. There, I was honored to meet her neighbor, the great English physician Thomas Sydenham and his friend and collaborator, the brilliant and influential philosopher John Locke.

Boyle had become far advanced in the science of chemistry, and through him, I was invited to attend meetings of the Royal Society, where I met many of the other members as well. Their discussions and their methods were like those of the *Investiganti*, but what was so impressive was the sense of real progress that these scholars were achieving among a society that possessed a better understanding of the importance of their efforts and was thus willing to support them.

When I returned to Naples, I was even more disturbed by the constant attempts at suppressing the new thinking. I became part of the small group of young scholars who gathered around Lionardo to discuss Natural Philosophy at his home in Naples. And it was there that I watched Giovanna DiCapua change from a shy girl into a delightful woman.

With the murder of the Marchese Concublet in 1675, I fell into the melancholy that seemed to inflict many of the progressives in Naples. I spent more and more time with Lionardo, although, I was also indeed pursuing my ever-increasing desire to be with Giovanna. Having a shy disposition and not physically becoming, I was poorly adapted for the role of suitor. Fortunately, Giovanna was a thoughtful woman, more interested in the intellectual than the physical qualities of a person. We were, it seemed, made for each other. The happiest days of my life were spent in her company.

When she became ill, Lionardo asked me to examine her, and it was I who confirmed his diagnosis of Typhlitis. When she died so suddenly, I came to believe that life was nothing more than a cruel and meaningless hoax. I lost all will to live. I could eat nothing for weeks, and I withdrew to my adopted home in Arena, where I prayed that God might take me from this living hell.

It was good Rosario, the closest person that I had to a relative, who stayed with me and supported me during that awful time. He slowly advanced my nutrition and activity level until I was able to do so on my own. It was his suggestion that I take a long trip out of the kingdom, so he accompanied me to Naples to help make the arrangements. There, I presented the idea to Cesare, who also needed to escape the city. I had established a friendship with him during our times together as part of his father's intellectual circle. Hence, our excursion to England.

* * *

When it was time to return to Naples after our vacation, I realized that I had no reason to go back. The intellectual environment in London was quite stimulating and appealing. I had friends there who did not know or care about my past. Besides, there were too many reminders in Naples, not just of my love, but also of my murdered uncle and his cousins, the loving sisters who had raised me. Cesare supported my proposal. I felt responsible for his safety, but he assured me that he could make the return trip on his own. He sent a dispatch to his father explaining my plan and Lionardo responded with his blessings, adding that he was certain that my deceased uncle would also have encouraged me in my new adventure.

Over the next several years, I remained in England, eventually settling down with my young wife on our estate outside of London. I became known as William (the English variant of my Italian "Guglielmo"), and I maintained the sir name of my wife's baronial family, Stuart, which was the same as that of my adopted mother. I kept in contact with Cesare, Lionardo, and my many other friends and acquaintances in Italy. I missed them all just as I missed the mild climate in the south, yet I harbored no desire to return to Italy.

* * *

It was upon receiving notification of Lionardo's death in 1695 that the time seemed propitious for a return to Naples. I wished to honor my dear maestro and to begin a serious pursuit of discovering my true parentage. To that end, I returned to the continent on many occasions over the ensuing years, by turns visiting towns in Holland, Spain, Sicily and Italy, always in pursuit of that key bit of information that would provide me with the answer that I sought. During my younger years, I was too engaged with the opportunities presented to me by my adoption to really care about my actual ancestry. After Cesare's drunken remark in that quayside bar in France, however, discovering my lineage became the slowly advancing obsession that eventually comes to possess many an orphan. The desire to learn my correct heritage, to understand the whys, to resolve the guilt, and perhaps to meet my father or mother—these were the forces compelling me to interview many people in many locales. In the process, I learned that in the town of Atri in the Abruzzo—more precisely, in the library of the Duke of Acquaviva—information might exist about Lionardo's life that was not included in Amenta's biography and that might clarify his relationship to me.

As I mentioned earlier in the book, most of DiCapua's papers ended up with the Duke of Atri, Giovan Girolamo Acquaviva, to whom they came after the murder of his cousin, the Marchese Concublet. Acquaviva had been forced to relinquish his *feudo* to an Austrian prince in 1707, and many of the papers from the members of the *Investiganti* that had originally passed to Concublet were lost. Yet, from among the disheveled gathering in the Atri library, I found a true gem. It was a sonnet, written in DiCapua's hand and torn irregularly in half. The first word, the name of the goddess "Proserpina" was crossed out and above it was written the name "Celestina." It goes:

Proserpina (Celestina) va via dal suo prigione
dal scuro inferno alla luce. Mi trovo
primavera e' beata col suo rinnovo
Vita comincia con questa stagione

Alberi e fiori alla sua stagione

Piccole bacche appaiono sul rovo
La terra puo' rinverdire di nuovo
Col suo arrivo comincia guarigione.

Qui lei rimane per meta' de l'anno
Ma presto sempre nel buio inverno
Poi i venti freddi d'autunno verranno.

Ora le nevicate de l'inverno
Lunghi giorni d'estate finiranno
Fino alla sua ricomparsa resteranno.

Translation

Celestina goes away from her prison
from the dark hell to the light. I find
springtime beautiful with its renewal.
Life begins with this season.

Trees and flowers at their season
Little buds appear on the branches
The earth turns green anew
With its arrival comes renewal.

Here she remains for half a year
But soon comes the darkness of winter
Heralded by the cold autumn winds.

Summer's long days will finish
Now the snows of winter will remain
Until she reappears.

Proserpina is the Roman equivalent of the Greek, life-death-rebirth goddess, Persephone. In mythology, she was the daughter of Ceres, the goddess of grains, and Jupiter, the head of the gods. She was abducted by Pluto, who took her to the underworld. Jupiter sent Mercury to order her release, but before Pluto let her go, he made her eat six pomegranate seeds (a symbol of marital fidelity) so that she would have to return to live for six months with him—an allegory to the barren darkness of winter.

By writing this sonnet, I believe that Lionardo was expressing the joy of his love for Celestina and the ultimate sadness of losing her. The final line hints at his hope that someday she would return to him when springtime might begin anew for the lovers. This was the only surviving love sonnet of the more than two thousand written by Lionardo around the time when he was finishing his medical studies and after he had returned to the Irpino. It was the one that had been torn by the brigands who had robbed him while he was on his way to have his poetry, plays, lessons, essays, and fables published in Naples.

The discovery of this sonnet corroborated the story that I had heard about Celestina and Lionardo from multiple, trusted sources. In the rather singular manner of its discovery, I came to realize the possibility—nay, the probability—that I was most eager to accept that Lionardo was my father and Celestina my mother. Hence, the poem was the tenon that fit snugly into the mortise of my dreams. Suffice it to say that I consider myself a scientist, and as such, I had to raise and dismiss all the other possibilities before I could accept the hypothesis that I desired. To that end (and this may seem foolish to most of you who know your parentage), I created lists of my potential fathers and mothers.

At the top of the lists, I wrote the names of Lionardo DiCapua and Celestina Carazutto. Thence, continuing under the maternal side, I listed Diana; the Mother Superior; an unknown noble woman with whom Celestina's brother, Giulio had one of his many affairs; one of the other sisters in the convent; or some other unknown woman. Below Lionardo's name, on my paternal side, I listed Giulio; Andrea Concublet (perhaps an amorous indiscretion in his youth); an unknown priest or higher prelate; or some other unknown man.

It was and remains not uncommon for children born out of wedlock to nobles and clergy to be raised in convents connected in one way or another to the parents. Of course, the truth will probably never be known, at least in my lifetime, since all the candidates from both rosters are dead and buried.

* * *

Before I end this tale, allow me, Benevolent Reader, to offer a final thought. In the introduction to this book, I hinted at the fact that the uncertainty of my parentage still, at times, haunts me. I suppose it is impossible to ever get over this dilemma completely, although by pursuing Lionardo's biography, and with the soothing balm of time, I can honestly say that I am at peace with the uncertainty.

I have received many blessings throughout my life, not the least of which is that I have now arrived at a very old age. And sometimes, in the darkness of a winter afternoon, when I fall asleep before the hearth, I awaken, not knowing for certain if I remain with the living or have passed over to the other side. It is then, in that fleeting moment of obscurity, that I am truly thankful for my good fortune, and I tell myself that the possibilities are good enough.

Appendix

Appendix A

A Brief History of the Kingdom of Naples

The Kingdom of Naples was once part of a great Mediterranean civilization aggregated as *Magna Grecia.* For centuries before the birth of our Lord, these Hellinistic states built opulent cities, like Neapolis, and prided themselves on their artists and philosophers and those who defended them. Legend has it that the great fortress-castle along the Bay of Naples, known as the *Castel dell'Ovo* (The Castle of the Egg) was built by the Roman poet Virgil who, by Medieval times, had attained the status of a wizard. Indeed, only a wizard would have been capable of constructing the improbable castle on top of an egg that was imbedded in the floor of the sea. Virgil knew of the earlier legend, when the tip of the land (upon which the egg rested) was said to be the final resting-place of the siren Partenope, whose dead body washed ashore after her song had been heard by Odysseus. *Partenope* translates to "Face of a Maiden." Through the centuries, such an unlikely beginning for a city with the dubious reputation of Naples has persisted in prose, poetry, and politics.

Since this is to be a brief history, it will be necessary to reduce the many years and a multitude of characters to a few printed paragraphs, and so we move from the kingdom's Greco-Roman roots, beyond that epoch known as the "Dark Ages," to arrive at the time of the Norman Conquest, which began around the year of our Lord 1016.

Norman warriors, originally from the frigid climes of the far north, came to southern Italy by way of France to fight in the Crusades. They expended at least some of their ferocity on the Turks and, in the process, acquired a gallant affect, such that their exploits in the south took on more romantic, if hardly less violent, ambitions. When the Crusades ended, Norman warlords allied themselves with various Italian dukes who eagerly sought their martial skills against other local principalities. From this original band of fighters, the mythic Robert "The Wise" Guiscard forged a Norman kingdom in southern Italy, and his younger brother, Roger, added to it by conquering Sicily.

In time, even the most brutal of warriors soften in the southern sun, hence the once ferocious Norman pugilists were subsumed by the German Hohenstaufens, who eventually ceded control of southern Italy and the isle of Sicily to the French House of Anjou. The "Great Captain" Gonsalvo de Cordoba defeated the French in 1503–1504, and the Spanish took control of the kingdom under King Ferdinand of Aragon and his wife, Isabella of Castille. Their unified dynasty eventually passed to their grandson Charles V of the Hapsburg line.

Charles V (*Carlo Quinto* as he was known to the Neapolitans) was a capable and generally respected monarch who realized the limits of ruling such an immense empire, upon which the sun never set. So, in 1556, he split his vast holdings, bequeathing the northern section—the German principalities, Bohemia, and Hungary—to his brother Ferdinand, while the larger portion of the Hapsburg Empire—including the Italian, Spanish, and Dutch holdings, plus the colonies in the New World—went to Charles's son, Philip II.

Typical of the time, the king of each division held several royal titles, although he kept his court in only one city. The actual title possessed by Philip II, "King of the Sicilies," is somewhat confusing. The Kingdom of Naples was described as the *"Regnum Siciliae citra farum"*—the kingdom of Sicily on the proximal side of the lighthouse at Messina. The *"Regnum Siciliae ultra farum"*—the kingdom of Sicily beyond the lighthouse—encompassed only the island of Sicily. And even though the same king ruled both regions, the two kingdoms were administered separate from each other. Charles had ruled his vast empire from The Hague until his abdication. The more Iberian-inclined Philip II moved his court to Madrid, leaving an appointed viceroy to run the government of the Kingdom of Naples. Throughout the many decades of Spanish rule, the king was absent from the kingdom. In his place, he appointed a nobleman as viceroy to rule as the king's direct representative.

Each of the successive viceroys' opulent court in Naples lasted a relatively short term, and they always maintained a strongly Spanish flavor (i.e., during the many years of Spanish control, none of the viceroys spoke the local dialect and none remained in Naples for more than nine years). Perhaps the main reason for the turnover was that the viceroy's power was intentionally circumscribed by multiple layers of a bloated administration that competed for jurisdictional control. First, and most importantly, the viceroy needed to secure the support of the king and the king's most influential advisers in Spain—the Council of State—that had appointed the viceroy and dealt with matters across the entire empire. He also needed the backing of the Council of Italy, which dealt specifically with Italian matters. Both councils set policy that the viceroy was expected to follow.

In addition to the Iberian power base, within the kingdom itself, the *Consiglio Collaterale* (Collateral Council) in Naples was the highest regional power. Its members were either Spaniards or from the Neapolitan elite. Then came the *elleti*, the highest of the city officials, made up of the feudal nobility. Below them was the *Parlamento*. The highest court in the kingdom was the *Sacro Regio Consiglio* that functioned under the auspices of the Collateral Council. An unending array of other minor councils further subdivided the administrative and judicial responsibilities within the kingdom, with each group scratching the others' backs, while engaged in their dizzying bureaucratic dance.

The viceroy rarely acted on his own without consulting the various councils. For their part, the Neapolitan elite—the barons and other officials—were happy, so long as their local prestige and power was confirmed by the Spanish. So, despite the competition among the bureaucrats and nobles, they all reinforced the prerogatives of the ruling class in the cities and hamlets throughout the kingdom.

The physical territory of the Kingdom of Naples stretched north to south, from the Papal States in the center of the boot to the Ionian coast along the heel, arch, and toe of the foot. From west to east, the land extended from the Mediterranean Sea to the Adriatic Sea. As mentioned earlier, Lionardo DiCapua's paternal family had lived within the kingdom in an area around Naples (*Capua*), or in the Campania for at least as far back as the eleventh century, most likely longer. By the time of Lionardo's birth, the Spanish had been in firm control of the territory for over a century, although the pope possessed a claim of homage from the king since, centuries earlier, the area had originally been assembled as a papal fief. Thus, the papacy maintained a strong influence over ecclesiastical and political affairs within the kingdom.

Appendix B

The Thirty Years' War

Political Incompetence and Religious Fervor

In 1588, in the north Atlantic Ocean, Spanish hegemony over much of continental Europe began a slow decline when the ponderous Spanish galleons of the great Armada were defeated by a smaller, yet more maneuverable, fleet of English ships. The rout was a disaster for Spain. Nonetheless, the Spanish Empire was so vast and so strong that one devastating loss could not bring it immediately to its knees.

The same, however, could not be said for the sovereign, Philip II who, racked with gout, died in September of the same year. His son, Philip III, became the king. This third Philip was a young and, by nature, timid sovereign who relied on an unscrupulous nepotist, the Duke of Lerma, to rule. The greed, mean-spiritedness, and miscalculations of Lerma, along with the extravagances of the opulent Iberian court, would push Spain into further deterioration.

With the decline of Spanish fortunes, the countries in the northern division of the former Hapsburg Empire (that part originally bequeathed to the Emperor Charles V's brother, Ferdinand I) became the front line of the Catholic Counter-Reformation, fending off the Protestants who had made significant inroads throughout the second half of the sixteenth century. Luther, Zwingli and Calvin on the continent and Henry Tudor in England had successfully cleaved a large portion of Catholic Europe from papal control, and the Church wanted it back.

But Ferdinand's kingdom was mired in its own political-religious bureaucracy. The German principalities were a tangle of fiefdoms, each with their own government, yet nominally supportive of the emperor. In Bohemia, the peasants favored the Catholics; the nobles and burghers were mostly Protestant. Hungary was the tenuous eastern border between the empire and the ever encroaching, heathen Turks, who were paid a tribute from the emperor to advance no further.

For decades, religion had been the great divider in the north. Attempts to resolve the religious jumble began with the Diet of Augsburg, in 1555, that produced the principle of *"Cuius regio eius religio"* (Whoever is the king, it is his religion). The religion of the leader of the principality would, per force, be the religion of the people, not necessarily Catholic like the emperor. Dissidents were expected to convert or withdraw to a site where the prince practiced a religion harmonious with them. Unfortunately, the amount of upheaval and hatred generated by this unsettling alternative created further animosities all around. Hence, both halves of the former Hapsburg Dynasty faced the reality of fading power, guided in their downward spiral by political incompetence and religious fervor.

In an effort to regain some semblance of their former glories, the Spanish and the Austrians decided to force the Protestants to resign all claims acquired during the Reformation, and the pontiff, Paul V, gave them his blessing.

Sadly, the passions of our species, then and now, lead countries to resolve their disputes through martial contests, for we have become far advanced in the production of war. Sadder still, after all the bombast and fluff is stripped away, the genesis of those disputes usually reduces to the economic claims of one state versus another. Or more correctly, to an argument among a handful of well-set gentlemen as to who will control the lands and the resources contained within them.

To stir their subjects to be much in want of the blood of their adversaries, the wealthy proponents—who stand to gain lands or money from the fighting—appeal to the ancient ties that bind the clan. The historical injustices committed against them are cited. Philosophic and, especially, religious ideals are touted. The enemy is made to appear grievous and inhumane and, of course, the people are assured that God is on their side. In truth, war is the sport of our baser instincts and we come to the notion of fighting as if by a natural persuasion.

As the sixteenth century came to an end, Catholics hated Protestants who reciprocated the sentiment, while also fighting among themselves. Calvinists despised Lutherans. Lutheran sects often hated each other as well as the Calvinists, and the combined revulsion of all these factions was directed at the Unitarians. When the Protestants finally broke their dance of mutual animosity and joined together to fight their common Papist enemy, the unleashed hatred eventually led much of Europe into one of its most deadly and protracted disasters.

* * *

Upon the canvas of a given century, history paints various images. When considering the first half of the seventeenth century, the predominant picture is one of chaos and destruction, and the predominant color is red as the blood of the countless victims slaughtered during the Thirty Years' War. The Spanish were already fighting their secessionist Dutch colonies in 1618, a year after Lionardo DiCapua's birth, when the war extended into north-central Europe, marking the nominal beginning of the conflict. The Thirty Years' War was based on religion when it began. But it was not simply a religious war. Historians have since noted that, whereas religion was a minor motive for the war among the leaders, it was used by them as a passionate stimulus, which, along with the feverish pitch of patriotism, lifted the populace to martial holocaust.

At various times, six different armies were involved in the fighting—Spanish, German, Danish, Bohemian, French, and Swedish—and, aside from the Swedes, the soldiers were mostly undisciplined mercenaries lacking any ties with the people for whom they fought. When an army moved through a region, it took what was needed and destroyed the rest. After a battle, the victors massacred their prisoners and, often, the local peasants as well. Peasant women left alive were herded into camps to service the soldiers of one army or another. Crops were stolen and fields were ruined. The people stopped replanting their crops, since the troops stole their harvests. By all reckoning, the devastation and carnage were on a scale never witnessed on the European continent.

Alliances and various subplots shifted between allies and enemies alike. Suffice it to say that, for the first half of the war, the Protestant side won no significant battles. Catholic Imperial armies usurped control of most of the northern German principalities from the Protestants, and they also defeated the King of Denmark. The triumphs emboldened the Catholic Emperor Ferdinand II to seize the opportunity to assert that God had granted victory to his forces for a higher purpose. But beyond his religious proclamation, the political ramifications of the emperor's success frightened his enemies as well as his allies.

The eventual consequences to the enemies were obvious. The very existence of the countries that practiced Protestantism was threatened, a fact carefully noted by the Swedes who had remained, up to that time, out of the war. The consequences to the allies were less clear, although still worrisome. And this is where matters got complicated.

If the Emperor defeated the Protestants and regained their lands, he would become an invincible power on the continent. That prospect frightened his allies—the Catholic princes—since the emperor might also choose to swallow up their fiefdoms. Similar subplots and jealousies aggrieved other allies, including the already-declining Venetians and the new pope, Urban VIII. Meanwhile, the French (another supposed Catholic ally) were in their ascendancy. Their goal was to weaken the Spanish Emperor whenever they could; thus, the crafty Cardinal Richelieu began providing monetary help to the German and Dutch Protestants and formed alliances with Protestant England, Sweden, and Denmark. The pope feigned outrage, and thence, behind the scenes, winked at the Cardinal's move.

Animated by the necessity of survival, Catholic France and Protestant Sweden re-doubled their efforts against the emperor. King Gustavus Adolphus of Sweden—the Lion of the North—actively entered the war and, with the financial support of France, his army of dedicated fighters soon began achieving the first "Protestant" victories. The brave and innovative Gustavus led an army made up almost entirely of native Swedes. They were an undermanned, yet highly disciplined, group compared to the mostly mercenary forces of the other combatants.

Without trying to diminish the sacrifices that occurred on many occasions during the war, suffice it to say that the battle of Leipzig, on 16 November 1632, marked a turning point in the Thirty Years' War. It has always been fashionable for men to sit around and discuss the glories of combat from the safety of their armchairs, and to proclaim this bloodbath as the "great" or "decisive" battle, while forgetting the countless minor contests. But Leipzig was indeed decisive. Gustavus led a regiment of his cavalry into the fray and was killed in the process, although the smaller Swedish force was inspired by the death of their beloved king to carry the day.

After Leipzig, the French added military forces to their financial support of the Protestants and, together with the Swedes, sided with the Dutch, who remained in their own intractable war for independence from Spain. The Thirty Years' War would drag on for thirteen more years. The result was the total impoverishment of the land, as great swaths of central Europe reverted to a state of desolate wilderness. Populous villages became extinct. Soldiers and civilians were decimated beyond imagination. Famine and disease rode with the scourge of war, and tales of infanticide and cannibalism spread throughout the continent.

Thence, by their circumstance as part of the Spanish dominion, did hardship befall the Kingdom of Naples during the Thirty Years' War. This was especially true for the peasants who were taxed, bled of their meager provisions, and forcefully conscripted into the armies of the emperor. Such has it always been with empires in which the well-being of the client states becomes important, to the extent that it contributes to the regular, ongoing operation of the empire. As for the Italian nobility, they may have fared much better than the peasants under the yoke of foreign domination. Yet, to a degree some of them came upon hard times as well.

Economic Realities and Brigandaggio

Ferdinand and Isabella took control of southern Italy from the French in 1504, and it became part of Philip II's realm in 1555, when Charles V divided the Hapsburg Empire. The Kingdom of Naples was a large geographic region and the area outside the capitol was almost completely organized as the feudal holdings of regional barons, both the old and new aristocracy. The Spanish government increasingly sold off its share of land to the aristocracy, such that by the middle of the seventeenth century, royal claims were less than 5 percent of the peninsula. Spanish decline meant increased political power for the barons and foreign merchants, particularly after the Armada debacle.

The reasons the Spanish sold their holdings and placed increased demands on their colonies came from failures in both domestic and military policies. As for the former, Philip II's son, Philip III, was possessed by a lassitude that left him incapable of leading. Filling that void, the Duke of Lerma ran the government with exceptional nepotism. The extremely lavish and increasingly isolated court life of Madrid had led to an indolent society of Spanish nobles who were likewise infused with religious fundamentalism.

The economically productive Christianized Moors, known as the Morisco, had been expelled from Spain (1609–1610) at the behest of the Archbishop of Valencia, who convinced Philip III that the many disasters recently befallen the country were God's punishment for harboring nearly a half-million infidels within its borders. The court—especially Lerma's friends and family—pocketed the resources from the expelled Moors. Since the nobles did not pay taxes, the government received nothing from the transfer. What officials within Lerma's government failed to consider was that someone had to do the work and pay taxes as the Morisco had done before their expulsion. It was an act of economic suicide that mirrored the same fate visited upon the Jews one hundred and seventeen years earlier under Ferdinand and Isabella.

As for military policy, Philip IV became king in 1621, when the Spanish—combined with the other half of the old Hapsburg Empire—were winning the Thirty Years' War and the simultaneous war with the rebellious Dutch. But as the tide turned in favor of the Swedes, their French allies, and the Dutch, revolutions erupted against the Spanish empire. In 1640, Catalonia and Portugal declared the Catalan Republic free from Spanish domination and initiated yet another war with Castile. Soon afterwards, the Sicilian Capital of Palermo rose in revolt. Meanwhile, the Kingdom of Naples seethed.

In the seventeenth century, the city of Naples was the largest in Europe with a population of around half a million. Wide boulevards with gracious palaces and, by some estimates, three thousand churches and monasteries created the impression of a splendid city. Yet, among the teeming masses, poverty was rampant. In the vast countryside outside the capital, more than two million people lived a feudal existence.

Aside from Naples, no other city in the kingdom exceeded twenty-thousand inhabitants. Most of the area was divided into small, isolated villages, and much of the population lived by subsistence farming. Peasants rarely owned the land they worked; they were essentially serfs to an aristocratic baron and their Spanish masters. Being satisfied with the arrangement, the aristocrats had no incentive to create a manufacturing economy. Consequently, a merchant middle class that produced goods from raw materials was nearly absent in southern Italy.

As to feeding the beast that trades in the propagation of war, the Spanish had devised a clever way to assure that they obtained their military materials while also recovering their costs. Sicily, Sardegna, the Kingdom of Naples, the colonies in the New World—even Spain herself—served, to varying degrees, as sources of raw materials that were sent north, where the raw goods were converted into provisions.

Thus, much of the manufacturing that was done for both branches of the former Hapsburg Empire occurred in Holland. Yet, for all its mercantile ingenuity, the Dutch hardly profited, since the Spanish recouped their expenses by levying exorbitant taxes on the enterprising northerners. Therefore, the producers of the raw materials and those that converted them into the final products were in the same predicament. Such has it always been with empires: The well-being of the client state becomes important to the extent that it contributes to the regular, ongoing operation of the empire.

Regarding the transportation of goods to and from the producers, the enterprising merchants of Genoa happily filled the need, with the result that commerce in Naples became, to a large extent, an extension of Genovese commerce. Consequently, Genoa's coffers filled with either cash or direct ownership of the regal holdings, which were being sold off throughout the kingdom. The Spanish and the Italian nobles were myopically content with the arrangement.

As the military situation worsened in the north, the royal government became increasingly desperate for money, goods, and troops. The regional barons accommodated those needs by pressuring their vassals. How the barons obtained their quotas was of little concern to the Spanish viceroy; hence, the aggressive use of feudal powers and privileges went unchecked, emboldening the aristocracy to worse abuse.

In Bagnoli Irpino, when the Duchess Eleanora denounced the *Capitoli*, the people were shocked and angered, but essentially left without recourse. The barons maintained control over their local courts, and any appeal to the royal jurisdiction in Naples would take forever to wend its way through the system. If a lawyer who had not already been bought off by the barons could be found, his fees would be enormous. The feudal community had little money to support their claim, since they usually owed money with interest to the local church or the baron himself. Thus, the ultimate outcome in most complaints opposing the aristocracy was usually pre-determined against the plaintiffs. The power of the barons essentially went unchallenged.

By the early 1640s, the financial burden on the kingdom had multiplied rapidly. The government used every means at its disposal to meet its requirements. The crown sold lands, offices, noble titles, and jurisdictions, which were acquired by the aristocracy, with the highest distinction going to those that owned feudal properties and belonged to one of five *Seggi* in Naples (like the Carazutti). The *Seggi* were gatherings of noble families in a specific part of the city. Two of them, Capuana and Nido, were granted increased weight over the other three—Portanova, Montagna, and Porto. The *Seggi* appointed all the *eletti* to the governing council of the city, except for the one *eletto* of the people. Hence, the nobles exercised enormous powers not only in the countryside where they were lords, but also in Naples by controlling the governing council.

As the war in the north dragged on, the demands from the Spanish crown on their client states continued to increase. Taxes were raised; yet, only a fraction of the money made its way into the royal treasury. This was due to an elaborate scheme in which the right to collect taxes was sold to intermediary financiers known by their descriptive name as "tax farmers." The tax-farmers were simply intermediaries who received the protection of aristocrats to collect from the peasants as much as they could. They acquired officially ratified powers allowing them to send their own private collectors into the communes. Worse still for the impoverished, the collectors could use whatever means necessary to gather the funds, such that, as the taxes increased on the already bankrupt areas, the use of violence by the collectors became commonplace and the desperate viceroy turned his back on the transgressions.

Compounding the problem was the fact that the tax structure was grossly unfair. The church and the clergy were traditionally exempt from taxes. The aristocracy managed to pay very little, if any, by flexing its bureaucratic and legal privileges. Any aristocrat who was a Neapolitan citizen, even if not living in the city, paid no taxes on property owned in the capital. Most taxes had to be approved by the General Parliament of the kingdom, which was composed of the barons and the *elleti*. After 1642, as the economic pressures escalated, Parliament was disbanded, and the political representation of the whole kingdom fell mainly on the old aristocracy through its control of the *Seggi*.

Southern Italy was a large and mostly untamed area unaffected by the peasant revolts that accompanied the religious spasms in northern Europe during the Protestant Reformation. In the expansive countryside, the only movement large enough to resist the authorities and protest their inequities was banditry. Throughout the south, people joined or provided material support for roving bands of *briganti*. Usually, the bands were small and made up of local men—and sometimes women—who knew well the rough, often mountainous terrain and used these advantages to strike quickly and avoid capture. Many groups formed out of expediency, stealing from anyone who passed their way. Very few of the bands shared their bounty with the people, but occasionally they accomplished what most peasants could only dream of doing: striking back at the endless injustices imposed by the elite.

Even though the brigands and the aristocrats historically opposed each other, oftentimes there was collusion between the powerful and the outlaw. It was nearly impossible for a small band of outlaws to last for long in their nefarious enterprises without the cover of the authorities, who then co-opted them with money and protection. The brigands then became either soldiers on the side of the Spanish or hired thugs and protectors of the local barons.

Ultimately, since *brigandaggio* failed to bring about any lasting social change, the only option left for the abused peasants was all-out revolution—a revolution led by a fisherman named Masaniello.

Marco Sciarra, The Italian Robin Hood

Most of the *briganti* who worked the roads and villages in southern Italy, like those that robbed Lionardo DiCapua, were thugs and thieves. They stole from the rich and poor and enjoyed the fruits of their work without sharing any of the spoils with the poor locals. Many of the bands were allied with—and often paid by—wealthy nobles. Among the few Italian Robin Hoods, however, one of the most famous was Marco Sciarra.

Sciarra came, as many did, from the Abruzzo region and, by 1585, had risen to the position of *Capo* of multiple smaller bands that roamed that wild, mountainous terrain. More than a group of thugs, he led a true military force composed not only of peasants, but also of a few educated men, monks, and priests. The tabloid papers of Rome, known as the *Avvisi*, mentioned that Sciarra's band of about one thousand strong was a force of disciplined soldiers, well financed and well equipped. This army extorted tributes from or directly attacked wealthy landowners in towns and urban areas, often with the support of the peasants. When the authorities responded with their own military expeditions into the countryside, Sciarra's men ambushed them across several southern regions. His army also confronted the bureaucrats sent to mobilize the villages against the popular bandits. In some areas, Sciarra set up provisional administrations and appointed magistrates to conduct tribunals and perform marriages. He endeared himself to the peasants by sharing the booty with them, keeping only what his army truly needed. Rape and plunder were forbidden.

Sciarra considered his activities to be a legitimate form of retaliation, an opportunity to redistribute the wealth back to those from whom the king, the viceroy, the barons, and the pope had stolen it. The messianic title he ascribed to himself summarized his calling: "Marco Sciarra, scourge of God and minister sent by God against usurers and rentiers."

In the countryside, this kind of class warfare was greatly appreciated by the people who directly benefited from it. In the cities (especially in Naples), the underlying political nature of Sciarra's activities became increasingly seen as an anti-Spanish revolt. Men of learning would draw comparisons with the grain revolt of 1585, and they began to support Sciarra. His group of disciplined bandits now became the spearhead of an all-out rebellion.

Such upheaval had to be crushed. The reaction of the controlling powers became increasingly harsh as the successes of Sciarra's guerilla war continued. The pope, the viceroy, and the regional nobility issued advisories that the relatives of the bandits were to be persecuted and known hideouts razed. Towns and villages suspected of supporting the thieves were to be destroyed, and government troops were given free rein to carry out these reprisals, thus promoting the inevitable abuses. The fight against the bandits soon became a fight against the rural countryside, with the peasants bearing the brunt of the reaction.

During the final decade of the sixteenth century, the Spanish amassed a force of four thousand soldiers, aided by papal militias and an army sent by the Grand Duke of Tuscany. Eventually, they surrounded Sciarra's band. Ever the fox, Sciarra and about five hundred of his followers accepted an offer from the Republic of Venice to lend their assistance in the fight against the Adriatic pirates. They escaped by boarding two Venetian galleys. The pirates had been disrupting Venetian trade within the Levant, and Sciarra's forces were recruited for a counter-attack. The Venetian Republic had always followed its own mercantile inclinations even when threatened by Rome, such that, when Pope Clement VIII demanded that Sciarra's group be turned over to the authorities, the Venetians demurred.

After stalling for several months, during which the thieves were pitted against the Saracen pirates in a series of battles noir, the Venetian Republic finally acquiesced to the pope's incessant demand. The bandits were attacked and overwhelmed by a large force. Somehow Sciarra again managed to escape and return to the Kingdom of Naples with four members of his army. In March of 1593, near Ascoli, his former lieutenant betrayed and killed him. After his death, Sciarra's legend lived on despite—or more likely, because—the conditions of the people who admired him continued to deteriorate.

Appendix D

A History of the Plague

The pestilence in Naples was but one sad chapter in the long and dismal history of the plague (*peste* in Italian). The effects of epidemic diseases had been written about for thousands of years in the Middle East, the Far East and Europe. Biblical references to early epidemics suggest that scores of people died; however, the cause, an accounting of the dead, or the distance the disease spread remains unknown.

The famed historian Thucydides wrote a detailed account of a virulent plague that infected Athens in the year 430 BC. Lucretius, the famed atomist poet, ended his lyrical poem *De Rerum Natura* with a description, taken from Thucydides, of the Athenian outbreak. By concluding his long masterpiece with such a vivid description of the plague, Lucretius aimed to support his assertion that the gods remained indifferent, even to the worst sufferings of mankind:

> Sunk in spirit and of every hope deprived;
> Fatigued with vain resources; and subdued
> With woes resistless and enfeebling fear;
> Passive, they sank beneath the weighty blow.
> Nothing but lamentable sounds was heard,
> Nor aught was seen but ghastly views of death.
> Infectious horror ran from face to face,
> And pale despair.

In the year of our Lord 542, a severe epidemic developed in Egypt and spread eastward to Byzantium. There, the Roman writer Procopius observed its ravages and left an accurate description of *vera pestis*—which, he noted, began at the coast before moving into the interior of the country. A few people recovered; most died. The results of the doctors' treatments were useless, and deaths occurred throughout all four seasons. He concluded:

> Indeed, the whole matter may be stated thus, that no device was discovered by man to save himself, so that either by taking precautions he should not suffer, or that when the malady had assailed him, he should get the better of it; but suffering came without warning and recovery was due to no external cause.

In 1347, a deadly plague—the "Black Death"— spread westward across the trading routes of India into the Crimea where the Black Sea port city of Caffa was under siege. When their Tartar attackers suddenly began to die in great numbers, the Christian defenders of the city believed that God had intervened on their behalf. The decimated Tartars were said to have catapulted the bodies of their dead comrades over the city walls as they abandoned their siege. The victorious Christian soldiers dodged the putrid corpses and boarded the Genovese ships that would carry them back to Europe.

During the voyage, many of them became ill. The ships full of dead and dying arrived at Messina in Sicily in October of the same year. No quarantine was declared at the time, causing the people who lived around the port to encounter the victims. Shortly thereafter, the locals began to develop the fevers and oozing buboes—the tokens.

As the disease spread northward to the continent, the second presentation (with a cough but without the tokens) became more prevalent in the crowded cities. Hundreds of people died each day for months on end. Nothing seemed to stop the advance. And, since neither medical nor religious authorities could allay the pestilence, people looked for scapegoats. The usual suspects were the Jews.

The role of the Jews as outsiders in a Christian Europe had always left them open to charges of sinister deeds such that the Black Death became the hub around which coalesced a litany of ancient, anti-Semitic biases. The most immediate accusation was that Jews were systematically poisoning wells. It was proclaimed a conspiracy, supposedly centered in Spain, where rabbis fabricated little packets of poison carried by their messengers throughout Europe. Confessions obtained under torture proved the charge. For centuries, the belief among many Christians was that Jews were performing ritual murders of Christian children and then drinking their blood. When they could not obtain young victims for their satanic rites, they were said to sneak into churches, steal the sacred communion hosts from the tabernacle and desecrate them.

In addition, it was widely believed that Jews became moneylenders for the same reason that some of them had fought on the side of the Arabs during the Crusades and were now poisoning the drinking wells: they wanted to obtain world domination over Christians. The massacres that followed in Savoy, Alsace, Brussels, the German principalities, and the Low Countries were also accompanied by the confiscation of Jewish property and goods. Pope Clement VI issued two bulls from his exiled palace in Avignon to try to stop the forced conversions, murders, and seizure of property, but to little avail. The pogroms, of course, did nothing to stop the pestilence.

By the time of the Neapolitan *peste*, the cause of the disease was linked to venomous atoms given off by rotting matter (including human and animal flesh) or from poisonous atoms within the earth. This pestiferous, sticky "miasma" is believed to be absorbed by pores in the skin or inhaled, thus causing disease inside the body, making the infected person a vector for further spread. The theory is logical and consistent with what is known and observed. It leads to the conclusion that the way to contain the disease is to prevent people from meeting other people or animals or goods from known infected areas.

When the plague struck Tuscany in 1630, a public health system, the most advanced in Europe at the time, had already been established. This Health Magistracy imposed a general quarantine throughout the city of Florence. Women and children under thirteen years of age were confined to their homes for forty days (thus the derivation of the word "quarantine" from the Italian number *quaranta*, or forty) to escape the venomous miasma.

Various cures were suggested, all of which were—at best—useless. Some physicians practiced bloodletting, some incised and drained the buboes. Enemas were popular, as were purgatives. The Tuscan Grand Duke's pharmacy probably ran out of scorpions while making *olio contraveleni*—the Tuscan version of Galen's famed "Theriac"—which was widely prescribed during the Tuscan outbreak. Not surprising, the Medici monopoly on the concession of this oil was a lucrative one.

The plague recurred multiple times throughout Europe after the outbreak of the Black Death. But considering the amount of mortality in Naples, probably none of the reappearances was as deadly as the Neapolitan outbreak of 1656. Recall that the London plague, in Defoe's telling, killed about 65,000 of a population of about 250,000. Whereas in Naples, around 240,000 to 300,000 people of a population of 400,000 to 500,000 died, making it one of the worst outbreaks ever witnessed on the European continent.

Luke Magnotto

In seventeenth century France, doctors who examined plague victims began wearing a long robe made of linen that had been coated with a mixture of wax and aromatic herbs. They covered their head with a waxed hat and, on their face, they wore goggles and a long leather beak stuffed with perfumes. One can imagine that an infected person, already delirious from the high fever, must have thought that they were in the presence of a demonic creature from the other side when the bedecked doctor appeared before them. In Italy, where fashion has always mattered, the outfit became especially popular. Its effectiveness was taken as confirmation of the miasma theory.

Appendix E

A Short History of Applicable Philosophy

The Whys and the Wherefores

Courteous reader:

In earlier sections, the theories of the atomists were explained in the lectures of Don Ruggero di Romano, and general notions of Aristotelian scholasticism were discussed. I feel that I would be remiss if I did not present the later philosophies that dominated the new ideas of the seventeenth century. Thus do I offer this short summary. As with all the historical chapters, I have covered just a few of the possible topics. Several excellent references are available at any reputable bookseller or, if you are blessed enough to have access to that treasure known as a good library, you may find them there.

In Don Ruggero's extra classes with Lionardo and Tommaso, he often contrasted Aristotle's system with other ways of thinking. The attempt at finding the teleological rationale for natural phenomena—the ultimate purpose, or the "why" of something—was a fundamental concept to Aristotle. His logic developed by using the syllogism, an argument in three parts: a major premise, a minor premise, and a conclusion. (For example: All mammals are animals./All cats are mammals./Therefore, all cats are animals.) Proof could be obtained by following the deductive method of moving from the known general to the unknown, with a correct conclusion—provided the premises are true.

In medicine, Galen followed Aristotle's lead and assigned a final cause to a particular disease or to the efficacy of a certain treatment. Hence, Galenism aligned with Aristotelian thinking and, for the next fifteen hundred years, progress in medicine was limited to an unshakable belief in Galen's teachings.

When Lionardo DiCapua began his medical studies during the first half of the *Seicento*, most of his teachers were steeped in Galenist medicine. These doctors of physick followed the master's ideas without questioning the theories or the training behind it. Their system had been rigidly reinforced by the profession, as well as by the Catholic Church. It would take persistent courage to challenge it.

Following Poggio Bracciolini's rediscovery of *De Rerum Natura*, some scholars began to emulate the atomists' ideas on natural phenomenon and, in the process, demonstrated the same excitement for learning that energized their atomist predecessors. The atomists were interested in everything, from all sorts of natural phenomenon (like volcanos and earthquakes) to religion, sex, and morality. Lionardo DiCapua's early exposure to atomism impelled him, as it had to so many others, to break the chain of orthodoxy in medicine and pursue a different approach to finding the truth.

Atomism is a purely theoretical philosophy, formulated without the technical apparatus to test it, which makes the veracity of the teachings that much more amazing. Neither Democritus, Epicurus, nor Lucretius was what would be considered today a true scientist, although each possessed what might best be described as a scientific imagination.

Francis Bacon, one of the great minds of the early seventeenth century, introduced inductive reasoning to natural philosophy, a careful leap from the particular to the general, based on detailed and repeated observations. Bacon opposed Aristotelian logic and referred to Democritus as the first among philosophers of his day. His inductive method was a new way of thinking that, coupled with atomist ideas, offered Lionardo DiCapua a new path to follow in his professional life.

Other famous philosopher-scientists of the *Seicento*, with whom Lionardo DiCapua and Tommaso Cornelio later interacted, studied the atomists and read Lucretius, as did the peripatetic Queen Christina of Sweden. Like Cornelio and DiCapua, the enigmatic Christina relied on a contemporary exponent of the "Two Truths," who showed them how to comfortably fit atomism into the religious framework of their lives. That man was a Catholic priest named Pierre Gassendi.

Gassendi's life was a series of contradictions. He was from a peasant family in Provence, yet he was able to rise to the position of professor of philosophy by age twenty-five. He became a Catholic priest while at the same time writing tracts in favor of Copernicus, Epicurus and Democritus and opposed to Aristotle. He unified two seemingly disparate systems by simultaneously proclaiming himself a Catholic and an epicurean-atomist.

Others had paid a visit to the torture chamber (or sometimes took a one-way journey to the stake) for supporting such heresy. Pierre, however, was a gentle soul who lived a life that Democritus would have admired. He was a true scholar who fasted often, took a vow of celibacy, modestly attended to his duties, possessed a congenial affect, and achieved his amalgamation of the "Two Truths" by making a few slight twists to Democritus's original concept of the atoms. Gassendi said that the number of atoms was not infinite but limited. Therefore, an infinite God could have projected the initial force onto the world and thus controlled the forms created by the atoms. After that, the world functioned on its own according to the natural laws. As for the soul (the main concern of most religions), Gassendi said that it was immortal; yet, concurrently, it was dependent on the physical body it inhabited for input through the senses. He pointed out the original nature of Epicurus's ideas on pleasure being the absence of pain and blamed their degradation on some of the early epicureans who preached the primacy of sensual excess.

Queen Christina invited Gassendi to visit her court in the frigid north in 1650, but Pierre cordially declined the invitation. He died five years later in the most contradictory way one would expect an epicurean might: He fasted too long, caught a fever and was too weak to resist its source.

Because Gassendi unified atomist teachings with Catholic doctrine, his philosophy had a strong resonance among the Academy of the Investigators *(Accademia degli Investiganti),* which DiCapua and Cornelio would initiate in 1663. However, the Neapolitan version of atomism was an eclectic blend of original Democritean teachings, along with Gassendi's purified form of Epicurus and Lucretius, plus the Italian atomism of Camillo Colonna.

Not much is known of Colonna. He was born in Naples sometime during the second half of the sixteenth century, and probably was a student at the University of Pisa where he met Galileo. He had a strong influence on a close friend of Lionardo's, Francesco D'Andrea, who brought Colonna's writings to the *Investiganti.*

The maternal nephew of Lionardo DiCapua, Domenico D'Aulisio who accompanied the group to the mountains to witness the *arco baleno,* was the last person known to possess Colonna's manuscripts, which were said to be written in the same highly refined, purist, Neo-Petrarchan style used by DiCapua. D'Aulisio's cantankerous arguments with DiCapua and the *Investiganti* leave one wondering why he would care to obtain Colonna's writings and what he might do with them. They disappeared and have never resurfaced.

As with other atomists of the time, Colonna was accused of atheism, but managed to somehow defy the Inquisition, possibly by dying before they could place him on trial. Like much of his early life, the date of his death remains uncertain. He disappeared from active contact with his contemporaries, some of whom have claimed that death came to him in the interval between 1657–1678, which leaves open all sorts of possibilities.

Besides the original and revised atomist teachings, two other ancient philosophies (originally introduced by Don Ruggero) influenced Lionardo DiCapua, Tommaso Cornelio and the other *Investiganti.*

The first was Stoicism. DiCapua read the writings of Seneca, the Roman Stoic who lived in the years immediately before, during, and after the time that Jesus walked the earth. At that moment in the history of Imperial Rome, the individual felt powerless in intervening in the politics of public life. Seneca was much affected by this situation. In his "Letters to Lucilius" written when he was an old man, he answers the questions of the young Lucilius, and in the process presents a practical method for living a meaningful life in difficult times, a situation familiar to Lionardo.

Seneca emphasized the power of the will, the control of the passions, the order of the universe, and the enjoyment of the simple pleasures of life. He scorned slavery, cursed the gladiatorial games for debasing humanity, spoke of a universal brotherhood as well as an ineffable soul of the world. These Stoic ideas resonated with the early Christians such that many believed, without any direct proof, that Seneca had secretly abandoned paganism in favor of the young religion.

DiCapua certainly spiced his Catholicism with neo-Stoic ideals of the kind that were a more moderate form of the unflinching asceticism for the public good espoused by the early Stoic practitioners. His writing of the constitution for the Republic of

Bagnoli Irpino during the revolution in the kingdom could be seen as a direct result of his neo-Stoic and atomist tendencies. It was unusual for literati to participate in the political events in the kingdom, and Lionardo must have understood the danger in doing so. Yet, he did pursue his anti-aristocratic beliefs for the benefit of his fellow citizens, even at the cost of having to flee Bagnoli for fear for his life.

The other influential philosophy on Lionardo and his circle was skepticism, which was related to atomism. It grew out of the teachings of early Greek philosophers, especially Sextus Empiricus, whose writings are the only ones that remain. The original members of the *Investiganti* were particularly fond of the moderate, academic strain of skepticism, the main contention of which was that it was doubtful whether one could achieve definite understanding of the natural world. Lionardo DiCapua confirmed this concept in print years afterwards when he wrote his *Parere*. The last phrase from the subtitle of that work makes the point: "[C]learly the uncertainty of medicine becomes apparent." This emphasis on uncertainty would hardly lead DiCapua or the other Investiganti to an immobilizing fatalism. Instead, they would use Bacon's inductive method and propose that, through detailed and repetitive observations, a probable understanding of the natural world was attainable.

Contemporary Influences

Lionardo DiCapua, Tommaso Cornelio, and their progressive circle were also influenced by other contemporary philosophers aside from Gassendi and Colonna. The most prominent were Galileo, Rene Descartes, and Thomas Hobbes.

For centuries, Catholic doctrine had taught that all knowledge came from God's inspiration. In that tradition, truth is attained through the revelation of Scriptures, which can be interpreted only by the Church. Any definition of "knowledge" had to be tempered by the demand for absolutes, and this rigid requirement led many Church leaders to resist the tentative ideas of natural philosophy.

As the new ideas of the emerging sciences evolved, however, it became apparent that knowledge *could* be obtained through observation and experimentation apart from divine influence. Epistemology—the study of how one obtains knowledge and its limits and validity—thus became a much-considered topic for philosophic discussions throughout Europe. One of the most influential people whose experiments and writings supported the new research was Galileo Galilei. He used his telescope to enhance a theory of the universe originally propounded by Nicholaus Copernicus who, in a rather singular manner, fractured the edifice of orthodoxy.

When the father of ten-year-old Nicholaus died in 1483, the young Prussian-Pole became the charge of his maternal uncle, who sent him to the University of Cracow to become a priest. He soon became disenchanted with the confining anti-humanism at Cracow and convinced his uncle to allow him to study in Italy. At the University of Bologna, he studied astronomy and mathematics and imbibed the ideals of the Renaissance.

Leonardo da Vinci (among several Italian thinkers) openly questioned the Ptolemaic model of an earth-centered (geocentric) universe in which a stationary earth sat at the center of a complicated and bewildering array of planetary epicycles, eccentrics and deferents. Another of those doubters, Domenico de Novara, taught astronomy at Bologna during Copernicus's time there. Novara introduced his students to Greek thinkers who lived well before Ptolemy and proposed a sun-centered (heliocentric) universe with the earth in its orbit. After completing his studies in Italy, Copernicus began working out the mathematics to prove a heliocentric universe.

It would take more than twenty years for Copernicus to complete his magnum opus, *De revolutionibus orbium coelestium,* and another thirteen years before it was published (1543). Here, in one astounding essay, was mathematical proof of a sun-centered universe, a new interpretation of God's order, and one of the greatest gifts of Renaissance scholarship. Nicollo Amenta, Lionardo DiCapua's biographer, did not mention Lionardo's stand on heliocentricity, but I can assure the reader that he read Copernicus's argument and accepted the science and mathematics that proved it.

A geocentric universe, as propounded by Aristotle and confirmed by Ptolemy, was the basis of the entire scholastic model of the world. By placing the sun in the center and the earth in orbit around it, the whole Aristotelian construct, the basic philosophy used to support Catholic doctrine, began to unwind. Planet earth was like all the other known planets, circling around the glowing sun.

In 1609, Galileo turned his telescope to the sky, and with each observation he became more convinced of the Copernican heliocentric universe. The heavens were revealed in all their physical glory. Their metaphysical implications were no longer pre-eminent. As a man of science, Galileo despised the endless metaphysical arguments that were common among philosophers of the day. Because the laws of physics and mathematics were precise and reproducible, he realized that knowledge could be obtained with certainty through repeated experimentation. His discoveries were proof positive of the inherent veracity of his method, and they placed him among the greatest scientists of all times. The religious authorities, however, were greatly disturbed.

Throughout the sixteenth century, the Church had been on the defensive, trying to fend off the challenges of Luther, Calvin, Zwingli, and Henry Tudor. The last thing it needed was another dispute that might undermine its fundamental authority. In addition to the political implications of his cosmology, Galileo's own aggressive personality left him with little patience for those who were pre-conditioned to question his ideas. Galileo's perceived arrogance, coupled with the wide distribution of his ideas through the printing press, left little doubt in the minds of the religious hierarchy that it must be contained. The inevitable effects of that confrontation would prove disastrous to both sides.

The punishment that Galileo received destroyed him physically. His retraction of the Copernican model kept him out of jail and away from the brutal practices of the Inquisition, but he remained confined to monitored house arrest. In time, the physical and intellectual isolation took its toll. He became depressed, his eyesight failed, and death, when it finally came in 1642, was a welcome relief. Despite, or maybe because, his books were listed on the Church's index of prohibited books, Galileo's writings enjoyed wide distribution in the northern countries of Europe; this meant that, as bad as it was for Galileo, the effects on the church in the long run, were much worse.

The attempt to suppress the physical reality of the universe initiated a conflict between religion and science that resonates to this day. Christianity could no longer claim to support the goal of attaining true knowledge of God's creation. The credibility of both the Catholic Church as well as the Protestant faiths that believed in a literal account of the Bible was irreparably damaged. In truth, many of the fundamentalist Protestant religious authorities would have preferred to enforce the same ban as the Catholics, but they were unable to gain political control of their governments as the Catholic Church had. Without a powerful religious force to stop them, many of the most brilliant minds that were advancing the new ideas observed what had been happening on the Italian peninsula and decided to apply their creative scientific energy in northern Europe. Hence, the historically great intellectual centers in Italy began a slow decline.

In hindsight, the message to the religious authorities should have been obvious: Truth can never be completely suppressed, a belief that was fundamental to Lionardo DiCapua and one that drove him onward, despite the obvious danger in doing so. DiCapua followed Galileo's plight while studying in Naples. He was old enough and certainly interested enough in Galileo's struggles to understand the implications to himself and his progressive friends. Beginning during his medical training and throughout his life, DiCapua faced multiple attempts to silence him, sometimes accompanied by implied threats of violence. But he believed that an enlightened synthesis of the Church's theology with Galileo's cosmology (and other evolving truths) could accelerate the rate at which science might advance, producing great benefit to mankind.

Indeed, as it was, many of the academies that developed throughout Italy during the seventeenth century, including the *Investiganti,* received their initial impetus through the Galilean tradition. But, as with all evolving disciplines, differences among followers of the new thinking would arise. These disparities were particularly evident when it came to the ideas advanced by René Descartes. Lionardo DiCapua discarded Descartes' idea that human reason was separated from sensory perception, while accepting other Cartesian principles. The same ambivalence was true with other philosophers. But none denied the impact

Descartes had on modern thinking.

Descartes was a mathematical genius whose rationalist approach to life ironically sprang from a mystical event that occurred in the solitude of his room on St. Martin's Eve, November 10, 1619, when he was twenty-three years old. He described the three dreams that happened that night as the source for his method, which was grounded in doubt. He rejected as false anything that possessed the least bit of doubt. His famous phrase, *"Cogito ergo sum"* (I think, therefore I am), reflects his deconstruction of reality down to the simple, indubitable fact that the thinker exists. The mind was, therefore, more certain than matter: I may not have a body; it could be an illusion. But I know that I am thinking; hence, I know that I exist. This would be his first principle upon which he would build his philosophy.

Descartes' epistemology began with the supremacy of human reason over divine revelation or sense perception. To him, the mind contained innate ideas that were separate from sensory input. The physical world around us could not be understood by the senses, except through man's most powerful tool: mathematics. Such straightforward thinking allowed science and mathematics to analyze the objective qualities of our environment and apply the accumulated knowledge to the improvement of the human condition. By placing mankind's rational self-awareness as the primary source of knowledge, he not only separated the human mind and the natural world from each other, but also both from God. His idea that thought was the prime, empirical certainty marked the beginning of modern philosophy.

A near contemporary of Descartes was Thomas Hobbes, an Englishman whose ideas were brought to Lionardo DiCapua and the other *Investiganti* by Tommaso Cornelio after a sojourn to several northern European countries. Hobbes studied Scholastic Philosophy at Oxford but found the ideas and life at the university too stifling. Through self-directed study, he became far advanced in Greek and Latin classics, which led to a position as tutor to Lord Hardwick, later the second Earl of Devonshire. With his pupil, Hobbes traveled to the continent where he was first exposed to the writings of Galileo and Kepler. Upon his return, the Earl introduced him to Francis Bacon, for whom he served as private secretary. It was through Bacon that Hobbes gained an appreciation for the importance of natural philosophy and the primacy of mathematics.

As the looming English civil war unfolded, Hobbes (who was an ardent monarchist) escaped to Paris, where he befriended Gassendi and was a critic of Descartes. With the former, he was aligned as an atomist and a materialist, whereas he objected to the latter's epistemology. He favored, instead, the materialist idea that all thought is ultimately derived through the senses, an idea that would have great resonance with Lionardo DiCapua and the other *Investiganti,* who were inclined to Hobbes's materialist way of thinking.

Appendix F

A Brief History of Medicine

The Gods and Their Agents

In as much as the structure of the human frame has been so set together by Nature that it is unable, from the continuous flux of particles, to remain unchanged; whilst from the action of external causes, it is subjected to influences beyond its own; and since, for these reasons, a numerous train of diseases has been pressed upon the earth since the beginning of time; so, without doubt, the necessity of investigations into the Art of Healing has exercised the wit of mankind for many ages before the birth, not only of the Greek, but of the Egyptian Esculapius, the latter being earlier by a thousand years than the former. And, indeed, as no man can say who it was that first invented the use of clothes and houses against the inclemency of the weather, so also can no investigator point out the origin of Medicine—mysterious as the source of the Nile.

Thomas Sydenham, *Medical Observations*
John Locke and Thomas Sydenham, Authors

The principles that guided the doctors of physick and were taught to Lionardo DiCapua during his medical training grew out of ancient mythological legends spun across the islands in the Aegean Sea. The gods and their earthly agents (represented by the two snakes wound around Mercury's staff to form the Caduceus) were believed to be sources of healing. Homer's epics *The Iliad* and *The Odyssey* were written in the ninth century BC and rendered a fairly accurate description of daily life, including the practice of medicine.

Homeric medicine consisted of both religious and secular rituals since disease was regarded as a punishment from the deities. Among the pantheon, Apollo was believed to be the main god in control of the health of mortals. Most of the others could cause or cure specific illnesses, and many could do both. In the lower sphere of earth, soldiers suffered mortal battle wounds and were treated by fellow warriors, among whom Asclepios and his two sons became the most prominent.

In the *Iliad*, Homer mentions Machaon and Podalirios, Asclepios's sons who were warriors skilled in the medical arts. They would become enshrined as the father of surgery and the father of medicine, respectively. Asclepios's other medically inclined offspring included a daughter, Panacea, who helped with treatments; another daughter, Hygeia, the goddess of health and prevention; and the youngest son, Telesphoros, who was always pictured accompanying his father on his medical rounds. He came to represent convalescence. Even Asclepios's wife, Epione, was gainfully employed in one of the busiest practices of the family. She was the soother of pain.

Eventually, the healing gods were enshrined in temples, and Asclepios became deified as Apollo's son. The interweaving of the secular with the religious led to the building of temples dedicated to Asclepios and his family. By the year 700 BC, those temples became the most important sites for healing, and the cult of Asclepios spread widely around the Aegean Sea and beyond to Egypt and Rome. Temples were built, and Asclepios either merged with the local gods of healing or replaced them.

These temples were more like a shrine and a spa than a clinic or hospital. The treatment ceremonies combined traditional methods with the supernatural.

A patient would go through a ritual purification at the *Tholos*, a round stone structure usually built over a natural spring. The process, sometimes preceded by a fast, would begin after sundown and include bathing and being anointed with oils before donning a clean white robe. The patient would then enter the *Incubatio*, lie down on a bed, and await the arrival of the priest who would do his rounds dressed as Asclepios. The priest/doctor would be accompanied by a retinue of actors dressed as his children, as well as medical assistants, and even animals (e.g., snakes, dogs, birds) trained to treat various diseases by a touch, a lick, or a peck. The cure was hoped for by morning, but it could take longer. Testimonials of dramatic cures for psychically based diseases increased the prestige of the temple. Patients showed their gratitude by leaving plaques inscribed with their story or a terra cotta votive of the healed body part. Before returning home, the cured person was expected to offer a gift commensurate with his or her economic station.

These elaborate rituals played well with a population presented, for the most part, with a choice between religious cures or charlatans. Gradually, however, a more rational, non-religious method for diagnosing and treating disease evolved in Greece. What caused the sudden rise in Greek civilization remains a mystery, but the disciplines of philosophy and science, which were one and the same to the Greeks, began around the sixth century BC.

Early Greek philosophers argued over which was the basic element—water, earth, fire, or air. Eventually, each was equated with its corresponding characteristic—wet, dry, hot, and cold—which became the basis for the humoral theory of medicine, a theory that would not be openly challenged for more than two thousand years. Even then, the humoral basis for treatment would continue in some quarters throughout Lionardo DiCapua's life, even unto the time of this writing and, most likely, beyond.

Arguably, no singular physician, including Galen, has had more of a lasting impact on the practice of humoral medicine than did Hippocrates who lived in the fifth century BC. He and other contemporaries provided rational etiologies for disease and omitted supernatural causes. In his extant writings (likely a combination of many sources), he aligned the four basic elements with the four humors of phlegm, yellow bile, black bile, and blood. The harmony of these humors is emphasized, and disease is seen as an internal imbalance among them. The physician is taught to take a good history and observe the patient and their environment using all of one's senses. The section on ethics advises the physician on the means of comforting his patients and implores him to lead a clean, structured and temperate life. Overall, his advice is summarized in the famous Hippocratic assertion, "First, do no harm."

More than two thousand years later, having read Hippocrates and other early physicians in the original Greek, Lionardo DiCapua wrote a series of medical essays (his *Parere*) reminding us that there was no unanimity of ideas, prompting written debates among physicians who disagreed with their peers:

And as for other disputes of those times, Hippocrates gives us an Account of some of them in these words: In acute diseases so various are the Sentiments of Physicians, that often times what one prescribes, as most helpful, others forbid as harmful; And for this reason the Art of Physick ought to be esteemed very like to that of Divinations, because the Physicians behave themselves just like to Soothsayers, some of which will have the same bird, if appearing on the right hand, to be an Augury of good Luck; but if on the left, of bad. But others again hold the contrary.

The "contrary" was common because much of the Hippocratic humoral method was based on the practitioner's philosophy rather than objective science. Medical schools, per se, did not exist. Pupils would study with experienced, often itinerant, physicians, but no formal curriculum existed, and the study of human anatomy was minimized.

Such was the basis for much of humoral medicine, a system that became the foundation for the training that Lionardo DiCapua and his contemporaries were expected to follow. The emphasis that Hippocrates placed on history-taking and direct observation, rather than relying on the precepts of authority, marked a great advance in the approach to disease, although somehow, to Lionardo's great sadness, those precepts were discarded somewhere during their two millennia journey to the Seicento.

The divisions that existed among the practitioners during the time of Hippocrates became more intense after his death. In his metaphysical writings, Plato emphasized reasoning over observation, whereas his pupil, Aristotle, used the observation of rational events to draw conclusions that possessed their own inherent, if incorrect, logic. For example, if you throw an object in the air, it falls to the earth. Repeating the toss a hundred times nets the same result. Thus, he concluded, bodies fall to the earth because it is the center of the universe with the stars, the sun and the planets all circling it. In another example, particularly relevant to Lionardo DiCapua, Aristotle held that one never sees more than a half-circle of a rainbow. Hence, a full circle was deemed impossible. In medicine, Aristotle performed detailed studies of animals, named the aorta, and taught the elements of fetal respiration. But he also taught that since the heart is the vital center of all activity within the body, it is the site where sensation and memory are perceived.

In the time of the Roman Empire, there were several important early physicians. All of them, however, were overshadowed by the singular personality of Caius Galen. He was born around 129 AD into a wealthy, educated family in Pergamum, presently the land of the Turks. He traveled widely and studied with itinerant physicians. His medical successes, which he was fond of recounting in his voluminous writings, eventually led him to Rome, where he became Emperor Marcus Aurelius' court physician.

Sixteen of Galen's works were accepted as his canon. Arabic scholars translated the Greek version into Arabic, and Galen became the revered fountainhead of knowledge in the Islamic world, as well. His correct teachings, as well as his mistakes, were codified into dogma, which was deemed irrefutable. Thus, the role of the physician, again to Lionardo DiCapua's great sadness and frustration, became one of interpreting the master. Unlike Lionardo, most medical students accepted Galen's tenets without question, but somehow forgot—or ignored, or perhaps were never taught—Galen's admonition to discover through experimentation. Like Hippocrates, Galen believed that knowledge accumulates within the wise physician who combines the ancient teachings with observations and practical experience, and thus comes to his own form of practice.

In Galen's case, the combination led to an association of each of the four humors with a specific temperament. A phlegmatic personality was sluggish and somewhat dull. A person quick to anger possessed too much yellow bile; one with too much black bile was melancholic. A sanguine personality had too much blood and was a passionate lover of laughter and music. Each temperament also possessed its own respective physical property: moist, dry, cold, hot. The physician was responsible for diagnosing the imbalance in the four humors, and then restoring balance using emetics, cathartics, purgatives, and the letting of blood. The medicines Galen used were of his own mixtures, each intended to counter the disease and return the patient to health. Hence, a moist medicine for a dry disease, a hot medicine for a cold disease, and so forth.

He carried his system of treatments to an extreme by creating a unique version of theriac, the multi-substance liquid touted as a panacea for poisons, pestilence, snake bites, infections, inflammation, and more. The mixture had a venerable history and was surrounded by such powerful legend that not even the wise Galen could resist its enchantment. As the story goes, Mithridates VI, King of Pontus in the early first century BC, was of a bellicose persuasion, convinced that his enemies were trying to poison him. So he started taking increasingly larger doses of known poisons to build immunity to them. It was a dangerous game, one that could prove fatal along the way; thus, he first performed experiments on his slaves, using varying doses to come to the correct formula.

After successfully battling against the Romans in Asia Minor and Greece during several campaigns, Mithridates was finally defeated and forced into the Crimea by Pompey. There, at the age of seventy, Mithridates had one of his surviving slaves run him through with a sword, for most likely no poison was left that might have killed him. In passing, he left behind his famous Mithridatium potion as a gift to the ancient world. He also left his name—a *mithridate*—to describe a universal cure for all poisons.

Nero's personal physician added viper's flesh, along with other interesting ingredients, to the Mithridatium, and the name of the potion became *theriac*, from the Greek for "wild beast." Whether Galen included it among the more than seventy elements in his secret mixture is unknown. Over the centuries, the number of ingredients has grown, although the main ingredient remains an essence of opium—thus its persistent popularity.

Galen believed that all of nature could be explained, and it was that kind of thinking that would have great appeal later, especially during medieval times when the daily reminders of the fragility of existence created a need for absolute truth. Even though he was not a Christian, his explanations fit nicely into the Aristotelian framework and were readily endorsed by the Catholic Church. After all, Christ had taught that the sin inside us would bring about our spiritual demise, just as the internal humoral imbalance brought about our death. Hence, for more than fifteen hundred years, and even in some circles today, have Galen's teachings been viewed as medical dogma.

When Lionardo DiCapua was a medical student at Naples, he read the original Greek edition of Galen. Writing years later in his *Parere*, Lionardo DiCapua clearly admired Galen's emphasis on experimentation, but he stumbled over his vanity and his pagan ideals. After Galen, DiCapua tells us, came the teachers of physick:

They foolishly followed the phantastical Chimera of Terms, and prattle, wherewith casting, as we used to say, dust in the eyes of the Multitude, they made them think Glowworms to be Lanthorns, and would make everyone believe that they knew all, when in Natural things, it cannot be affirmed that they knew anything. But in time this vain shadow of Philosophy, sinking together with the Majesty of the Roman Empire, gave the last plunge, drawing with it also Physick.

Itinerant Physicians

When Lionardo DiCapua began his medical studies in the first half of the seventeenth century, the system of medicine propounded by the doctors of physick was dominant throughout all of Europe. The Galenic principles handed down over many centuries were parsed and reinforced by the proponents. Physicians were paid well for their services, and they enjoyed a respected position within society. Few would dare to stray from the accepted canon. In practice, that meant that a patient who suffered from a given disease in the year of our Lord 150, during the Roman Empire, would have received a similar treatment (purging, emetics, cathartics, or bleeding) as a patient afflicted with the same disease during the height of the Spanish Empire in 1650. Usually, neither patient would have been healed, and both might have been harmed.

At the same time, around the beginning of the Seicento, progressive practitioners began advocating for the establishment of careful research, mastering anatomy, bedside observation, and experimentation in pursuit of healing the patient. During his years of medical study, thanks to the guidance of Marcaurelio Severino, Lionardo DiCapua concentrated on human anatomy as the way to observe the intricacies of the body. He also read of the curative properties of chemical mixtures and realized that chemistry was an important discipline that merited study. Once he completed his formal studies in Naples, he arrived at a critical juncture in his life, both professionally and personally. Leaving aside those issues of a personal nature, consider his professional challenges.

Lionardo DiCapua was not a Galenist; he did not support their rigid and financially compromised positions, nor the innumerable errors that they espoused. DiCapua's atomist studies had opened his mind to other possibilities. However, no established name for this new approach to medicine had been given, which was initiated by an eccentric rebel ninety years before Lionardo's birth, on the evening of June 24.

For centuries, the short night of Midsummer was the balancing point of the year, the best time to purge the world of its evil magic and its flagrant sinners. Later, Christians transformed the day into a celebration of the life of the wandering mystic, John the Baptist. On that day in 1527, in the courtyard at the University of Basel, students encircled a giant bonfire, singing the traditional rhymes while tossing their class notes into the flames. The only teacher who participated in the revelry was the newly appointed professor of medicine named Theophrastus Phillipus Aureolus Bombastus von Hohenheim, known simply as Paracelsus. In his hands were two books—a copy of the Latin translation of Galen's works and Avicenna's *Canon*—the two tomes that contained the essence of what was handed down by the pillars of western medicine. After delivering a scathing diatribe, he tossed the books into the pyre. "Thus, the realm of medicine has been purged!" he yelled. The cheering students could hardly have appreciated what this seemingly harmless prank meant.

Like Hippocrates and Galen centuries earlier, Paracelsus was an untrained, itinerant physician who traveled widely, gathering medical knowledge from peasants, gypsies, barbers, and alchemists, which he then applied to the compounding of new medicines. His most precious concoction, his opium-laced, cure-all "Laudanum," was always nearby, hidden in the handle of his large sword.

Just as Galen's reputation as a healer had led him to treat the rich and revered in Rome, so also did the growing reputation of Paracelsus lead him to consult for the wealthy publisher, Johann Froben of Basel, Switzerland, who suffered from a lingering leg infection. Froben had heard of Paracelsus's success treating intractable cases, and he summoned him with an offer to advance his fees. Paracelsus lived in Froben's home with another houseguest, the great and wise Erasmus of Rotterdam.

Paracelsus's treatments cured Froben as well as the fragile hypochondriac, Erasmus. "I cannot," wrote Erasmus, "offer thee a reward equal to thy art and knowledge, but I surely offer thee a grateful soul. . . . May fortune favor that thou remain in Basel." Froben and Erasmus used their connections to make sure that Paracelsus did remain near them in Basel, arranging for his appointment as municipal doctor and professor at the university.

Their efforts, however, soon proved disastrous when the bombastic Paracelsus went out of his way to anger the other university professors, all of whom held a diploma in medicine. "For I tell you boldly," Paracelsus announced to his fellow professors, "that the hair from the back of my head knows more than all your writers put together; my shoe buckles have more wisdom in them than either Galen or Avicenna; and my beard more experience than your whole academy." The doctors of physick and their students ridiculed his use of the German vernacular to teach his radical new theory of disease based on specific etiologies outside the body.

When Froben died suddenly, less than two years after Paracelsus's appointment, the authorities knew that his temper and his problems with drink would lead to Paracelsus's own self-destruction. Forced to flee Basel in disgrace, he resumed his peripatetic ways. For the next twelve years, he would remain long enough in various German and Austrian towns to anger the local doctors and clergy before being forced to move on. In 1541, broken, penniless, and unpublished, he died at the age of forty-eight. The doctors of physick tried to suppress his works from reaching distribution. But copies of his writings soon spread throughout Europe via the printing press.

About one-hundred-and-twenty years later, Lionardo DiCapua wrote a series of essays summarizing the history of medicine and the current state of the art. In the first essay of his *Parere,* he praises Paracelsus as the man who revived the wisdom of ancient folk methods and attempted to mix it with chemistry to cure diseases that the doctors of physick had failed to heal. But he tempered his enthusiasm for the oft-romanticized hero by adding, "Theophrastus Paracelsus wrapped and concealed his Doctrine in obscure Aenigmes, and ambiguous Allegories usual with Chemical Authors."

He was referring to the strange mixture of astrology, cosmology, metallurgy, and theology contained in Paracelsus' teachings; theories that would blow open the archaic doors of physick and force the art in a new direction. A movement long overdue.

The Awakening

Thomas Aquinas cemented the Aristotelian model in the thirteenth century with his philosophy of scholasticism, in which supernatural intervention took even greater precedence over the natural world. Universities remained under the direct control of the church, and Aristotle and Galen reigned supreme. The most famous Persian medical philosopher was Avicenna, whose *Canon* also became a standard text in Christian universities, which was why Paracelsus felt compelled to toss it into the Midsummer bonfire, along with Galen's writings.

When the Black Death struck northern Italy in 1348, the Paduan health authorities required that all indeterminate deaths have a post-mortem exam to account for their cause. This decree presented numerous opportunities for the medical students to perform human dissections, and probably was the main reason that the University at Padua became the center for anatomical studies that culminated with the monumental work of Andreas Vesalius.

Vesalius was appointed Professor of Surgery in Padua at the age of twenty-three and surprised his students by descending from his chair to teach through his own dissections. Since the amphitheater provided little space to get a close view of the topic, Vesalius produced large anatomical charts, which became much admired among his pupils. The charts contained three drawings of the vascular system, which Vesalius had sketched, and three sketches of the skeleton, drawn by his fellow countryman now living in nearby Venice, the artist Jan Stefan van Kalker. This *Tabulae Anatomicae Sex* was Vesalius's first publication and a great success.

Over the next few years, Vesalius continued teaching and working on his magnum opus. He sometimes obtained specimens for dissection through contact with a local judge of the criminal court who became interested in Vesalius' work and secured the bodies of executed criminals for him. It took Vesalius four years of diligent work to complete his masterpiece. Throughout Italy, the Renaissance was in full flower with artists producing works that faithfully represented the natural world. Vesalius's texts were intended for the art student as well as the medical student. Yet, as it became known later, he was not the first to think of creating such a comprehensive book.

Leonardo da Vinci had planned on producing a textbook for art students with the anatomist Marcantonio della Torre in the latter part of the fifteenth century. As with many of da Vinci's ideas, it was never completed. The drawings were lost for centuries and, when some were rediscovered, it became clear that if they had been published as planned, the great genius of the Renaissance would have produced perhaps his most famous work. The surviving sketches are beautifully rendered with precise detail. They were obviously the products of careful study created under trying conditions. Oftentimes the autopsies were performed at night when the lighting was poor and the mood more somber. Leonardo da Vinci apprises his students of the task before them:

And though you have a love for such things, you will perhaps be impeded by your stomach; and if this does not impede you, you will perhaps be impeded by the fear of living through the night in the company of quartered and flayed corpses, fearful to behold. And if this does not impede you, perhaps you will lack the good draughtsmanship which appertains to such a representation; and if you have skill in drawing, it may not be accompanied by a knowledge in perspective; and if it were to be accompanied, you might lack the methods of geometrical demonstration and methods of calculation of the forces and the strength of the muscles; or perhaps you will lack the patience so that you will not be diligent.

Vesalius's publication of *De Humani Corporis Fabrica* in June 1543 marks one of the great moments in man's quest for knowledge. Along with the *Fabrica* came the companion *Epitome*, a mostly pictorial guide with minimal description, much like his earlier *Tabulae Sex*. The result was an innovative synthesis of science and art, for which Vesalius deserves an honored place in the history of science. His great work confirms the historical reality that the inevitable expression of truth sometimes takes thousands of years to unfold.

We know that Vesalius performed dissections and was a good enough draftsman to make sketches of his studies, as the first three figures in the *Tabulae Sex* demonstrate. His overall skills as an artist, however, were not to the level of the Fabrica. Questions arise: who drew the illustrations, and who cut the wood blocks for the printing? Based on careful reviews, historians of art believe that the drawings came from Titian's school in nearby Venice. Enough technical variations exist within the collection to support the notion that more than one artist was involved, including the unassuming Jan Stefan van Kalkar, as well as a landscape specialist from Titian's school named Domenico Campagnola, and probably others. These artists worked under the direction of Vesalius, who also drew some of the sketches.

As for the production of the wood blocks used in the first and second editions (1555), all that is known is that they were struck by hand in Venice by unknown artisans and then sent to Basel for printing. The detailed craftsmanship was clearly extraordinary. Their subsequent history has been one of disappearance and partial rediscovery.

Soon after *the Fabrica* and the accompanying *Epitome* were released, the latter had a much greater reception with the public, a fact that initially disappointed Vesalius. This was probably due to the high cost of *Fabrica* and the detail of its text, which required knowledge of anatomy that few people possessed. Many of those that did—that is, the older professors whose lives had been spent upholding a system they now interpreted as being denounced—proclaimed their unfavorable reviews. Jacobus Sylvius, Vesalius's renowned and influential instructor, was incensed. He demanded a retraction and begged the Emperor to physically punish his former student. Vesalius stood firm, although not before burning the notes of his original manuscript in a rage of anger and sadness. Commenting on the violent reaction of Sylvius in his own history of medicine in the first essay of his *Parere*, Lionardo concludes, "Now what more, I pray, could he (Sylvius) have done, had poor Vesalius been guilty of High Treason not only against Monsieur Galen, but even against Cesar himself?"

Vesalius's experience bears witness to the saying that a prophet is often despised in his own homeland. In Italy, however, the reception was quite different. Andreas returned in triumph to Padua, then continued his victory tour south, for a lecture and demonstration at the medical school in Bologna and then Pisa.

Vesalius's work was a blessing for Lionardo DiCapua, who began anatomy studies under his maestro, Marcaurelio Severino. In Amenta's biography of Lionardo, he says that DiCapua did particularly well in anatomy, which was undoubtedly due to Severino's supervision, as well as the availability of Vesalius's pictorial guides.

Andreas Vesalius remains among the pantheon of great physicians and innovative scientists. But another character is important in this story, yet oftentimes receives little attention in the telling. That person is the printer of the *Fabrica*, Johannes (Herbst) Oporinus of Basel. He worked at the printing house of the previously mentioned Johann Froben and eventually set up as an independent printer in 1539. Oporinus came from a poor family and, perhaps, because he had experienced the deprivations of poverty, he was said to be of a generous nature, which was a rare companion trait to the successful businessman—then or now. Not surprisingly, his firm struggled financially. But he had a reputation as a thorough artisan and a man willing to take a risk on a project if he believed in it. He understood the significance of Vesalius's masterpiece and he produced it with the reverence it deserved, not knowing at the time whether he would ever recoup his investment.

Johannas Oporinus connects us back to where we began the first part of this history, back to Basel, the home of Froben and his eccentric houseguest, Paracelsus. After taking a job with the famed printer, Oporinus became a student and secretary to the fiery Paracelsus and accompanied the mercurial iconoclast on his wanderings throughout the continent. Ultimately, Johannas came to see his mentor as an impossibly cantankerous, loud-mouth drunk, and they parted ways.

One other physician who, like Paracelsus, recognized the importance of chemistry in the teaching and practice of medicine was Jan Baptista van Helmont. He became a physician in 1599, yet his dissatisfaction with the Galenists led him to choose private research in his native Holland. He opposed Galenist therapeutics like purging and bloodletting and, instead, promoted the use of chemical cures. In this regard, he became a model for the advocacy of chemical therapeutics that Lionardo DiCapua would later follow.

At the dawning of the seventeenth century, probably the greatest contribution to medicine and physiology came from William Harvey's confirmation of the continuous circulation of blood. Science builds on its established foundation, and Harvey's discovery was built on the theses of his teachers at Padua. It would take several decades and the precise microscopic studies of Marcello Malpighi, an acquaintance of Lionardo DiCapua, to truly close the vascular loop, not through holes in the heart chambers as Harvey had thought, but through the capillaries (Malpighian Tubules), the tiniest bridges between the arteries and veins.

Ultimately, the seventeenth century would come to be known as the cradle for anatomical and microbiologic discoveries, as above half of the known structures in the body were identified and named during that time. Medical science was awakening from its millennial slumber, and Lionardo was hoping to profit from its new direction. He mastered human anatomy during medical training, and he hoped to use his knowledge to develop a better method of treating his patients based on careful observation and open experimentation.

Appendix G

On Magic, Astrology and Animism

The Iconoclasts

In the year of our Lord 1639, while Lionardo DiCapua was completing his formal medical curriculum, the eccentric Dominican monk, Tommaso Campanella, died in Paris, having struggled for most of his legendary life in Italy. Lionardo had read Campanella's texts and wrote about the similarities between the famous Dominican's stormy relationship with the religious authorities of his time and the disputes that the bombastic Paracelsus had with the doctors of physick.

Both men lived fascinating, raucous lives that ended naturally (as far as is known), having barely avoided a hasty dispatching in a straw pyre or at the hands of some hooded executioner. Both were iconoclastic dreamers whose inspiration evolved from the ideals of the Renaissance. Paracelsus was already buried by the time of Campanella's birth in 1568, in the Calabrian town of Stilo, in the Kingdom of Naples. Tommaso grew to be an imposing man with thick black hair, intense dark eyes, and a brooding face dotted with a conspicuous mole on his right cheek. Indeed, he was proud of all seven protrusions emanating from his face and head, for he believed that they represented the seven planets, marking him as a magus. His powerful physical presence undoubtedly added to his charismatic appeal.

By age fourteen, he had entered a monastery in southern Italy. The Dominicans had long been the order that defined and defended Catholic theology. Thomas Aquinas and his teacher, Albertus Magnus, both Dominicans, formulated the medieval scholastic tradition central to Catholicism. In Rome, the Dominican Order had maintained an authoritative position during the Inquisition of the sixteenth century. Farther south, however, opposite forces were brewing. The propagation of contrary ideas within the southern monasteries seems like a paradox, until one considers the role of the order within the political milieu of the region. As defenders of the true faith, the Dominicans were exposed to heretical ideas that strayed from official doctrine. Through repeated interrogations of the accused and an intimate study of their writings, the reviewers would have acquired detailed knowledge of an apostate system. Some of those concepts must have generated more than just dispassionate interest among some of the brethren.

As for the political milieu, the earlier writings of two influential philosophers from the south were an indication that unorthodox ideas had already gathered considerable strength by the time Campanella was born. Giambattista della Porta's *Magia Naturalis*, published in 1559, was a neo-Platonic text in the tradition of earlier "Hermetic" writers. And in 1565, Bernardino Telesio, who would become Campanella's maestro, released his own *De rerum natura,* which was a decidedly non-Aristotelian account of natural phenomena.

Any attempt on the part of the authorities to address these fermenting ideas was hampered by another particularly southern Italian reality. With its reputation for banditry or *brigandage*, the south was not the safest place to travel. Consequently, the centers of dissent—the monasteries in the south—remained distant from the watchful control of Rome, allowing the beliefs to ripen within a region where a political backdrop served as the active yeast.

Political unrest against the Spanish and the ruling barons resonated with the monks. Often the sons of poor southern farmers, they could not help but be affected by the growing divergence between rich and poor in the sixteenth century. In the cities and in the countryside, wages were decreasing, prices were rising. Extravagant spending by the wealthy few became even more conspicuous when contrasted to the sufferings of the many. This decline in charity among mankind and the consequent discord stirred the consciousness of those who took the teachings of Jesus to heart.

Over the next decade, on two separate occasions, the nobles (with the support of the viceroy) petitioned the pope to replace the Dominican monks at two monasteries in Naples. In both cases, the radical monks—with the support of the local people and the threat of violence—kept their monastery. Tomasso Campanella was not among the resisters in Naples since he was in the last year of a three-year imprisonment for a controversy involving the religious authorities in Padua. This early incarceration, however, failed to cool his passions.

With the dawning of the seventeenth century, the wild forces that, throughout history, have accompanied a *fin de siècle* seemed to reinvigorate the persistent radicalism within the southern Dominicans. Beginning in 1598, Campanella led a group of ill-prepared supporters in a revolution against the Spanish monarchy in Calabria. He was convinced that the year 1600, being a multiple of the auspicious number "4," would be a magical year, ushering in a new age. The signs in the heavens foretold it. The sun was coming closer to the earth, he announced, and the reformed utopia that he would later summarize in his book *Citta del Sole (City of the Sun)* was at hand. He would be the high priest and political leader who would actuate a renewal of the wayward church. Catholicism would combine with ancient natural magic, and mankind would begin to grasp the "universal mind." This new era would start in Calabria and then spread to the rest of the world.

Campanella may have been a fantastical dreamer, but he was an awful general. He planned the first phase of the war, and apparently stopped there. Unfortunately for his followers (like Andrea Concublet's previously mentioned grandfather, the Marchese Scipione), the Spanish had a seasoned army. Likewise, their post-Armada navy was still powerful enough to keep the small fleet of Turkish ships (engaged by Campanella to send naval help) at bay. The Spanish also employed a clandestine network of spies within the rebel chain of command.

The naïve, emotional fervor that propelled the rebellious band to consider taking on the powerful empire seems almost comic in retrospect. The Spaniards and the Church hierarchy, however, were not amused. When two members of the conspiracy betrayed the plot, the survivors were thrown into prison, including Campanella who began a sentence in November of 1599 that would last twenty-seven years. During that time, he was tortured and escaped death by famously feigning insanity. Yet, through it all, he managed to survive by cleverly adapting his reformist beliefs like a man travelling on the boat of life, constantly trimming his sails.

In the early seventeenth century, science was still in its infancy and few people could appreciate its evolving potential. This was a world in need of the support derived from a belief in the occult. And even though many in positions of authority were publicly opposed to the magical arts, privately, they were often the most ardent supporters. They were latter-day followers of mystical sentiments, which had dominated the Renaissance mindset. Given the political, religious, and economic upheaval of the early fifteenth century, classical humanists saw the history of mankind as regression from the glorious font of ancient times. To the Renaissance humanist, progress meant a rebirth of antiquity. The farther back in the mystically shrouded past that the belief or writing or practice could claim its origin, the closer, it was believed, to the pure, unvarnished truth, and hence the more earnest was its appeal. Thus, the Greeks were great thinkers, but the Egyptians were considered wiser. This search for the venerable wisdom of the distant epochs fired the passions of learned men (like Poggio Bracciolini) to discover, translate, study, and circulate manuscripts from that pristine golden age. In time, a revival in the magical interpretation of nature resulted.

This "animist philosophy" competed with Aristotle's scholastic philosophy, as interpreted by Thomas Aquinas, challenging the authority of the Catholic Church. Consequently, during the last part of the fifteenth century, the initial proponents of the revived animist magic tried to unify their ideas with the accepted teachings of the Church and distance themselves from sorcery and black magic. They realized the potential conflict and tread carefully. Later animist proponents—like Tommaso Campanella and his Dominican contemporary Giordano Bruno—however, were not as reserved, pursuing their arguments with the Church and the ruling elites at their own peril. Both men were visionaries with charismatic personalities and great personal pride. Their struggles, as misdirected as they might have been, completed the bridge begun by their predecessors upon which mankind would pass into a modern era. Yet this new age, beginning at the dawn of the seventeenth century, would be vastly different from what these earlier reformers had anticipated, precisely because the animist tradition remained rooted in the past.

Lionardo DiCapua read the writings of Campanella and Bruno. He appreciated their willingness to reach beyond the stifling dogma of scholasticism, but he found their egotistical pronouncements based on their interpretation of magic to be impossibly subjective and short sighted.

375

Animism minimized the importance of science and mathematics in favor of "natural magic." Consequently, the Copernican theory of a sun-centered galaxy was seen as proof that the portents of a new, magical age were at hand. Those who proclaimed this truth, they argued, should be appreciated. However, the animists went on to say that, notwithstanding the validity of their insights, mathematicians could not possibly be expected to comprehend the deeper significance of heliocentricity. Such understanding was the purview of the enlightened Magi.

Magia Simpatica

Tommaso Campanella was the last of the great animist visionaries who considered himself a Magus. His animist beliefs,
derived from the Renaissance tradition, considered the origin of
wisdom to have been well before the Greeks in the pre-Mosaic
time of the Egyptians. This truth was supposedly confirmed in
a manuscript from Macedonia that was brought to Cosimo de
Medici in Florence around 1460. Cosimo insisted that his head
translator, Marsilio Ficino, put aside the complete works of Plato,
which had been carefully assembled for translation, to work
on this new, much anticipated find, the so-called "writings" of
Hermes Trismegistus. The fact that Cosimo prioritized Hermes
above Plato reflects the reverence afforded to Hermes, whom
some of the early Church fathers had praised as an Egyptian
priest and prophet.

The Hermetic manuscript translated by Marsilio Ficino
contained fourteen treatises, which he titled the *Pirmander
(On the Power and Wisdom of God)*. Like other scholars of
his time, Ficino had read commentaries written centuries earlier. Cicero had enthusiastically endorsed the Hermetic texts
as profoundly important, whereas some of the early Church
fathers, like Augustine, had been critical of them. Despite their
differences, however, none of them questioned the existence
of Hermes Trismegistus, placing him in the pre-Mosaic time
of Noah. Ficino considered Trismegistus to be the source of the
most ancient theology.

The origin of the name "Trismegistus" (Thrice Blessed)
evolved from the medieval tradition that referred to his supposed three roles as priest, philosopher, and ruler. In those
capacities, he was said to be the wisest of the ancients, his brilliance a reflection of his Egyptian roots. *Pirmander* confirmed
those truths for Ficino. He was amazed at the prophetic nature

of the writings. In one of the treatises came a description of the creation, an "Egyptian Genesis," in which man is made in the image of God and then falls into the corporeal world just as in the Old Testament. Even more inspiring was the prediction of the coming of the Son of God made by a man who had preceded Jesus, presumably, by thousands of years.

Augustine had written that the Hermetic teachings contained black magic, and Ficino proceeded carefully when disagreeing with Augustine, who was a canonized saint. Ficino believed he had discovered another, more orthodox, side to Hermes, a teacher who admonished his followers to live a holy life in order to regain their eternal nature. In the Hermetic texts, man maintains part of the divine through his intellect and is taught the methods whereby he can use his mind to reconnect with the universal wisdom that enhances the living world.

No literary sleight of hand, however, could cover the fact that an astrological outline clearly framed the texts of *Pirmander*, and Ficino never denied its presence. All of nature was assumed to be under the rule of the stars and the seven planets. The magic of Hermes did not derive from dark forces, Ficino explained. Instead, the practice came to be known as sympathetic magic (*magia simpatica*). The underlying theory was that every object was infused with occult sympathies that originated with the planet to which it was connected. The magus could evoke the power of a particular planet by learning the material connections—the plants, colors, animals, scents, metals, rocks—that were attached to it. With precise astrological timing, he would inscribe the image on a talisman, which then possessed the power of the planet for later use.

Such practices hinted at black magic. To get around this conundrum, Ficino placed God at the apex of a complex, multi-layered universe. Thus, the Magus was using his knowledge of sympathetic magic in conjunction with his religion.

His talismans were devices used to connect the divine with the material world. As mentioned, in projecting this ideal, Ficino proceeded with great care. His renowned pupil and fellow member of Lorenzo de Medici's Platonic Academy, Count Giovanni Pico della Mirandola, became a much more forceful advocate.

In the year 1486, the self-assured, erudite, twenty-four-year-old Count Mirandola went to Rome carrying his "nine hundred points." Anyone who accepted his challenge and came to Rome for an intellectual joust over his ideas would have all expenses paid by the count himself. It was his belief (which he was certain he could prove in public debate) that each religion was compatible with the others. He admired Arabic and Jewish thinking. Several of his friends were Jews, and one of the most famous Jewish writers of the fifteenth century, Eliah del Medigo, a philosophy instructor in Padua and Florence, was his teacher.

Pico learned Hebrew to read the original Scriptures. This Hebraic connection led him to the spiritual magic called Cabala, which was believed to be a mysterious doctrine begun by Moses and passed on to a few select followers. The mystical teachings of Cabala are based on the study of the Hebrew alphabet. Ten names for God (the doctrine of the "Sephiroth") form one great name. Through deep meditation of these names, the practitioner gains an understanding of God and his divine creations. Pico believed that by learning Cabalist secrets, one could gain a true understanding of Christ and the mystery of the Trinity.

The theologians that reviewed those points did not care at all for Pico's genuinely pious beliefs. They refused to debate the propositions and advised Pope Innocent VIII to sanction Pico. The pope responded by appointing a commission, which quickly condemned many of the points as heretical. A year later, Pico replied with an apology that became part of his famous essay titled "The Dignity of Man." This noble work of Renaissance thinking was more of a defense and hardly a retraction. Thus, his obstinacy occasioned an even stronger rejoinder. Bishops from the Inquisition took charge of the matter.

Like other Italian thinkers over the centuries that ran afoul with the Church, Pico fled to the north. Papal nuncios tracked him down and imprisoned him in France. He was tried and exonerated in the more favorable French courts and eventually allowed to return to Florence, a concession achieved by the intervention and support of "The Magnificent" Lorenzo de Medici. Although still shy of thirty years, much of the starch had been taken out of the noble scholar. Pico sought a quieter life and found it within the strict asceticism of the reactionary monk Savonarola at the Dominican convent in Florence.

Innocent died and was succeeded, in 1492, by one of the more outrageous characters to ever sit on Peter's throne. Rodrigo Borgia took the name Alexander VI. By the time he became pope, he had at least five children, including his ruthless son, Cesare, and his famously beautiful daughter, Lucretia. The former lived comfortably on the largesse of his father's flagrant nepotism. Rumors of incest resulting in an illegitimate child with the latter could not be dismissed. This Borgia pope maintained his own strong belief in the power of magic and astrology. He had read Count Mirandola's books and, early in his reign, sent Pico a personal letter praising him for describing the nexus between Christianity and Cabalistic magic, and absolved him of any heresy.

The Catholic Church did not universally accept Pope Alexander's blessing of Pico. Many clerics were concerned that, no matter how much the magus claimed to be employing his techniques to connect with sacred forces, darker powers were being tapped and any connection of magic to religion became worrisome—at least in public. Likewise, following the Reformation, Protestant sects became harsh critics of Renaissance animist ideas and practices. The idolatrous Catholics adored statues and venerated relics. This combination of Hermetic magic with religion, the Protestants asserted, was further proof of the superstitious nature of Catholicism. Hence, just as they were about to flower, the intellectual ideals unleashed by the Renaissance were doomed by the prejudices and animosities of all the Christian religions.

From Pico's Oration on the Dignity of Man comes a most eloquent assertion of the central humanist ideal that each person possesses the potential to rise or to fall:

> Thou mayest sink into a beast, or be born anew to the divine likeness. The brutes bring from their mother's body what they will carry with them as long as they live; the higher spirits are from the beginning, or soon after, what they will be forever. To thee alone is given a growth and development depending on thine own free will. Thou bearest in thee the seeds of a universal life.

This critical insight remains the firm foundation of the bridge across which humanity would pass from medieval to modern. Pico's combination of naturalist magic and Cabala with the more accepted disciplines of Christian theology, mathematics and logic freed the Renaissance person to take charge of his own destiny.

In 1494, a year after Alexander issued his absolution, Giovanni Pico della Mirandola died suspiciously in Florence. Many years later, poisoning was proven to be the cause. He was thirty-one years old.

In the process of reading Pico's writings, Lionardo DiCapua came across an argument the count had raised with Aristotle's assertion against a circular rainbow. Pico argued that the rainbow could be a full circle given the right setting. In La Vita,

Amenta mentions Pico's contention, which DiCapua used to support his own calculated theory.

A Passionate Mistake

Tommaso Campanella remained in jail for twenty-seven years after leading the Calabrian revolt. His *Citta del Sole* (*City of the Sun*) was written in the early years of his incarceration and published during his last years in jail. The book summarizes the communal ideals of a society founded on a magical, Christianized-Hermetic structure, which inspired his followers to attempt the irrational seizing of Calabria from the Spanish. But during his long incarceration, Campanella transformed his revolutionary rhetoric to a more conciliatory tone that reinforced a Christian interpretation of Hermes and argued against the use of demonic magic. The Spanish monarchy became the vehicle for his world government, with the pope as its spiritual leader. How persuaded he was of his newfound orthodoxy is questionable. He showed a remarkable ability to adjust his methods while holding to the ultimate mission of finding a royal personage to inspire the magical revival.

Soon after Campanella was released from jail, he probably thought he'd found that person when an eclipse was due to arrive, and the pope summoned him to Rome to perform a magical ceremony to protect him from his enemies. Four years earlier, Urban VIII was elected pope, conveying with him to the Vatican artists and scholars, and the sincere hope for an informed papacy, since it seemed that he, Maffeo Barberini, was an enlightened man. He was well read, had befriended Galileo, and did not oppose the essentials of heliocentricity. He possessed a keen interest in the natural world, wrote poetry, understood the importance of art, and appreciated architecture enough to appoint the incomparable Gian Lorenzo Bernini in charge of completing St. Peter's Basilica. Campanella heralded him as a new "David."

Still, it is surprising that even an enlightened pope would beckon Campanella, recently released from inquisitorial jail. But belief in the occult, as noted earlier, was common among the hierarchy of the Church, and Campanella's reputation as a magus preceded him. In the appendix to his book *Astrologica,* he described the actual ceremony: The private chamber was sealed and hung with white cloth. Propitious planets were summoned with the correct talismans, colors, flowers, and music. Herbs were burnt and appropriate liquors consumed. Each part of the Hermetic ritual was intended to call down protective magic.

Having saved Urban, how sad it must have been for Campanella to watch his David fall under the restraining influence of a conservative hierarchy. His despondency made him realize the futility of placing his hope on any leader of the Catholic Church. Thus, he followed the well-worn northern path from Italy. He went to Paris, where he transferred the central role as ruler of his universal City of the Sun to the French monarchy. While in Paris, Campanella performed a magic ritual on his own behalf near the end of his life in 1639. The effect, if any, was short lived. By then, Campanella had already become an anachronism.

During the early seventeenth century, atomist ideas summarized in Lucretius's great poem led the way to natural philosophy, which would evolve into what we now call "science." A new world was unfolding. During that transition, the entire edifice of the Hermetic tradition began to unravel just a few years before Lionardo DiCapua's birth, when the perceptive Greek scholar Isaac Casaubon showed that the references, styles, and dates within the Hermetica came from multiple authors in a much later era.

Casaubon was born in Geneva in 1559, after his Huguenot parents had fled France. They returned to France during his childhood and, for much of his life, he was buffeted by the religious intolerance of the times. As a youth, he was often in hiding with his family and friends, at times living in mountain caves where, it was said, he received his first Greek lessons. His facility with the language was soon recognized and he became the most noted Greek scholar of the period, working, at various times, under the protection of either French Catholic or English Protestant kings.

James I of England set him to rebut a newly written Counter-Reformation Catholic history, which had relied, in part, on the Hermetic writings. Casaubon's detailed argument against the authenticity of the texts was buried within the rest of his eight hundred pages, so it failed to ignite the coverage it should have received. Campanella never knew of it. Nonetheless, Casaubon exposed the writings for what they were: the works of various unknown Greek Gnostics from the second through fourth centuries AD. Casaubon allowed that Hermes Trismegistus could have been a real person from Egyptian times, but he was definitely not the author of the Hermetic texts. The rebirth of what was thought to be the "ancient" wisdom of a great magician-prophet turned out to be a hoax. Indeed, this must be one of the great ironies of history, that the earliest rumblings of modern science, which relies on discovering truth to proceed to greater truths, began as a passionate mistake.

By the time Casaubon's discovery had become well known, a new age of philosophizing had arrived. The rebirth of ancient magic during the Renaissance had been a way for man to obtain knowledge and make life better on earth. To seventeenth century scholars like Lionardo DiCapua, science, in its evolution from natural philosophy, offered the same possibilities. DiCapua's mission was to improve the practice of healing through a "free philosophizing" of medical science. He and his companions proposed experimentation, observation, physiological and chemical studies, and, above all, openness to the concept of uncertainty.

The goals of sympathetic magic and science were the same. The major difference between them was the means used to obtain that end.

The Shaman and the Conman

To the Renaissance magi, the combination of mathematics with magic could lead to a true understanding of the forces of nature and, ultimately, to a better life for mankind. Among this miniscule group of unorthodox thinkers, none believed or practiced that concept more than the brilliant Englishman John Dee.

Born in England in 1527, when Copernicus was still finalizing his proof, John Dee followed the Hermetic tradition espoused by the man he called "noble Earl of Mirandula." Like Pico, he studied mathematics and stressed its importance in daily life, then applied his considerable mathematical skills in the seemingly contradictory effort to understand nature through Cabala.

The *Zohar* is the title given to the mystical text written in Spain around 1295, and it contains the essence of Jewish Cabala. Catholic practitioners of the Cabala believed that hidden within the obscure text was proof that Christ was the Son of God. One method of practical Cabala called "Gematria," assigns a number to each of the twenty-two Hebrew letters. Words represent a sum of those numbers and, by adding or subtracting, multiplying or dividing these word-numbers, deeper meanings are revealed. Gematria is used especially for interpreting the names of angels. Thus, by deciphering the intricacies of the various names of the seventy-two angels, an opening to the understanding of the Sephiroth and, ultimately, to the one great Name of God can be obtained.

This combination of mathematics and mysticism was especially appealing to a man like John Dee who wished to call down the angels for an audience in which they would reveal the tenets of "natural philosophy" to him. Like Pico, he was a devout man who approached his studies of magic with a mystical reverence and wonder. Dee was the epitome of the Renaissance magus: a man who could move between mathematics and magic, Cabala and Christianity, science and seances, and find common ground between them.

In his younger days as a student in Louvain, Dee made it a point to meet as many mathematicians and cartographers as possible while he traveled from city to city on the continent. He spent time in the workshop of the renowned cartographer Gemma Frisius, where he befriended one of Frisius's star pupils, the famous mapmaker Gerard Mercator. Dee shared his observations on the heavens with the respected stargazer Tycho Brahe, who was impressed with Dee's brilliance in astronomy. The breadth of his intelligence soon brought offers of royal patronage with university appointments—which he refused, citing the stifling environment within academia. Instead, he wrote and drew packed audiences to his lectures in Paris on Euclid's geometry.

Dee returned to England and eventually became astrologer and cartographer for Queen Elizabeth. Among other things, he used his acquired skills to compose maps and charts of the North American continent. He built mechanical contraptions for the theater; proposed the political necessity of the British Empire; published a book on the position of stars; taught British naval captains how to use their instruments and calculate their position on the high seas; and, at the same time, held angel-summoning sessions with his assistant, Edward Kelley.

Shakespeare was said to have admired Dee so much that the character of Prospero in *The Tempest* is based on the great conjurer himself. With his long, white beard pointing in an upside-down delta (the Greek letter for "D," the way he referred to himself in his voluminously detailed diaries), he looked the part. And if Dee is Prospero, Kelley (who first presented himself to Dee as Edward Talbot) could have played Othello's nefarious servant, the conniving Iago.

What is known about this somewhat mysterious man is more legend than fact. Yet, by all accounts, Edward Kelley was a bad egg. When Dee met Kelley, his ears had been cropped or deformed in such a way as to suggest an earlier sentence for forgery and counterfeiting. Another unconfirmed story charges him with necromancy, the enlivening of a freshly dead body to predict future events. He was said to be a capable ventriloquist and used his skill to deceive Dee into believing that angels were talking to Dee through him. Dee, for all his brilliance, was an easy mark. He prepared for the sessions with prayer and fasting and was apparently sincerely persuaded by the charade. Kelley often relied on baser spirits before gazing into his crystal ball and relaying Dee's questions and various angels' responses.

Perhaps due to his alcohol problem, Kelley often acted in an unpredictable, impulsive, and childlike manner, behavior seen by Dee as typical of a "scryer." At that time, many wealthy English patrons included a scryer among their household retinue of gardeners, cooks, maids and servants. They were often capable, literate men from the countryside who came to the city with a good story to tell. They probably knew of herbal treatments and folk remedies and could be counted on to predict the future, read a fortune or transmit spiritual messages across the void. Because they dabbled in the occult, their behavioral idiosyncrasies were tolerated, even expected, as a sign of great potential.

Edward Kelley, despite his selfishly scheming ways, was a fine actor. His ability to convincingly play the various angelic parts for nearly six years of friendship with Dee was a masterful run. The show finally came to an end in Bohemia when, over the course of a few sessions, Kelley had transmitted the idea that the two men should exchange wives for the purpose of "cross-matching." The gullible Dee fretted and prayed over this seemingly irreconcilable suggestion, but eventually relinquished.

About this time, Kelley, who must have realized the extent to which he could manipulate Dee, began to seriously experiment with alchemy, the ultimate in spiritual and pseudo-scientific quests. Not long after he had first met Dee, Kelley claimed to have been directed by a spirit to a site in the country outside London where he had found a book, a scroll written in a strange alphabet, and a red powder that could turn base metals into gold. Dee believed that Kelley had located the much sought-after Philosopher's Stone.

In Bohemia, using his sleight of hand cunning, Kelley demonstrated his ability to use his magic powder and create small nuggets of gold. This apparently astounding skill and Kelley's promise to duplicate the feat on a grand scale amazed the English observers and representatives of Rudolfo II, the Holy Roman Emperor from nearby Prague. Dee, on the other hand, made no claim to possessing the skill. Consequently, both the English Court and Rudolfo's retinue ignored Dee and instead competed to secure Kelley's services. Kelley chose to remain in Bohemia for good reason. He became a well set-up gentleman, was made a baron, inherited estates and became an adviser to the emperor.

What happened to finally end his successful run remains part of the Kelley legend. One version of the saga claimed that Rudolfo became angered at Kelley's chicanery. He was thrown into jail and was thought to have died in 1595 after sustaining serious injuries in a fall while trying to escape. However, there were reported sightings of the resourceful man as late as 1598.

By that time, John Dee and his family had already returned to England for nearly a decade. When they arrived home, they found that the house and Dee's famous library had both alike been ransacked and destroyed. Dee was without any source of income to repair his home or care for his family. Thus, he petitioned Elizabeth. His plight was brought before the aging queen who took pity on her loyal servant and appointed him warden of Christ College. He outlived his beloved regent to reach a full and fascinating eighty-one years, and he was still searching for spiritual enlightenment when he died in 1609. The intensity that he brought to that universal search remains part of his legacy; it is kept alive in the societies that still honor his ideals and his name.

Although his naivete made him easy prey for a charlatan like Edward Kelley, John Dee appreciated the commonality of all religions in the hope that one day they would be unified into a pure theology derived from the ancients, as Pico della Mirandola had proposed. Dee was also lucky enough to have been born and raised far from Rome; he was canny enough to resist invitations to travel there to convince Church authorities of the truth inherent in the idea of a universal religion, as Pico had attempted to do.

The Nolan

In 1583, just before John Dee left England with Kelley and their families to meet Rudolfo II in Prague, the estranged Dominican priest, Giordano Bruno, arrived in London, hoping to obtain a lectureship at Oxford. He had spent several years making his way north from Italy. Bruno's philosophy was rooted in the Hermetic tradition in common with Marsilio Ficino, Pico della Mirandola and John Dee. But Giordano Bruno was of much different stock. He was self-assured, quarrelsome, and often proclaimed his iconoclastic ideas in a frenetically pompous manner that, at the same time, could be mystically poetic.

Bruno was born in Nola near Mount Vesuvius in 1548. Scholars have noted that he never lost traces of his volcanic, Neapolitan origin, for he was proud to call himself "the Nolan," born under a kindly sky. The story is told that when he was an infant, a serpent appeared from a hole in the wall of his house, an ancient portent of a courageous fate. The Nolan was baptized "Filippo" but changed his name to Giordano when he entered the famous Dominican monastery in Naples at age sixteen. He received Holy Orders in 1572, although his doubts about the tenets of Catholicism and his vow of celibacy continued. Most likely, he was also influenced by the unrest that was fomenting throughout the southern Italian monasteries at the time. In 1576, unable to suppress his sexual desires, and after repeated problems with his superiors, he abandoned his habit and fled Naples. For the next seventeen years, he would follow a hectic path that commenced and concluded in Rome.

After his first stop in the Holy City, he continued north to Padua, Venice, Torino, and Bergamo. He crossed over the Alps to France, then moved on to Geneva, Switzerland, the center of Calvinism, where he obtained a job correcting manuscripts. Never one to remain judiciously quiet, he was expelled from the city because he listed numerous mistakes in a lecture presented at the University of Geneva by a Calvinist theologian. His expulsion must have been a sorrowful eye-opener when he realized that Catholics and Protestants both and alike were intolerant of free thinking.

From Switzerland, the Nolan moved back to Paris where he taught King Henry III the secrets of his memory skills through mnemonics. In 1583, he left Paris for London. Whether he actually met John Dee in London is uncertain, but Dee's friends warmly received him and accompanied him to Oxford. There, he tried to convince the professors of the truth of his magical insights into a sun-centered universe. His ideas, presented in his irascible and bombastic style, were not well received. Yet, despite the conflict with the Oxford Dons, he found comfort and camaraderie among the literate circle of Sir Philip Sidney and the great Queen Elizabeth herself. This support, plus the pride of the English in their own language, inspired him to write his most imaginative works in his own Italian vernacular during his two years there.

He returned to Paris where the flames of religious intolerance—lit by the horrendous brutality of the St. Bartholomew's Day Massacre of Protestant Huguenots eleven years prior—were once again being stoked. Without Henry III's protection, Bruno departed for Germany. He was accepted as a lecturer by the Lutheran professors at Wittenberg and remained happily for two years before heading to the court of Rudolfo II in Prague. There, Bruno would again cross paths with John Dee who was leaving Bohemia about the time of the Nolan's arrival.

Whether they had intersected during this period is, again, unknown. Edward Kelley had stayed on in Rudolfo's court, presenting the tantalizing, but unsubstantiated, possibility that Bruno might have met him, as well. Such an occasion would have provided the stuff for a comedy or, better still, a farce worthy of a contemporary talent like Shakespeare. (Would Kelley bamboozle the irritable Bruno, or would the Nolan see through the great charlatan and tear him to shreds in a pithy, poetic monologue?)

Bruno obtained a position at the University of Brunswick in Helmstedt where he lectured and wrote poetry on the infinite expansion and the infinite minuteness of the universe; this reflected the strong influence that the atomist philosophy of Democritus and Lucretius had upon him. In 1590, he went to Frankfurt to have his poems published. Thence, in August of 1591, after wandering for over fifteen years across the frontiers of Europe, the Nolan took the fateful step of crossing back into Italy, where the Inquisition had branded him an outlaw. On the face of it, he made this move to teach a wealthy Venetian his magical secrets of memory, even though he felt no strong attachment to the man. Certainly, his fame could have easily provided more rewarding employment on the continent. Some have suggested that he returned to Venice thinking that he might find protection by the lenient, worldly inclined Venetians. Whatever the reason, to Italy did he come.

Once there, the imprudent Bruno went beyond the necessary mnemonics curriculum to expound several heresies to his devoutly Catholic pupil, Giovanni Mocenigo. Not wishing to open himself to the Inquisition, the fearful Mocenigo related the details to his confessor, which led to Bruno's arrest by the Holy Office of the Inquisitor of Venice in May of 1592. Over the next several months, Bruno underwent periodic examination, during which he admitted to some of his errors and begged forgiveness. The head of the Holy Office in Rome asked the Venetians to hand over the prisoner and, after months of resistance, the Venetian government acquiesced. In February 1593, Giordano Bruno was transferred to Rome, completing the circle he had begun after seventeen years and thousands of miles of wandering.

For the next seven years, the prisoner was occasionally questioned and then intentionally ignored. He remained in his cell for extended periods between interrogations, probably to break his spirit. Nonetheless, the deprivations he suffered did not produce the desired effect. The repentant mood he exhibited in Venice hardened into a firm recalcitrance throughout his long ordeal in Rome. He was charged with various heresies and given multiple opportunities to recant, which he refused to do.

At his sentencing, Bruno replied to the cardinals: "Perhaps you who pronounce my sentence are in greater fear than I who receive it." (Whether this is apocryphal is less meaningful than the fact that most scholars would find it believable.)

It has been said that the heretic is more dangerous than the assassin, since the assassin destroys one man, while the heretic destroys the beliefs that influence many. The Inquisition followed that premise when, on February 19, 1600, the convicted heretic, Giordano Bruno, was mounted on a donkey and led into the Campo dei Fiori bound and gagged, with his head shaved bald. A nail was placed from one side of his face, through his tongue and out the other cheek and his lips were pinned together to prevent him from speaking. He was tied to a metal stake and burnt to death, and afterwards his ashes were scattered.

Bruno was a unique, mercurial character whose life was constantly in flux. The only consistency was his mission to return Christianity to its pure, Egyptian-Hermetic roots, even if his methods of fulfilling that goal were peculiarly erratic. This was the one guiding principle of his life—one that he followed to his death: "For love of true wisdom and zeal for true contemplation, I tire, torment, and crucify myself."

As a young novitiate, he had used the great library of the Dominican monastery in Naples to its fullest, reading the Hermetic texts; atomist philosophy; the memory tricks of the fourteenth century Spaniard, Raymond Lully; the rebellious medical mysticism of Paracelsus; Cornelius Agrippa's handbook on the occult (which was also a reference guide for John Dee) ; and the infinite universe ideas of Nicholas of Cusa, among others. His expertise in the art of mnemonics led him deeper into the use of talismans, numerology, and Cabala during his travels. By the time of his return to Italy, he was writing about a purely Egyptian magic that would link the magician with the angels as well as the demons, the gods, and the goddesses, who could connect the practitioner with higher celestial spheres. His was the kind of "black" magic that Ficino and Pico della Mirandola had gone out of their way to disavow.

It is impossible to truly understand events surrounding historical characters in isolation from each other. In Bruno's day, the Counter Reformation had begun in earnest, and the Catholic hierarchy did not appreciate a wayward priest who aggressively attacked the established order while mingling with Protestants. Born under the kindly Campania sky, Bruno was predisposed to despise the strongly Catholic Spanish monarchy, which had been bleeding the Kingdom of Naples for decades. The unsettling events taking place in the monasteries in Naples and throughout southern Italy during the last part of the sixteenth century could only increase his animosity. At the same time, his proclaimed admiration for the Anglican Queen Elizabeth; his fond regard for the professors at Wittenberg; his early expressions of hope for the not-yet-converted, Protestant, French King of Navarre; plus his denial of Christ's divinity, the Trinity and the doctrine of transubstantiation inflamed the Inquisition.

Bruno, in a sense, floated in a separate sphere above the mortal fray, always holding to his deeper purpose of religious reform. As events unfolded across the continent, he adapted his methods by connecting back to the world around him, attaching onto one or another monarch in the constant hope that they would be the focal point, the one who would initiate the long-awaited magic renewal. There is no reason to doubt his sincerity toward each royal patron. His repeated shifts of allegiance, along with his ceaseless peregrinations, should, instead, be seen as a reflection of his deeper sense of mission. At the same time, they demonstrated a personality whose ego was as boundless as his thoughts. Here was a man who saw the teachings of the Catholic and Protestant faiths, the professors at the great universities, even the regents of Europe as imperfect vehicles to the mystical truth, which he, the Nolan, would bring to the world. And nowhere was this megalomania more obvious than in his writings about mathematicians like Copernicus.

Bruno strongly supported heliocentricity since the Egyptians and the early Greeks had already recognized it. He admired Copernicus, as well and defended his sun-centered cosmos against its critics, but he did so in a pedantic and patronizing way. According to Bruno, Copernicus understood the universe based on mere mathematical principles, while completely failing to understand the deeper, magical implications of his theory. He, the Nolan, had applied himself to a strenuous study of philosophy and all aspects of magic, giving him an elevated insight into divine wisdom, which the study of mathematics alone would never offer.

To prove his point, Bruno, indeed, went beyond Copernicus. Using his fertile imagination, enhanced by the writings of earlier mystics and Lucretius, he postulated the scientific view of an infinite universe composed of numerous worlds all moving through space. Our planet is just one of an inconceivable number of celestial bodies, he said, and those of us who inhabit the earth are just a miniscule bit of an infinitesimally large cosmos. He did not use mathematics to make the leap. Instead, he based his theory on the religious principle of "plenitude"— that the powers possessed by God, the infinite cause, are limitless.

Apart from the baffling question as to why he returned to

Italy, another persistent question arises regarding Giordano Bruno, which has to do with the timing of his death. As mentioned, he was imprisoned for nearly eight years, during which he was occasionally interrogated and then ignored, sometimes for months on end. Why, after all that time, was he executed in February of 1600? Was Bruno's death related to the restlessness within the southern Dominican convents, of which Tommaso Campanella's ill-conceived and magically inspired Calabrian revolt of 1599 had been the epitome?

Attempts at reforming the southern Dominicans, begun nearly fifteen years earlier, had met with minimal success. Furthermore, Campanella was being tortured and his surviving followers were in prison at the time of Bruno's execution. Were the Catholic hierarchy and their Spanish supporters sending a message to the agitators in the south? A religious institution that once was the home of the Church's most luminous scholar had become a gathering place for open discussion on prohibited topics, and Bruno's execution may have been timed to send the clearest signal that such behavior would no longer be tolerated. If that were the reason for his execution, it appears to have been successful since much of the turbulence within the Dominican order in Italy was quelled after the failed Calabrian revolt and the execution of Giordano Bruno.

Bibliography

1. *Vita di Lionardo DiCapoa dello fra gli Arcadi*
   Alcesto Cilleneo
   Amenta, Niccolo
   Pub: Vinezia 1710

2. *Tipographia Storica*
   Dell Irpinia
   Vol. IV
   LaStoria del Pensiero Irpino
   Angelo M. Jannacchini
   Stab. Tipog. Edoardo Pergola
   Avellino 1894

3. *L'Alta Valle del Calore*
   Vol V
   Il Feudo ed il Municipio di Bagnoli Irpino
   Napoli, Istituto della Stampa
   1954

4. *Breve Saggio Monografico su Lionardo DiCapua*
   (1617-1695)
   Edito a cura del: Circolo Sociale "Lionardo DiCapua"
   di Bagnoli Irpino
   Con il contributo della Regione Campania

5. *Parere del Signore Lionardo di Capua*
   Bulifon
   Napoli, 1681

6. *Lezioni Intorno alla Natura delle Mofete*
   Lionardo DiCapua
   Salvatore Castaldo
   Napoli, 1683

7. *Vita di Andrea Cantelmo*
   Lionardo DiCapua
   Giacomo Raillard
   Napoli, 1693

8. *Breve Sagio Monografico su Lionardo DiCapua*
   Scienziato, Medico, Filosopho Bagnolese
   Gabrielle Rapucci
   Ed: Circolo Sociale "Lionardo DiCapua"
   di Bagnoli Irpino, 1995

9. *History of the Kingdom of Naple*s
   Benedetto Croce
   Ed. H. Stuart Hughes
   The University of Chicago Press
   Chicago and London, 1970
   Originally published as Storica del regno di Napoli
   Bari: Laterza & Figli, 1925

10. *Per una Teoria dell' incertezza tra Filosofia e'medicina*
    Studio su Leonardo DiCapua (1617-1695)
    Salvatore Serrapica
    Liguori Editore, Napoli 2003

11. *On the Nature of Things – De rerum naturam*
    By Titus Carus Lucretius
    Translated by Charles E. Bennett
    Classics Club – Walter J. Black,
    New York 1946

12. *The Seekers*
    The Story of Mans' Continuing Quest
    to Understand his World
    Daniel J. Boorstein
    Random House
    New York 1998

13. *The Story of Civilization VII*
    The Age of Reason Begins
    Will and Ariel Durant
    Simon and Schuster
    New York 1961

14. *The Story of Civilization VIII*
    The Age of Louis XIV
    Will and Ariel Durant
    Simon and Schuster
    New York 1963

15. *Two Renaissance Book Hunters*
    The Letters of Poggius Bracciolini to
    Nicolaus De Niccolis
    Translated and annotated by Phyllis G. Gordan
    Columbia University Press
    New York and London 1974

16. *Pathfinders in Medicine*
    Victor Robinson MD
    Marcello Malpighi p. 155-185
    Medical Life Press,
    New York 1929

17. *A History of Western Philosophy*
    Bertrand Russell
    The Atomists p. 64-73
    Simon and Schuster
    New York 1945

18. *Treasury of Philosophy*
    Editor: Dagobert D. Ranes
    Philosophical Library
    New York 1955

19. *The Origins of Philosophy*
    Its Rise in Myth and the Pre-Socratics
    A Collection of Early Writings
    Selected, Edited, and with Explanatory Essays
    Drew A. Hyland
    Capricorn Books
    G. P. Putnam & Sons,
    New York 1973

20. *Giovanni Pico della Mirandola*
    Stanford Encyclopedia of Philosophy
    June 3, 2008

21. *Pico della Mirandola*
Walter Pater
Chapter 2 The Renaissance p. 24-40
Modern Library Edition
Originally written 1871
New York circa 1960

22. *Olivia Sabuco de Nantes Barrera*
A History of Women Philosophers
ed by Mary Ellen Waithe
Vol. 2 pp. 261-284
1989

23. *The Continuity of Feudal Power*
[The Caracciolo di Brienza in Spanish Naples]
Tommaso Astarita
Cambridge University Press
Cambridge 1992

24. *The Continuity of Feudal Power*
[Aristocratic Strategies for the Preservation
of Family Wealth]
Tommaso Astarita
Cambridge University Press
Cambridge 1992

25. *Italy in the Baroque: selected readings*
Edited and translated by Brendan Dooley
Selected Italian texts written between 1583-1704
Copyright 1995 by Brendan Dooley

26. *The Illustrations from the Works of
    Andreas Vesalius of Brussels*
    Dover Publications Inc,
    New York 1950

27. *The Fever Bark Tree: The Pageant of Quinine*
    M. L. Duran-Reynals
    Doubleday
    Garden City, N.Y. 1946

28. *Quinine's Predecessor: Francesco Torti and
    the Early History of Cinchona*
    Jarcho, Saul
    Johns Hopkins University Press
    Baltimore 1993

29. *Leonardo da Vinci*
    Corpus of the Anatomical Studies in the Collection of her
    Majesty the Queen, at Windsor Castle.
    Kenneth D. Keele & Carlo Pedretti (Eds)
    Johnson Reprint Co. Ltd
    London 1978-1980

30. *The Swerve*
    How the world Became Modern
    Stephen Greenblatt
    W.W. Norton & Co.
    New York 2011

31. *The Academy of the Investigators in Science, Medicine, and History*
    Vol. 1, pp.521-563
    Fisch, Max H.
    Collected and Edited by E. Ashworth Underwood
    London: Oxford Press 1953. Reprinted 1975
    by Arno Press.

32. *Una Teoria dell' Incertezza*
    (note sulla Cultura Napoletana de Sec. XVII)
    Rak, M
    Filologia Letturatura 15, 233-297, 1969

33. *Evangelista Torricelli*
    Letter to Michelangelo Ricci Concerning the Barometer -
    Florence June 11, 1644
    Collected Works Vol. III
    [From William F. Magie, A Source Book in Physics –
    New York: McGraw-Hill, 1935]

34. *The Eruption of Vesuvius of 1631*
    In the words of two witnesses:
    Giulio C. Recupito; 1635
    Giulio C. Braccini; 1632

35. *La Rivolta Antispagnola a Napoli,*
    Le Origini (1585-1647)
    Laterza
    Bari 1967

36. *Masaniello: Contemporary and Recent Interpretations*
    Past and Present, 108 (1985)
    pp.117-132

37. *Faith, Reason, and the Plague in*
   Seventeenth Century Tuscany
   Carlo M. Cipolla
   W.W. Norton & Co
   New York 1977

38. *A Collection of Very Valuable and Scarce Pieces*
   Relating to the Last Plague
   in the Year 1665
   London 1721
   To which is added:
   Account of the Plague at Naples in 1656

39. *Historia del Contagio di Avellino*
   Abbate Michele Giustiniani
   Lazari
   Roma 1662

40. *On the Proper Administration of Bloodletting,*
   for the Prevention and Cure of Disease
   Henry Clutterbuck MD
   London 1840
   From UCLA Louise M. Darling Biomedical Library
   Los Angeles, CA January 2002

41. *Bloodletting Over the Centuries*
   Gilbert R. Seigworth MD
   New York State Journal of Medicine
   December 1980 pp 2022-2028

42. *Lionardo Di Capoa's Parere (1681)*
Philosophy in the Sixteenth and Seventeenth Centuries
Conversations with Aristotle
Nancy Struever
(Aldershot: Ashgate, 1999) p322-336
Ed by S. Kusukawa & C. Blackwell

43. *The Tarantella*
Antonio Melechi
Fortean Times
November 2006

44. *History of Intrigues and Gallantries of
Christina Queen of Sweden*
London, 1927

45. *Queen Christina*
Georgina Mason
Farrar, Straus & Giroux
New York 1969

46. *Christina, Queen of Sweden*
The Restless Life of a European Eccentric
Veronica Buckley
Harper Collins, New York 2004

47. *Chemistry and Medical Debate*
Von Helmont ro Boerhaave
Science History Publication
Watson Publishing International
Canton, MA 2001

48. *The Queen's Conjurer*
    The Science and Magic of John Dee,
    adviser to Queen Elizabeth I
    Benjamin Wooley
    Henry Holt & Co.
    New York 2001

49. *Giordano Bruno and the Hermetic Tradition*
    Frances Yates
    Routledge Second Edition
    September 2015

50. *Dizionario Biografico degli Italiani*
    Biographies of: Lionardo DiCapua/ Francesco D'Andrea/
    Andrea Conclubet/
    Tommaso Cornelio/ Camillo Colonna/ Sebastiano Bartoli/
    Niccolo Amenta/ Giovan Girolamo Acquaviva
    Istituto dell'Encyclopedia Italiani
    Multiple volumes
    Italy 1960-2020

9 781954 604087